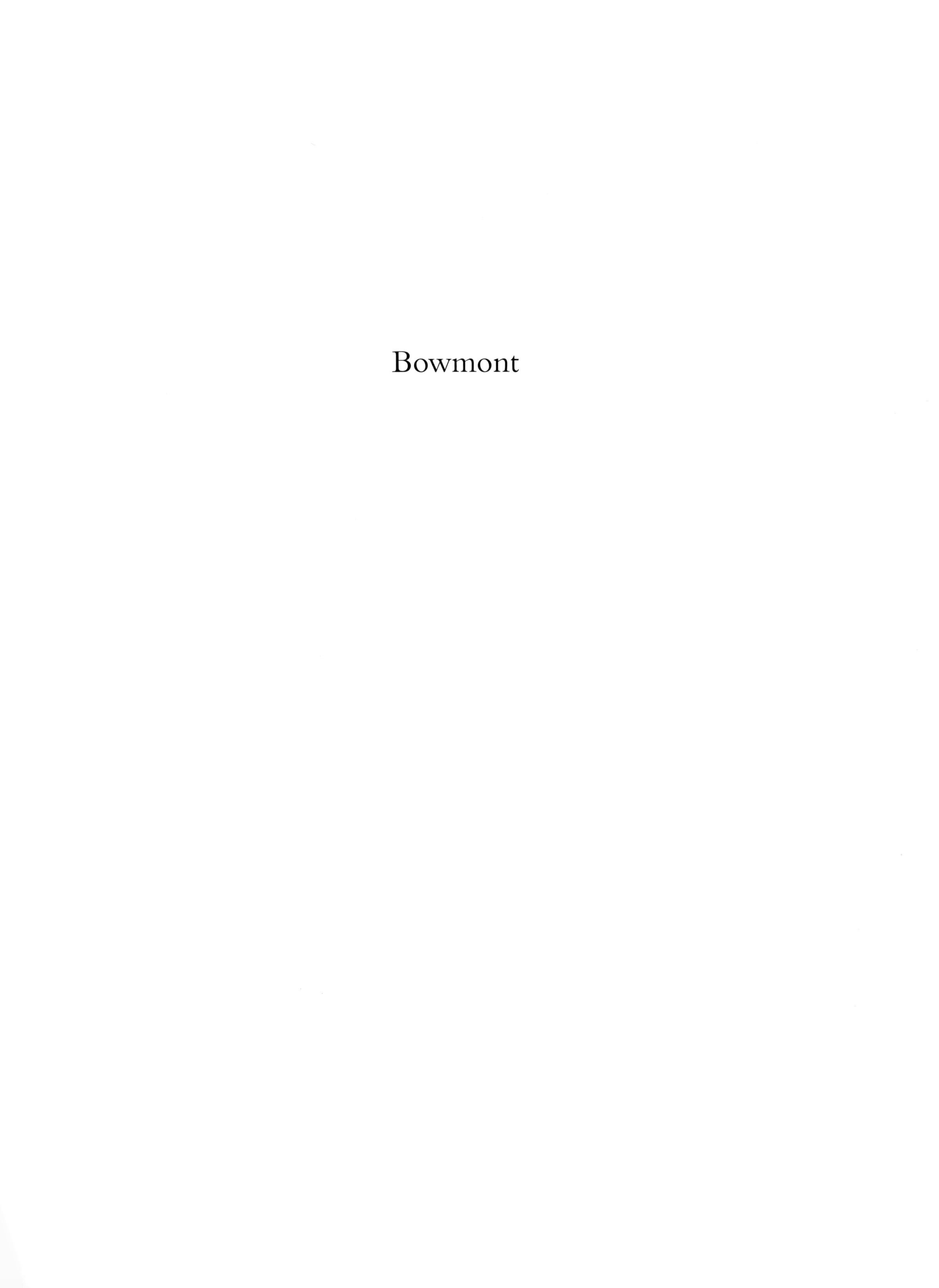

Bowmont

Bowmont

An Environmental History of the Bowmont Valley and the Northern Cheviot Hills, 10 000 BC – AD 2000

RICHARD TIPPING

SOCIETY OF ANTIQUARIES OF SCOTLAND
Edinburgh
2010

Cover image © Tomasz Szatewicz/Alamy

Published in 2010 by Society of Antiquaries of Scotland

Society of Antiquaries of Scotland
National Museum of Scotland
Chambers Street
Edinburgh EH1 1JF
Tel: 0131 247 4115
Fax: 0131 247 4163
Email: administration@socantscot.org
Website: www.socantscot.org

The Society of Antiquaries of Scotland is a registered Scottish charity no. SCO10440

British Library Cataloguing-in-Publication Data
A catalogue record for this book is available from the British Library

ISBN 978 0 903903 49 3

The Society of Antiquaries of Scotland gratefully acknowledges funding towards the publication of this volume from Historic Scotland.

Design and production by Lawrie Law and Alison Rae
Typeset by Waverley Typesetters
Printed by Gütenberg Press, Malta

Contents

Acknowledgements

During the course of a project of this nature and scale, thanks are clearly due to a great many colleagues. First and foremost, thanks are accorded to Roger Mercer, now Secretary of the Royal Commission on Ancient and Historical Monuments (Scotland), but in 1986, at the start of my involvement in the project, Reader at the Department of Archaeology, University of Edinburgh. Without his kind invitation to participate in the work, his constant support, involvement and enthusiasm for the environmental reconstructions, the work would probably not have been undertaken, and this report would not have been written.

At the same time, thanks in equal measure go to the staff of Historic Scotland, and in particular to Patrick Ashmore, Noel Fojut, Richard Welander and Gordon Barclay, not simply for committing substantial funds to the project, but also for their understanding of the problems encountered, their ready accession to numerous requests, and their keen interest in the products of the investigation. Astrid Schweizer, who contributed data in Chapter 6 from her Diploma dissertation at Johann Wolfgang Goethe-University, Frankfurt, received financial support for fieldwork from the Hermann Willkomm Stiftung. Fieldwork at Akeld Steads (Chapter 7) was provided by the British Geomorphological Research Group and the University of Edinburgh Research Fund. Access was freely given by the Duke of Roxburghe, by other landowners and by the tenants of many farms.

Enormous support came from the staff of the Bowmont Valley Project: Angela Wardell, Gordon Thomas, Peter McKeague and Jane Blair. Assistance in the field came from a great many willing helpers, and I am grateful to the following (in alphabetical order) for their commitment, often in decidedly inclement conditions: Andy Akhtar, Nick Branch, Chris Burgess, Harry Chrisp, Geraint Coles, Richard Corrigan, Nyree Finlay, Bill Finlayson, Andy Hoehn, Helen Hoehn, Anthi Koutsoukou, Peter McKeague, Bob McCulloch, Mary McCulloch, Frank Matsaaert, Gunter Nagel, Anthony Newton, Marion Pagan, Sukhivar Palmer, Carl Phillips, Charles le Quesne, Melanie Smith, Astrid Stobbe, Angela Wardell and Jane Webster.

Professor Denis Harding kindly ensured that sampling equipment, laboratory time, space and consumables, and accommodation, were unstintingly provided by the Department of Archaeology at the University of Edinburgh. The Department of Geography at the University of Edinburgh provided space and laboratory facilities for Astrid Schweizer, as did the Laboratory of Archaeobotany, Frankfurt University, and the Laboratory of Palaeobotany and Palynology at Utrecht University. Astrid was guided in Germany by Dr Joop Kalis. Help with laboratory work was given by, among others, Andy Akhtar, Richard Kynoch and Richard Corrigan. Bob McCulloch is thanked for support in computer programming. Particular thanks go to David Aitcheson, cartographer and author, who prepared with skill and patience the illustrations in this report, and who undertook the preparation of the final product with the support and assistance of Bill Jamieson at Stirling University.

The reliance on dating controls will become clear in the following pages, and the financial support of Historic Scotland, through Patrick Ashmore, is much appreciated in the provision of radiocarbon dates assayed at the Radiocarbon Laboratory of the Scottish Universities Research and Reactor Centre, East Kilbride, where Gordon Cook and his staff generously gave of their time and experience in supplying dates and discussion. Similarly, the Natural Environment Research Council Radiocarbon Steering Committee approved funding for assays determined at the NERC Radiocarbon Laboratory, also at East Kilbride. The innovation of Douglas Harkness and Brian Miller and their staff in the dating of different organic fractions added greatly to understanding the chronology of the fluvial sequences. Gus Mackenzie (SURRC) was very enthusiastic in developing the technique of ^{210}Pb dating for the peat stratigraphies. Martin Aitken and Eddie Rhodes (Research Laboratory for Archaeology and the History of Art, Oxford University) were more than willing to test the potential of the Bowmont Water fluvial sediments for OSL dating (Chapter 7).

The ideas and interpretations presented have developed from discussions with innumerable colleagues, but many thanks go especially to the following (again in alphabetical order): Patrick Ashmore, Keith Barber, Sjoerd Bohncke, Colin Burgess, Chalmers Clapperton, Geraint Coles, David Cowley, Jim Dickson, Piers Dixon, Robert Dodgshon, Lisa Dumayne Peaty, Robert Evans, Ian Fraser, Paul Frodsham, David Gilvear, Strat Halliday, Caroline Hardie, Jim Innes, Bob McCulloch, Peter McKeague, Angus MacDonald, Mark Macklin, Roger Mercer, Jane Murray, Dave Passmore, Susan Ramsay, Barbara Rumsby, Peter Topping, Judith Turner, Angela Wardell, Graeme Whittington, Pat Wiltshire and colleagues on field visits by the Association for Environmental Archaeology and the British Geomorphological Research Group. In particular, Dave Cowley, Strat Halliday and Piers Dixon patiently and encouragingly read, many moons ago, an earlier draft of Chapter 8. The ideas, errors and erroneous interpretations are mine, however.

Finally, the publication of this report is possible only through the assistance of colleagues at Historic Scotland, and particularly Patrick Ashmore and Rod McCulloch, in providing financial support in 2003 and 2004. My thanks go to colleagues at Stirling University who allowed sabbatical leave in completion of the writing, and Eileen Tisdall who shouldered the burden of my teaching for several months. Finally, my thanks go to Erin Osborne-Martin and Alison Rae of the Society of Antiquaries of Scotland for their speedy production of this report.

RICHARD TIPPING
May 2010

List of figures

List of tables

List of plates

Chapter 1

THE NORTHERN CHEVIOT HILLS AND THE BOWMONT VALLEY

1.1 First impressions

The intentions of this work are to reconstruct and describe the changing landscapes of the northern Cheviot Hills, and of one valley in particular, the Bowmont, from the beginning of the present interglacial to the present day. It is the first of two major publications on this valley. This report will describe the environmental histories of the diverse landscapes within these hills and will establish the often complex links between different factors, natural and anthropogenic, in landscape change. Beyond this, it is hoped that this analysis will enable the archaeologist and historian to understand more how the historical environmental sciences work, and what they can reveal. A second report (Mercer in prep.) will incorporate detailed data and discussion on the types of archaeological remains and the archaeological landscape.

The Cheviot Hills are in both south-east Scotland and north-east England (Figure 1.1). The northern Cheviot Hills are those parts of the border ridge that descend to the Teviot and Tweed Valleys and the Merse. Frontiers are different to other regions (Phythian-Adams 2000), but the Anglo-Scottish border has been a dominant political factor only for the last 1000 years (Mack 1924). The landscape, its comparative poverty and the sharing of its history by both countries, may be typified by the ballad *Chevy Chase*. The ballad describes the battle of Otterburn (1388 cal AD), in Redesdale (Figure 1.1), and was probably written soon after. There are both English and Scottish versions, and different geographies evoked in each, but natives on both sides would recognise:

> The Otterburn's a bonnie burn;
> 'Tis pleasant there to be;
> But there is naught at Otterburn,
> To feed my men and me.
>
> The deer rins wild on hill and dale,
> The birds fly wild from tree to tree;
> But there is neither bread nor kale,
> To fend my men and me.
>
> (Marsden 1990, 29)

The isolation of the hills can be measured in distance from the nearest urban centres, with Edinburgh 90km to the north-west and Newcastle almost as far to the south-east (Figure 1.1). It is further emphasised by the comparative scale of the Hills. Although the highest summit, The Cheviot itself, is only 776m high (2670'), not high enough for a Scottish 'Munro', its gently rounded bulk and long unforgiving slopes rising from the surrounding lowlands make it feel truly mountainous (Plate 1.1). Daniel Defoe fancied The Cheviot to exceed two miles in height. In 1724, Defoe climbed to the summit from Wooler, and although fanciful and embedded in symbolism, his description is beautifully evocative. From the narrow valley of, probably, Harthope Burn (Figure 1.2; Plate 1.2)

> 'it was evident in the winter season' that 'not streams of water, but great rivers came pouring down from the hill in several channels, and those (at least some of them) very broad; they were overgrown on either bank with alder-trees, so close and thick, that we rode under them, as in an arbour'. As the party climbed on horseback 'the height began to look really frightful' ... 'and we rode up higher still, till at length our hearts fail'd us all together' ... 'so we work'd it upon our feet, and with labour enough, and sometimes began to talk of going no farther.' But the effort was worth it: 'I must acknowledge, I was agreeably surprized' by 'a most pleasant plain, of at least half a mile in diameter; and in the middle of it a large pond, or little lake of water', and, only a few years after the Act of Union, a 'view of both the united kingdoms, and we were far from repenting the pains we had taken'.
>
> (Defoe 1974 (1724), 355–7)

Archibald Geikie, a somewhat more seasoned and more acute observer than Defoe, nevertheless saw in these hills 'a dreary expanse of bare hill-top and bleak moor – wide lonely pastoral uplands, with scarce any further trace of human interference visible from this height than here and there a sheep-drain or grey cairn' (Geikie 1887, 288). Equally poignant but more bitter comes this paean from Wainwright's *Pennine Way Companion* (1968, 9) as the route reaches the Border ridge at the head of the Bowmont Valley: 'Most walkers will arrive ... already tired ... and none

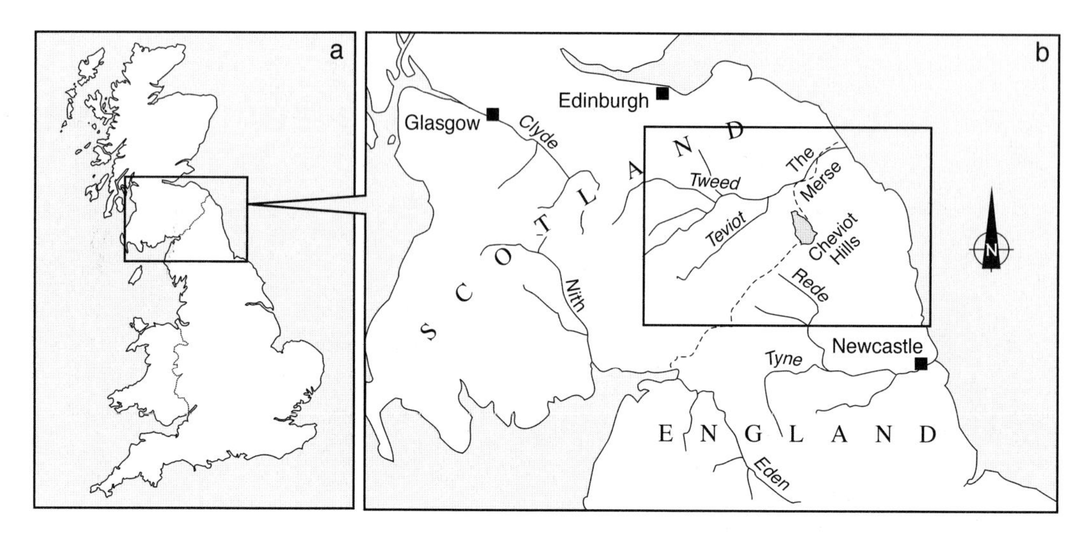

Figure 1.1
The Bowmont Valley in context: (a) southern Scotland and Northern England, straddling the current border, the region in essence providing the context for the work; (b) the region and the Anglo-Scottish border in relation to the major urban centres and the major drainage systems draining the Southern Uplands of Scotland and the northern Pennines in England. The box outlines the area depicted in detail in Figure 1.2. The small shaded lozenge lying mostly on the borderline is the upper Bowmont Valley, described in detail in this report.

the richer but a good deal wearier after floundering for two miles through filthy and pathless peathags that demolish the spirit and defeat the flesh without even the reward of a good view.... The Cheviot is too much for ordinary mortals. The Cheviot stands well away from the Border, wholly in England, and after experiencing it one can readily understand why the Scots wanted no part of it.'

1.2 Environmental reconstruction, environmental history and archaeological survey

The Bowmont Valley is one of the richest archaeological landscapes in southern Scotland (RCAHMS 1956). In this alone, Archibald Geikie (1887) missed much. The abundance of archaeological monuments is due to the extraordinary levels of prehistoric and historic settlement and land use, described in later chapters, but the preservation of so many monuments is because of a long prehistory and history of pastoral activity, as Geikie rightly observed, leaving an upland of grass and soils bound tightly together by the dense root mats of Cheviot turf (Muir 1956). Threats to some of the recorded monuments from, principally, afforestation, led in 1984 to the establishment of the Bowmont Valley Project, under the auspices of Historic Scotland. Over the next six years, archaeological field survey attempted to record, as completely as possible, the upstanding settlements and traces of cultivation within the catchment of the upper Bowmont Water. At the same time, the data reported here were collected. This report, completed in 2005, was for no good reason not submitted until 2008: publications after 2005 have not been incorporated – my apologies to those colleagues. Archaeological surveys of many uplands have yielded valuable data on the extent, density, altitudinal range, broad chronology and relations of successive settlement phases (e.g. Fleming 1978; Mercer 1991; RCAHMS 1997; Everson & Williamson 1998). In broadening the scope of archaeological enquiry from individual sites, landscape archaeology has vastly extended our understanding of prehistoric and historic geographies. Techniques for understanding change in 'natural' landscapes developed independently (Gregory 1985), but increasingly the influence of the landscape on people, and of people on the landscape, came to be regarded as seminal problems in palaeoenvironmental research (e.g. Oldfield 1969; Evans 1975; Simmons & Tooley 1981; Birks *et al* 1988; Chambers 1993; Simmons 2001).

The archaeological survey of an entire river catchment, as in the Bowmont Valley Project, has a resonance for the physical geographer, who has long understood that the drainage basin is 'the fundamental geomorphic unit' (Chorley 1969, 30). It

Plate 1.1
The broad bulk of The Cheviot rises above the surrounding rounded summit ridges and slopes of the northern Cheviot Hills. The view is east from the high altitude plateau of Mow Law.

Plate 1.2
In contrast to the airy summit ridges of The Cheviot, the radiating valleys approaching the hills are frequently narrow and deeply incised preglacial valleys. This is the College Burn in its upper reaches, east of and parallel to the Bowmont Valley, looking from the rough pasture of the valley floor towards The Cheviot in the distance.

was hoped that in the Bowmont Valley the adoption of a suite of compatible techniques, archaeological and palaeoenvironmental, each designed to function at comparable scales, had the potential to move beyond a depiction of the natural world as a mere backdrop to human settlement, and could explore more fully the complex dynamism of the linkages between natural and anthropogenic processes and rates of change.

When the project began, this synthetic approach and holistic view of the relevance for people of landscape change was becoming the norm (e.g. Fleming 1978; Jarman, Bailey & Jarman 1982; Jones 1983), perhaps most positively in Scotland (e.g. Whittle *et al* 1978; Renfrew 1985; Affleck, Edwards & Clarke 1988). However, the working relations between environmental scientists and archaeologists have been eroded as the concerns of archaeology have self-consciously moved from explanation in economic terms to more social and cultural drivers, most provocatively argued by Thomas (1990). One product of this erosion is the disengagement of many archaeologists and landscape archaeologists with what are seen as fads and fashions (O'Connor 1991; Wilson 1995; Rackham 2000; Taylor 2001). A more positive approach is to argue anew the need for holistic landscape histories (Evans 1999; Tipping *et al* 2004). One argument for this latter position is the old one, that people spent a substantial part of their life engaged in economic activities, and we should want to know why and how, and new connections relate the often exciting ideas emerging within social archaeology to their testing by scientific observation (Jones 2002). It is a misconception that scientific analyses can only answer questions pertaining to economic activities. Most techniques are descriptive of past environments. To understand how people moved within a landscape (Fowler 1998; Edmonds 1999), walked through a wood (Austin 2000; Tipping 2002a), processed from monument to monument (Barrett, Bradley & Green 1991; Parker Pearson 2000), discovered and regarded natural places (Bradley 2000), created and made special their own (Tilley 1994; Richards 1996) and transformed landscapes (Bruck 2000), just to consider major themes to emerge in the last decade within later prehistory, we need to understand those landscapes. Many ideas within social archaeology, as in cultural geography (Cosgrove & Daniels 1988; May & Thrift 2001) are more explicitly engaged with understanding place and landscape than in the 'new' archaeology of the later twentieth century. Almost all of these ideas are able to be explicitly tested by reconstructions of landscapes and environments (Butler 1995; Tipping *et al* 2004). There is more need now to forge closer links between archaeology and the natural sciences.

Given this, there is a need to explore how the explanation of past human behaviour in all its multi-faceted ways can emerge from an holistic depiction of their living in the landscape. Such an analysis should not only account for economic behaviour, but should inform on the choices and the decisions that communities made in other aspects of their life, daily and in the long term, the routine and commonplace as well as the special, to become a more complete story. This is a deeper purpose of this book.

This book is called an environmental history. It is not an archaeological text, although it is concerned with human beings and archaeologists will see their data used throughout. The book also draws on archival data, but this is not an economic or social history. It is perhaps closest to landscape history, and shares many of the biases and influences described by Williamson (2002, 21), a focus on the physical landscape and the 'subtle interplay of the natural and the cultural, the social and the environmental'. This is a purposefully generalist reading. Specialists will find much to quibble over, but synthesis requires a broad brush. Like Williamson's text, it is the case in this book that 'humans are not, perhaps, placed quite so close to the centre of the stage': central but not dominating, not getting in the way of the view. However, environmental history is different still. It should be more fully interdisciplinary (Tipping 1999; Tipping & Watson 1999), inclusive of all data sets and truly holistic. It recognises the differences between disciplines but draws up rules to ensure they work together (Worster 1993). It is more prepared to move people away from centre stage: Rackham (2000) has suggested, perhaps tongue in cheek, that an environmental history of Mars is not inconceivable. Environmental historians will, more persistently than economic or agrarian historians, pursue the links from human management to environmental degradation, writing histories less confident and Whiggish. Perhaps most importantly, where landscape history and landscape archaeology can sometimes paint a series of static portraits, environmental history explores the dynamism and mechanisms of change (Simmons 2001). Landscapes are commonly perceived as having been transformed, with the emphasis on dramatic change (e.g. for recent times by Devine 1994; Overton 1996; Williamson 2002), but this view at least in part results from discontinuities in the story introduced by different data sets, archival and archaeological (Horden & Purcell 2000). Data sets that sometimes are capable of describing landscapes with greater continuity are explored in this report to test the apparent abruptness of change (Tipping 1999).

1.3 Landscapes and the description of spaces

By trying to record all the upstanding monuments in a catchment, the archaeologist has immediately moved to a spatial scale of analysis, the landscape scale, that is closest to that of many palaeoenvironmental techniques. However, some of these techniques will not effectively describe this scale. The spatial resolutions at which some palaeoenvironmental techniques function best are not those of the landscape archaeologist. Equally critically, not all such techniques describe the same space, and not all applications of the same technique are comparable in how they describe space. For example, conflicts between pollen and land snail analyses in the description of the extent of open ground around archaeological sites (Dimbleby & Evans 1974) are resolved only when it is recognised that each technique describes a different space: land snails describe a smaller part of the landscape than most pollen analyses (Davies 1999; Davies & Wolski 2001). Charred plant assemblages are not comparable to pollen analyses in the space they describe: this difference is fundamental to explanations of later prehistoric agriculture in northern Britain (van der Veen 1992; Tipping 1997a), considered in detail later in this report. Pollen analyses from on site contexts and soils reflect a very much smaller space than pollen analyses from peat-filled basins and lakes (Jacobson & Bradshaw 1981; Tipping, Carter & Johnston 1994).

These conflicts are difficult to resolve. There should be an optimal spatial resolution for merging archaeological and archival data with palaeo-environmental analyses. When a microscopist adjusts what he or she can see through binocular eyepieces, he moves two fields of view of the object so that they overlap. The same adjustments have to happen in multidisciplinary environmental history. This thinking was developed at an early stage in the Bowmont Valley Project, because it determined in part the techniques that could be pursued and the locations of the sites sampled. The analysis is in no way sophisticated, and is unsurprising. It takes as its basis the simple idea that a landscape like the Bowmont Valley can be divided into more or less discrete landscape elements. These elements will be repeated across a landscape, not necessarily regularly, and can be mapped. They will appear as a patchwork or mosaic when mapped. Each landscape element can be expected to function in the same way because it has a consistent relation to topography, energy inputs and outputs, microclimate, etc. Identifying how one typical element has functioned will define how all those same elements within the landscape functioned. Different elements will then be nested within a landscape. The need is then to define the different elements, and to analyse one example of each element. The analogy is that of establishing the minimum number of colours to separate different regions on a map. Some assumptions in applying this approach, particularly to past landscapes, are considered below (Section 1.6), but it is now appropriate to introduce the physical geography of the northern Cheviot Hills and the Bowmont Valley in more analytical detail than provided in Section 1.1 by previous visitors.

1.4 The geography of the northern Cheviot Hills

Figure 1.2 depicts the physical and settlement geographies of south-east Scotland and north-east England (see Figure 1.1). The Moorfoot and Lammermuir Hills separate the Tweed Valley from Edinburgh. From the heart of the Southern Uplands west of Hawick, the River Teviot flows north-east to join the River Tweed near Kelso. To the south of the Teviot–Tweed river system, the Cheviot Hills are readily differentiated topographically by the long ridge of rising ground higher than 180 to 200m above sea level (asl). From The Cheviot the rivers radiate from the central dome in an echo of the preglacial drainage pattern (Hall 1991).

The Rivers Teviot and Tweed collect water from north-flowing tributaries across much of southern Scotland (Figures 1.1, 1.2). North-east of Jedburgh, constraints exercised by the patterns of glacial deposition and erosion force these rivers draining the Cheviot Hills to flow parallel to the Tweed (Clapperton 1967, 1970, 1971a; Gordon & Sutherland 1993) including lower tributaries of the Kale Water and the lower course of the Bowmont Water. The northern watershed of the Bowmont Water, paralleling the River Tweed south-east of Kelso, forms one boundary to the northern Cheviot Hills (Figure 1.2).

To the west, the Teviot watershed culminates in the Anglo-Scottish border south-west of The Cheviot. The highest ground reaches more than 600m asl on Peel Fell, south of Hawick, and an unbroken summit surface higher than 450m asl extends to The Cheviot

Plate 1.3
The high altitude plateaux surfaces of the northern and western Cheviots from the Mow Law – Craik Moor looking westward down Heatherhope Burn to the Southern Uplands and Carter Bar. The two uplands are indistinguishable. Some moor burning is still undertaken here, the effects seen in the foreground, although acid grasses today dominate the uplands.

(Figure 1.2). The west part of this ridge is called the Southern Uplands, the east part the Cheviot Hills. Topographically and geologically there is little to distinguish the two, and today they share the same patterns of grazing and afforestation (Plate 1.3). Only in a restricted outcrop on the higher dome of The Cheviot does the geological control of the Cheviot Granite emphasise differences. Where the Southern Uplands become the Cheviot Hills is difficult to define. Both were within the old county of Roxburghshire and the Scots Middle Marches (Tough 1928), so that people have not found it necessary to define this too closely. Carter Bar, a meeting place during the Border Wars (Tough 1928), is often seen as the boundary, as it is here (Figure 1.2), but largely because it lies on the Edinburgh to Newcastle road, not because of any natural line.

To the south, the Rivers Rede and Coquet drain south and east (Figure 1.2). They are part of the Cheviot Hills in all natural ways, only divided politically, but the Anglo-Scottish border forms a convenient southern boundary to the study area. To the east, the importance of the navigable River Tweed determined the political boundary, so that the border runs north, cutting across the Cheviot Hills and the east-flowing river valleys to Coldstream (Figure 1.2). The artificiality of this line is clear, and topographically the northern Cheviot Hills end in the east at an extraordinary scarp rearing above the Milfield Basin at Wooler (Plate 1.4), part of the catchment of the River Till looping south and east to the River Breamish, completing the circuit (Figure 1.2). Within the northern Cheviot Hills, the Bowmont Valley is undistinguished, save for the intensity of the work to be described in this report.

1.5 The geography of the Bowmont Valley

This section briefly reviews the geological and glacial history, and hence the physical setting of the Bowmont Valley, nested within and typical of the northern Cheviot Hills (Figures 1.2, 1.3). Also described are the present climate, soils and vegetation. The purpose is not simply descriptive, however, because by analysing these factors, the landform elements, the building blocks of the landscape introduced at a general level in Section 1.3, might be identified. A level plain

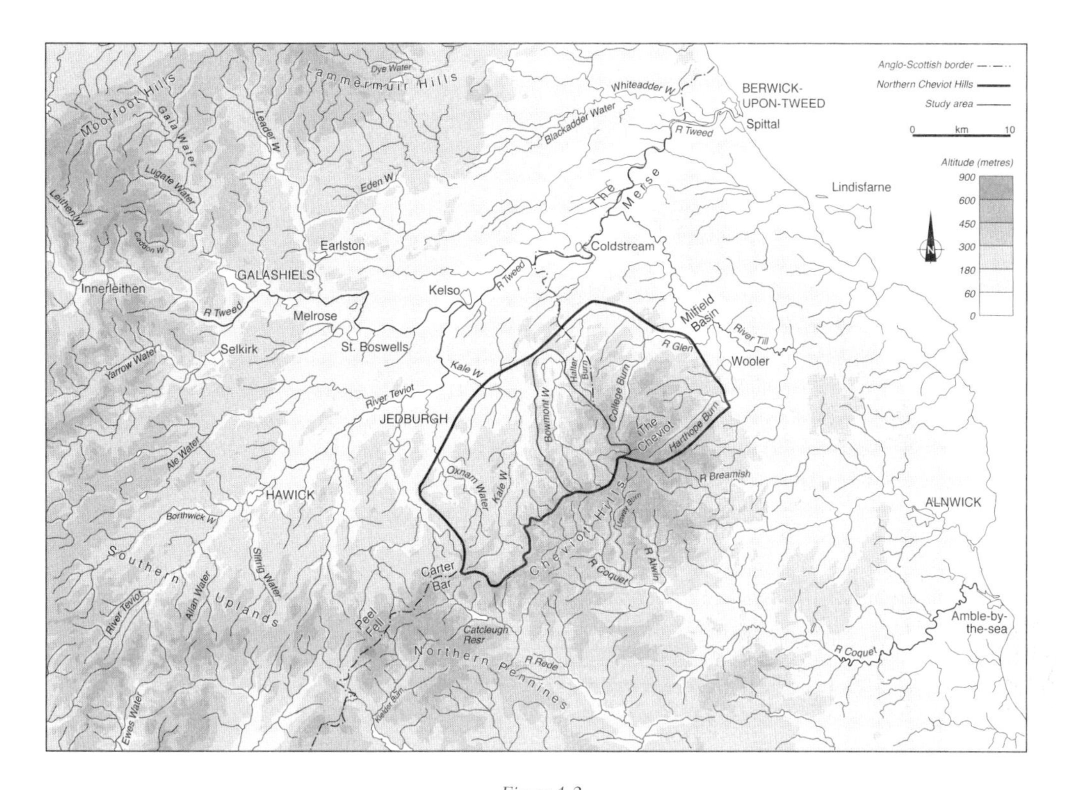

Figure 1.2

The physical and settlement geographies of south-east Scotland and north-east England, defining the northern Cheviot Hills and the study area in the upper Bowmont Valley.

Plate 1.4

The fault scarp of the eastern edge of the Cheviot Hills at Yeavering Bell, rearing above the flat enclosure landscape of the glaciofluvial and fluvial surfaces of the Milfield Basin.

stretching forever is a single landscape element. However, upland landscapes are heterogeneous and complicated. Their high relative relief tends to create a greater range of ecological niches, characterised by different plant and animal communities. They are more dynamic environments than lowlands, and respond to environmental stresses more readily.

Figure 1.3 depicts the major landforms, summits and rivers in the surveyed area. The area selected for archaeological survey extends to the entirety of the Bowmont Water drainage network from Primside Mill at 114m asl, south of the villages of Town and Kirk Yetholm (Figures 1.3, 1.5, 1.6), to the summit ridges north-west and south-west of

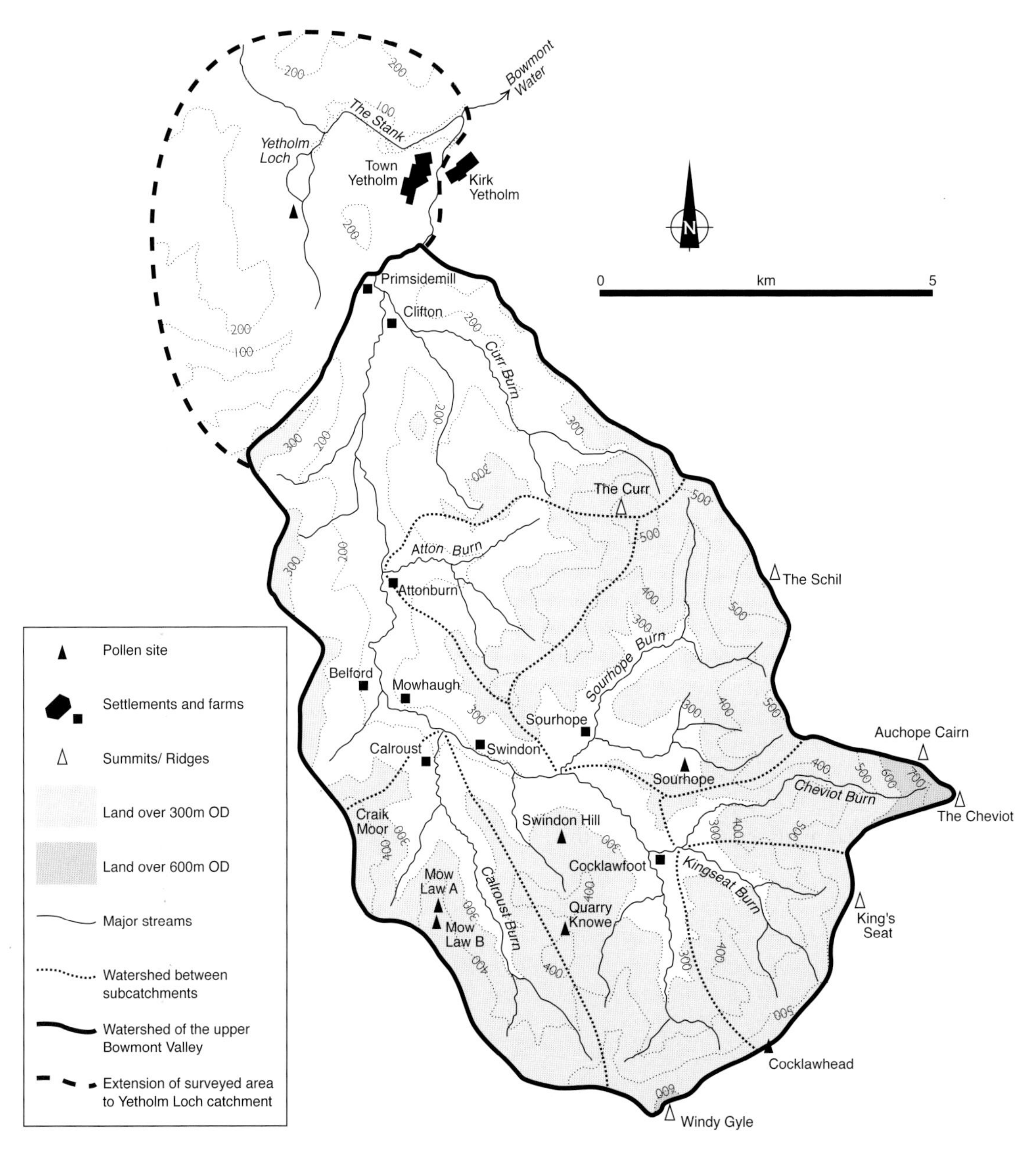

Figure 1.3
The physical and settlement geography of the upper Bowmont Valley, with the watershed defining the area archaeologically surveyed, and the extension examined to understand lowland landscape evolution, showing the villages of Town and Kirk Yetholm in the lower valley and the modern farms in the upper valley and tributaries, the drainage system and the different fluvial subcatchments. Also shown are the locations of pollen sequences described in this report.

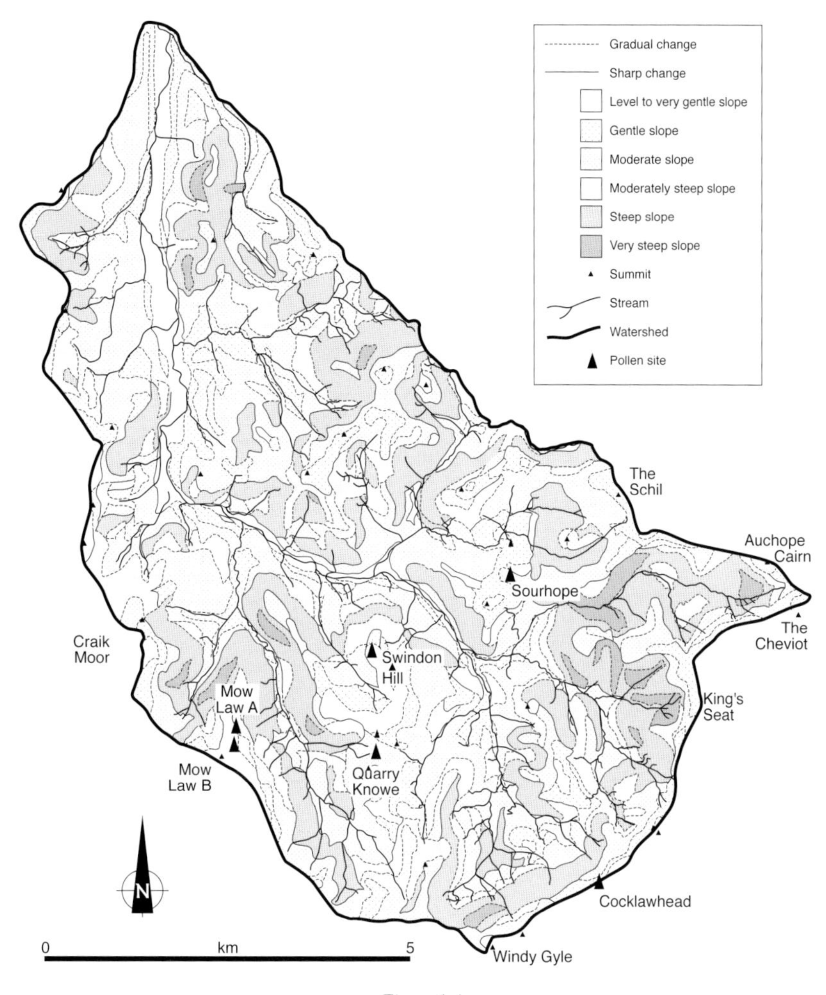

Figure 1.4
Slope elements in the upper Bowmont Valley in relation to the pollen sequences described in this report.

Auchope Cairn at 737m asl. Like Wainwright, the archaeological survey avoided The Cheviot itself. The palaeoenvironmental analyses presented in this report extend the surveyed area north of Primsidemill to include the subcatchment of Yetholm Loch and the delightfully named The Stank to Kirk Yetholm, at 100m asl (Figure 1.3). This extension represents a distinctive lowland landscape not seen in the higher valleys. The total relative relief, the difference between the highest and lowest ground, is 637m. The catchment is around 60km^2, with a perimeter of 50km and basin length in a straight line from Windy Gyle to The Stank of 14km.

Figure 1.4 shows the distribution of slope elements within the archaeologically surveyed area. Because the Yetholm Loch catchment was not surveyed for the project by archaeologists, these low and gentle slopes were not characterised in detail. The map is a simplified representation of slopes defined by the relative relief in 100m^2 squares from mapped contours on Ordnance Survey 1:10560 sheets. Contours are thus generalised and not sensitive to small scale changes in relief. The slope classes are defined in Table 1.1, and are comparable to those of Young (1972).

The upper Bowmont Valley

There are no major discontinuities in the distribution of slope classes: all slopes are smooth. One reason for this uniformity lies in the bedrock geology. Within the archaeologically surveyed area (Figure 1.3) there is a single bedrock, a series of Lower Devonian lavas called the Cheviot Volcanic Series (Carruthers *et al* 1932). These are dark grey, purple and reddish, jointed, medium to coarse grained pyroxene andesites. These

Table 1.1
Slope classes within the archaeologically surveyed area.

Description	*Slope angles*	*Percentage in archaeologically surveyed area*
level to very gentle	0 to 3°	5.6%
gentle	3.1 to 8°	14.1%
moderate	8.1 to 14.5°	34.5%
moderately steep	14.6 to 18°	18.5%
steep	18.1 to 31°	24.9%
very steep	31.1 to 42°	2.3%

lavas occasionally exhibit, on hillsides, the stepped appearance typical of successive lava flows, too small to show as breaks of slope on Figure 1.4. Common (1953) suggested that some of the more prominent steps may have formed the cores of cultivation terraces on steeper slopes. Emplaced into the lavas was the Cheviot Granite. It is exposed over a small area south and east of the border, outside the surveyed area. Associated with emplacement of the granitic intrusion are dyke swarms and fracture zones. The latter form extended linear belts of crushed and shattered bedrock up to 100m wide. These run in two principal orientations, north-east and north-north-west. The straight reaches of several rivers in the Cheviot Hills such as the Harthope Burn south-west of Wooler (Figure 1.2), were probably formed in preglacial times by selective fluvial erosion along these narrow fracture zones. The approximate south to north parallelism of the middle courses of the upper Kale, Bowmont and College Burns (Figure 1.2) may also imply a similar structural control (Common 1953).

The radiating Cheviot valleys predate Quaternary glaciation. They are probably of Tertiary age (Sissons 1967; Hall 1991, 1997). Parts of the highest surfaces above the valleys are also probably of Tertiary age. Auchope Cairn is substantially higher than other ridges, but summits such as Windy Gyle and The Schil rise only tens of metres above a high level plateau at 490 to 520m asl (Common 1953), remnants of a once

Plate 1.5
The gentle rounded slopes of the summit ridge between the Bowmont Valley in Scotland to the right and the College Valley in England to the left from The Schil, looking towards Auchope Cairn and, to the right on the skyline, The Cheviot.

Plate 1.6
Looking south and west from the summit ridge at The Schil, the convex upper slopes steepen to deeply scoured meltwater channels and basins in the tributary valleys, here above Sourhope Farm. The block of conifers behind Sourhope Burn is on Fasset Hill. To the left and above the plantation is the large nineteenth-century walled intake, and behind this is the pollen site of Sourhope (Chapter 4). Beyond this is the ridge of Bonnie Laws, looking back to where the front cover photograph was taken, in front of the large conifer plantations to the right on Swindon Hill. Windy Gyle dominates the skyline.

more continuous preglacial surface (Frontispiece; Plates 1.1, 1.3). Summit ridges are usually gentle slopes (Plate 1.5), although very extensive high level plateaux can be remarkably level, as on Mow Law in the south-west of the valley (Figure 1.4). Summit ridges on this highest surface can be punctuated by small tors in well jointed Devonian andesite. These may be products of initial deep weathering in the warmer climate of the Tertiary period (Linton 1955; Hall 1996), although their exposure probably occurred during periglacial erosion and removal of weathered rock from around them (Common 1953, Ragg & Bibby 1966; Douglas & Harrison 1985).

All slopes change from convex to concave between the summit ridges and the valley floor (Plate 1.6). Below the watershed and the highest plateau, slopes carry a number of lower altitude plateau surfaces (Plate 1.7), level to very gentle slopes on interfluves between streams; the most extensive occur between Quarry Knowe and Swindon Hill (Figure 1.4). Common (1953) defined three such surfaces in the Cheviots, at (i) 455 to 395m asl, (ii) 365 to 300m asl, and (iii) 230 to 160m asl. Their origin is unclear, but they are probably preglacial in age.

No slopes in the Bowmont Valley, and very few in the Cheviot Hills, are precipitous (45 to 70°; Young 1972), despite the impression that Daniel Defoe sought to impart to his readers. In the northern Cheviots there are cliffs only at Hen Hole and the Bizzle at the head of the College Burn, immediately north of Auchope Cairn (Figure 1.3). These two localities probably represent corries freshly excavated when ice last accumulated, during the final stages of the Devensian glaciation, in the Loch Lomond Stadial (*c* 12 500 to 11 500 cal years ago) when glaciers readvanced in many parts of upland Britain (Clapperton 1970; Harrison 1994a). These deep, north-facing corries are the only areas in the Cheviot Hills thought to have collected ice in this period, and glaciers probably flowed only hundreds of metres from the back walls. Earlier glaciations were longer lasting. Evidence of glacial erosion and deposition in most of the Cheviot Hills is thought to date to the last major glaciation in the area, the Late Devensian or Dimlington Stadial, which ended *c* 15 000 cal years

Plate 1.7
The separate but comparable low altitude plateau surfaces of Fasset Hill and Bonnie Laws above the deeply incised tributary valleys. The parallel ridges cutting the slope of Bonnie Laws in the foreground mark the edges of a set of shallow subglacial meltwater channels.

Plate 1.8
Filling the former floor of the upper Bowmont Valley are very thick accumulations of reddish-brown glacial lodgment till, here forming a cliff incised by the Bowmont Water at Belford.

ago. The Cheviot Hills probably developed a small ice cap (Clapperton 1970). If models developed for the Cairngorm are appropriate, ice on summit surfaces had insufficient speed to demolish tors (e.g. Sugden 1968; Hall 1996), but valley glaciers accelerated as they flowed down preglacial valleys to merge with massive ice sheets streaming east along the Tweed Valley from the Southern Uplands. Some glacial landforms in the upper Bowmont Valley are erosional. The rounding of higher slopes relates to such processes, as does the scouring of deep basins such as the enclosed Sourhope basin beneath extensive very steep slopes at the foot of The Schil (Figure 1.4). Subglacial meltwater channels were excavated on slopes (Plate 1.7; Clapperton 1967, 1971b).

Other landforms of glacial and periglacial origin in the upper parts of the valley are depositional. On the highest summits, as around Auchope Cairn (Clark 1970; Douglas & Harrison 1985), shallow mass movement deposits are thought to be products of a periglacial climate following deglaciation from the Dimlington Stadial. Though undated, they are assumed to date to the Loch Lomond Stadial, when the climate was cold enough to generate glaciers at the head of the College Burn (above). Very thick deposits of probable Dimlington Stadial till are found on the lower slopes, below 300m asl (>8m thick near Belford and upstream of Swindon Cottage; Plate 1.8). Overlying the till, very extensive sheets of banded soliflucted sediment mantle the concave lower slopes of all upland valleys (Douglas & Harrison 1984, 1985; Harrison 1993, 1994b). In section the sheets are bedded and sorted sands and stony sands (Plate 1.9). They can be shown to have been derived from the till, and so are later. These vary from low angled (6 to 7°) terraces to shorter, steeper (18°) slopes. The sheets thicken as they approach the lowest slopes, and this is a reason for the concave and gentle slopes lining wide valleys (Figure 1.4). This downslope reworking of sediment is another reason the slopes of the Cheviots are so smooth. Also undated, these solifluction sheets may have been formed as frozen slurries at the end of the Dimlington Stadial and in the intensely cold climate of the Loch Lomond Stadial (Douglas & Harrison 1987). The same periglacial conditions may have led to deeper seated rotational landslips which pockmark very steep slopes (Plate 1.10), and to the formation of gravel river terraces above the present valley floor, mapped in the high valleys fringing Kingseat Burn.

The concave solifluction sheets, believed to have last formed 11 500 cal years ago, flowed to and partially filled contemporaneous valley floors, but Plate 1.11 shows that these now lie some 10 to 15m above the present valley floor. Downcutting of these valleys probably occurred in the earliest Holocene period, discussed fully in Chapter 7, resulting in the distinctive trenched cross profile of southern Scottish valleys. Mapping this trenching of valley forms in the upper Bowmont Valley shows that the drainage pattern and density has not changed significantly in the last 10 000 to 11 000 cal years.

The upper Bowmont Valley has several subcatchments. A way of defining subcatchments is to measure

Plate 1.9
The very poorly sorted reddish-brown till in the lower part of this section near Swindon Cottage in the upper Bowmont Valley is overlain by a succession of better sorted sediments to the soil at the top. These sediments are less consolidated than the till, and so they hold water more and appear darker here. They have been derived by slope erosion from till on the valley sides, and so can be very coarse. Although not dated, they seem to have formed by periglacial processes in the later stages of the Devensian Lateglacial.

Plate 1.10

On steeper slopes are large incipient, not fully formed corries which are the seat of deep slope failures, probably active at the end of the last glacial stage and now filled with peat. This example is on the steep west side of Percy Law in the north of the upper valley. Below the corrie, the small stream has at some time been incised to form a narrow gully. The lower till slopes carry beautiful adastral curves of broad rig cultivation, but the wide valley floor in the foreground has lost any trace, partly because it is probably younger than the ploughmarks and partly because post World War II ploughing has destroyed the evidence.

Plate 1.11

Looking south by the farm of Swindon Cottage, the incised floor of the Bowmont Water can be seen. The low cliff by the conifers across the valley marks the depth of fluvial downcutting from till and colluvial sediments (Plates 1.8, 1.9) on the lower slopes of Swindon Hill. These lower slopes carry well preserved cultivation terraces and lynchets. Below the cliff, the valley floor is marked by smaller arcuate cliffs that are the edges of former channels, and separate different terrace surfaces, mapped and described by Tipping (1993) and considered in Chapter 7.

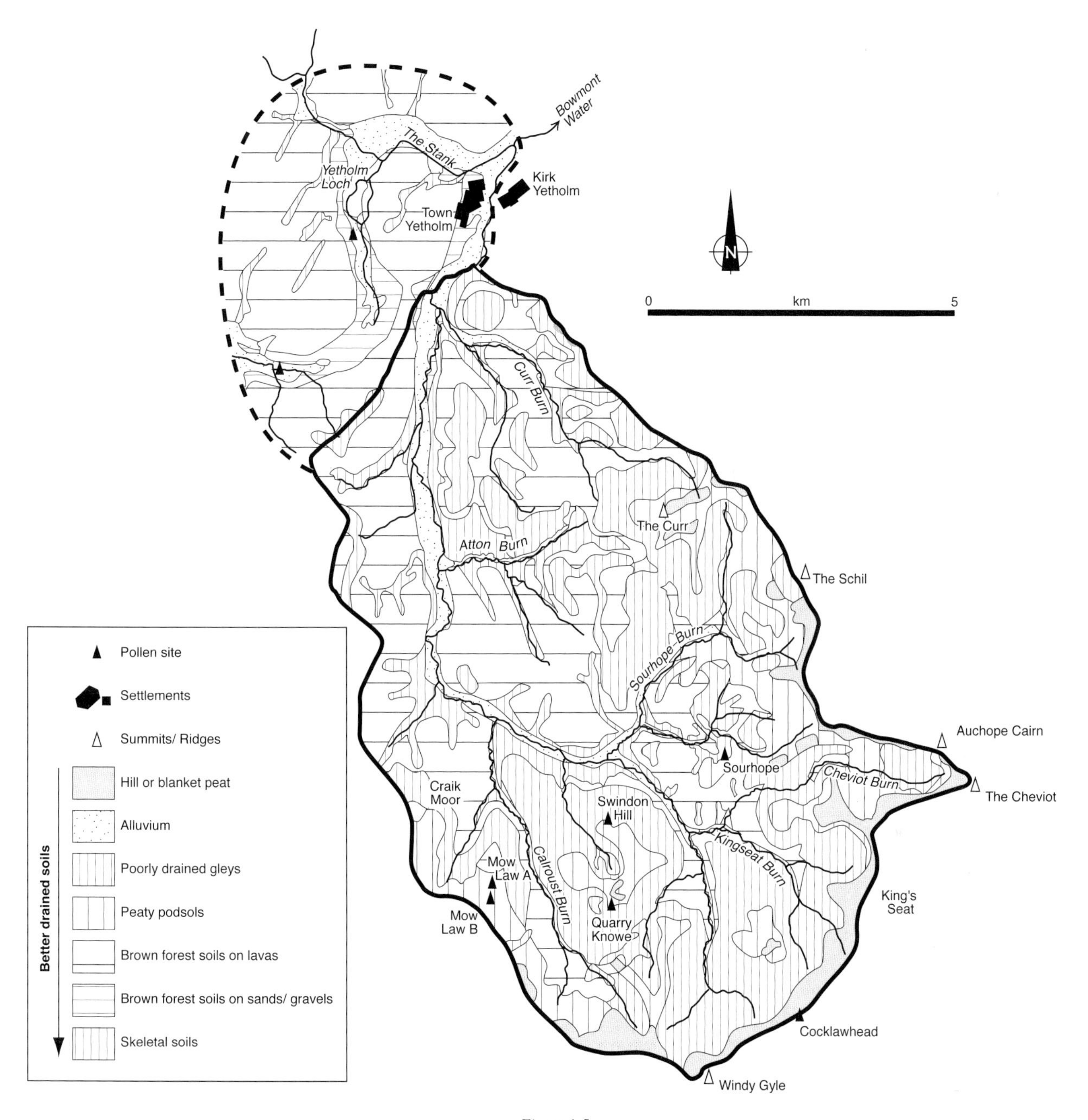

Figure 1.5
Soils in the upper Bowmont Valley (from Muir 1956; Ragg 1960) in relation to the pollen sequences described in this report.

stream order (Gardiner 1975): in Strahler's (1952) scheme all unbranched streams are 1st Order; when two of these join, the downstream section is 2nd Order; when two 2nd Order streams join the downstream section is 3rd Order and so on. Figure 1.4 shows the drainage pattern (the best estimate of drainage density, taken from Ordnance Survey 1:25 000 mapping of the blue line river network), and Figure 1.3 outlines the watersheds separating 4th Order river catchments. Kelsocleugh Burn, below Windy Gyle, is the head of the Bowmont Water. The different shapes of subcatchments, linear (Calroust, Kelsocleugh Burns) or more regular (Sourhope), are determined by geological structural controls. Catchments draining from Auchope Cairn, the Kingseat and Cheviot Burns, have a high density of streams on the steeper slopes

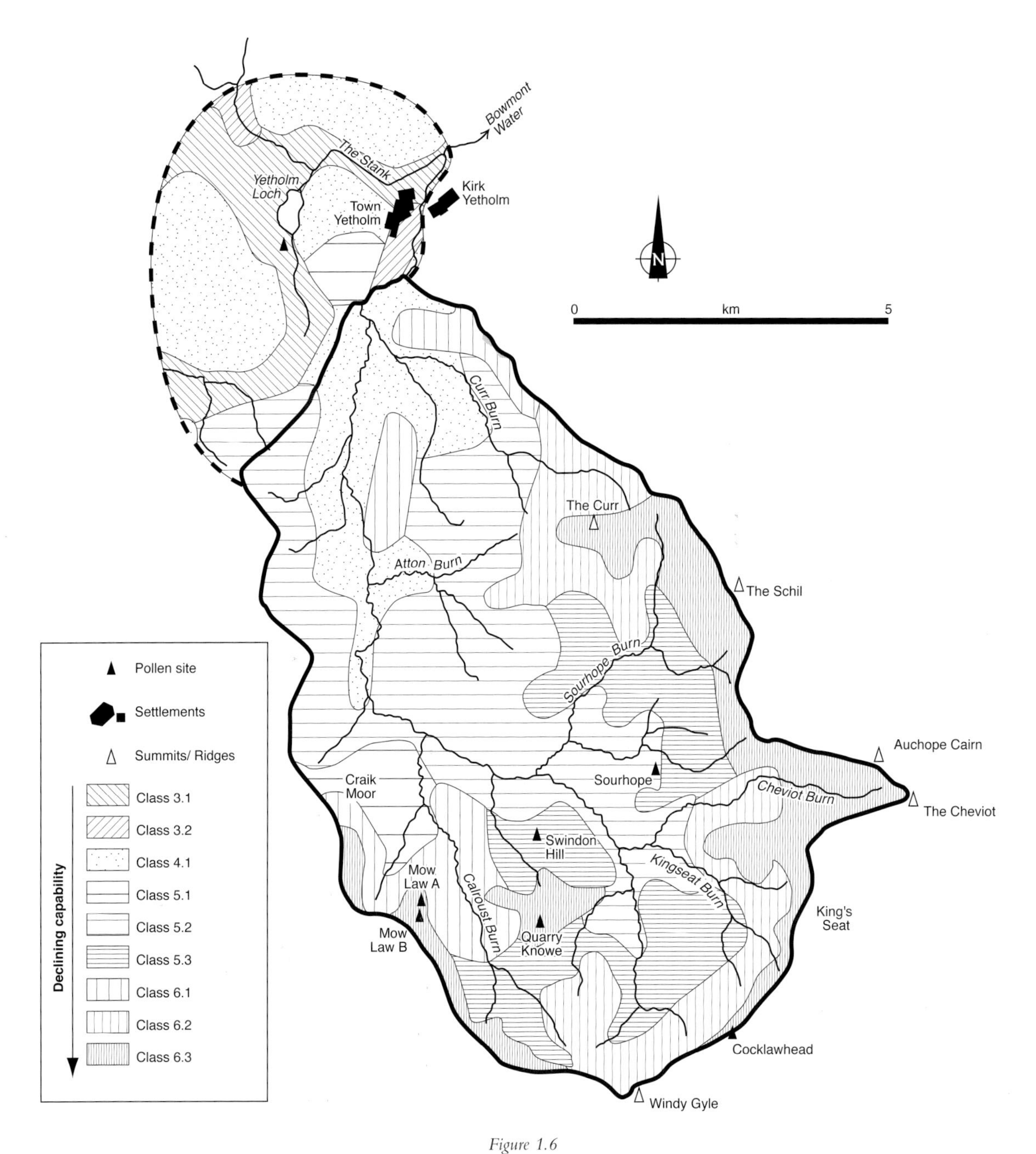

Figure 1.6
Twentieth-century land use capability classes (Bown & Shipley 1982; see Table 1.1) in the upper Bowmont Valley in relation to the pollen sequences described in this report.

below the summit ridges, and consequently become 4th Order streams quickly. Drainage is very effective from steep bedrock slopes in most of the valley, but drainage density is noticeably lower, and the 4th Order catchment consequently larger, from the moderate and gentle till covered right bank slopes of the Curr Burn draining to Primsidemill. The Bowmont Water is a 5th Order (Strahler) stream as far upvalley as Cocklawfoot, where the Kingseat and Cheviot Burns join, and does not grow larger where it exits the archaeologically surveyed area at Primsidemill. From Cocklawfoot to Primside Mill, the Bowmont water falls at a mean gradient of 11.3m/km over its 11.5km length. Stream number (Shreve 1967) increases regularly and linearly

Table 1.2

Classes and descriptions of current (1970s) land capability for agriculture (from Bown & Shipley 1982).

Class	*Description (Bown & Shipley 1982: Sheet 7 – Land Capability for Agriculture)*	*Percentage occupied**		
3.1	land 'capable of producing consistently high yields of a narrow range of crops (principally cereals and grasses) and/or moderate yields of a wider range'	n.d.	9.6	6
3.2	'capable of average production but high yields of barley, oats and grass ... Other crops are limited to potatoes and forage crops. Grass leys are common and reflect the increasing growth limitations for arable crops'	n.d.	13.8	9.4
4.1	'suited to rotations which ... include forage crops and cereals for stock feed. Yields of grass are high'	n.d.	10.3	4.8
4.2	'primarily grassland with some limited potential for other crops. Grass yields can be high but difficulties of conservation or utilisation may be severe, especially in areas of poor climate or on very wet soils. Some forage cropping is possible and, when the extra risks involved can be accepted, an occasional cereal crop'	8.9	10	6
5.1	'Establishment of a grass sward and its maintenance present few problems and potential yields are high with ample growth throughout the season. Patterns of soil, slope or wetness may be slightly restricting but the land has few poaching problems. High stocking rates are possible'	2.8	4	2.4
5.2	'Sward establishment presents no difficulties but moderate or low trafficability, patterned land and/or strong slopes cause problems. Growth rates are high' ... 'satisfactory stocking rates ... are achievable'	38.5	12.9	7.8
5.3	there are 'serious trafficability and poaching problems' which result in rapid 'deterioration in quality' of sward. 'The land cannot support high stock densities without damage and this may be serious after heavy rain even in summer'	16.4	10.3	8.7
6.1	'high proportions of palatable herbage in the sward, principally the better grasses'	8.3	2.2	2
6.2	'Moderate quality herbage', e.g. bent grasses, rush pasture and herb rich moorland	10.8	5.5	7.2
6.3	'low grazing values, particularly heather moor, bog heather moor and blanket bog'	14.2	17.5	40.1

* 'Percentage occupied' excludes urban areas: (a) archaeologically surveyed area in the upper Bowmont Valley; (b) SE Scotland; (c) Scotland
n.d. not determined

downstream in the archaeologically surveyed area, emphasising the unity of the valley and the uniform geology.

In the upper valley, the streams are gravel rich, and are bordered by low gravel terraces on the floodplain: their evolution is discussed in Chapter 7. They overtop their low banks regularly and are capable of very violent flood events: in 1986 an agricultural researcher was killed when his Land-Rover was swept from the road at Belford (Archer 1992). The Bowmont Water is only monitored by hydrologists when it becomes the River Glen, below the confluence with the College Burn at Kirknewton (HMSO 1983), but here the flood regime is not significantly more 'flashy' than the River Tweed itself.

The distribution of soils is related to geology, aspect and slope angle (Figure 1.5). Despite the uniform geology, the distribution exhibits considerable complexity. Soils in the UK are classified into Associations determined by parent material and Series indicating contrasting soil properties. Within the archaeologically surveyed area, all soils belong to a single Association, the Sourhope Association, derived from parent materials associated with Devonian lavas, from bedrock or from tills and soliflucted sediment containing large amounts of lava rock fragments.

These parent materials most commonly disintegrate to a coarse gritty sandy loam. The Soil Series principally vary in their drainage state, which is a product of aspect (the drying of south-facing slopes in direct sunlight) and slope. Slope angle (Figure 1.4) is critical for many significant soil forming processes through the erodibility of the soil. In the Lammermuir Hills to the north across The Merse (Figure 1.1), a similar landscape to the Cheviots, Whitfield and Furley (1972) found that slope angles steeper than 18 to 22° (steep to very steep slopes; Figure 1.4) were critical for accelerated soil erosion. The erodibility of the soil in part determines the chemistry (pH), organic content and dominant particle sizes of soils.

In the upper Bowmont Valley, the highest summit plateaux and ridges between the head of Heatherhope Burn and The Cheviot, on level to gentle slopes, have a blanket of peat (Figure 1.5). This morass is that not so fondly described by Wainwright in Section 1.1. The evolution of this blanket peat cover is fully described in Chapter 6. As the slopes become convex and steeper, and drainage efficiency increases, the peat thins to a clearly defined edge. Under present land uses and climate over 35% of the blanket peat in the Cheviot Hills is being degraded by gullies cut into these edges (Wishart & Warburton 2001). Archer (1992) described one spectacular catastrophic failure of shallow blanket peat in July 1893, just over the border on Bloodybush Edge when a summer convective storm caused a peat slide, still visible in 1987.

On steeper slopes are immature soils called rankers or skeletal soils (Figure 1.5), thin and unstructured because soil particles have been lost by surface erosion. On moderate to steep slopes skeletal soils form complexes with more mature freely drained brown forest soils of the Sourhope Series. Soil stability, and so position on a slope, is the major control on soil development, rather than altitude, because high level plateaux also support brown forest soils. More limited in extent are freely drained peaty podsols of the Cowie Series on gentle plateau slopes at lower altitudes (350 to 450m asl). More poorly drained gley soils of the Atton Series are found on concave gentle to moderate lower slopes in till or soiliflucted sediment (Muir 1956).

The distribution of soils in the Bowmont Valley (Figure 1.5; Muir 1956) is closely related to slope class (Figure 1.4). The correspondence between steep to very steep slopes and skeletal soils suggests current soil instability on slopes steeper than 20°, around 28% of the valley. However, away from the eroded blanket peat active erosional features are very few, even on steep slopes. There is little evidence that skeletal soils are actively losing sediment at the present time. The majority of deeply incised gullies at the heads of streams on the steepest slopes appear, for example, to have formed in the past and to be relict features, now grassed over and stable. Evidence of extensive slope failure is absent, and small sheep scars and terracettes are the most commonly observed erosional elements. Slope angle is thus not the only determinant of soil erodibility, and the densely rooted grass sward restricts significant soil movement at the present day.

However, slope angle is critical in current land management regimes such as ploughing (Muir 1956; Bown & Shipley 1982). The logistics of employing heavy farm machinery are commonly defined by slope. Arable crops are not harvested on slopes steeper than gentle (up to 11°), and slopes more than moderately steep provide little scope with modern equipment for improvement (Bown & Shipley 1982). The pattern of present day land uses (Figure 1.6) shows this relation. The best land under the present climate, agricultural economy and technology is still of only limited potential for arable farming (Class 4.2); all other areas are today considered suitable for improved grassland (Class 5) or only rough grazing (Class 6). Table 1.2 shows the markedly higher proportion of very good grazing land (Class 5) in the Bowmont Valley compared to other parts of southern Scotland, predominantly because soils are developed on comparatively nutrient rich andesitic parent materials (Muir 1956).

Grasslands dominate the landscape of the upper Bowmont Valley. *Calluna* (ling heather) heath is common only on less intensively grazed areas (King 1960) and on the summit blanket peats (Figure 1.5). There are different grassland communities, however, with contrasting dominant grasses and associated herb floras. The acid grassland developed on the Sourhope Series provides good pasture. Atton Series soils generally support poorer quality grasses, and provide moderate to poor grazing, as do the wetter Cowie Series soils (Muir 1956). These grassland communities have been described in detail by King (1955, 1962), Hunter (1962) and King and Nicholson (1964) because within the valley the Hill Farming Research Organisation has maintained an experimental hill grazing farm at Sourhope (Figure 1.3). Because the development of these hill pastures is one of the key questions in this report, detailed discussion is left until Chapter 8.

As a relief to the unremittingly open vistas provided by these grasslands, most farms in the valley established shelter belts and avenues of trees in the eighteenth century cal AD, many not native to the region, as at Clifton, Attonburn and Belford. Their planting and the agricultural improvements that accompanied them are part of the story pursued in later chapters.

The lower Bowmont Valley

Almost every aspect of the landscape changes immediately north of Primside Mill and the protective flanks of the northern Cheviots. This contrast was the reason for trying to understand how the lowland valley had developed using palaeoenvironmental techniques, and how the two regions, upland and lowland, might have been linked in the past.

Immediately south of Morebattle, and following the line separating the archaeologically surveyed area and the subcatchment of Yetholm Loch (Figure 1.3), Devonian lavas are replaced by younger Old Red Sandstone calcareous sandstones and conglomerates. These are more readily erodible than the Cheviot lavas, and the landscape is lower. The highest point in these sedimentary rocks is at 256m asl to the west of Yetholm Loch (Figure 1.3), and the valley floor throughout the subcatchment is at 100m asl. Slopes at their steepest are only moderate.

Yetholm Loch receives water from a stream so small as to have no name. The watershed with the Kale Water is barely higher than the valley floor (Figure 1.3). During the Dimlington Stadial, beneath the powerful east-flowing ice sheets that moulded the landscape, the Kale Water flowed eastward to the Bowmont Water (Common 1953; Clapperton 1970). The Yetholm Loch subcatchment is the only part of the Bowmont Valley where the valley floor is a substantial spread of fluvioglacial sands and gravels. The Kale Water descending from the Cheviots was captured during deglaciation by west-flowing streams. The valley floor north of Morebattle was a large lake throughout the Devensian Lateglacial period, persisting through the Loch Lomond Stadial and into the Holocene (Mannion 1978). The sediment and pollen records from this former lake, at the extant Linton Loch are discussed in Chapter 8.

The sands and gravels on the valley floor support freely drained brown forest soils of the Eckford Series (Figure 1.5; Muir 1956; Ragg 1960). These are the best quality soils in the Bowmont Valley (Figure 1.6). The gentle slopes above, on gley soils of the Atton Series, are comparable to those in the upper Bowmont Valley except that parent materials and soils are more base rich (Mannion 1978) and are ploughed, the only extensive area of arable land in the Bowmont Valley.

Climate and microclimate

In understanding a landscape of high relief as in the Cheviots, small scale contrasts in climate are more significant than regional patterns for understanding soil development, slope stability, natural plant communities, human settlement and land uses. The complexity of these microclimatic patterns cannot be fully constructed for the Bowmont Valley because there is no network of meteorological stations, but can be defined in simplistic terms.

The prevailing wind across southern Scotland is from the south-west (Harrison 1997). At the regional scale there is no significant difference in temperatures between west and east Scottish coasts. Within inland hills, however, the decrease in temperature with altitude can be rapid: for every 100m increase, maximum temperatures fall by around 1 °C, minimum temperatures by around 0.4 °C. At Sourhope, deep in a large basin at 275m asl, temperatures ranged (1952 to 1958) from an average in winter (January and February) of 1.25 °C to 13.85 °C in July and August (King 1963). On Fasset Hill, immediately north of Sourhope, the summit at 371m asl will experience mean winter temperatures close to freezing. However, the high relief and steep slopes of the inner recesses of the northern Cheviots accentuate differences in the benefit of sunlight: a 20° south-facing slope receives twice as much radiation in winter than a level surface (Geiger 1965). Steep north-facing slopes on the south side of the Sourhope Burn receive no direct sunlight until very late in the spring. The sensitivity of this relation is profound in ecological processes and land uses. Temperature is the main determinant in assessing the growing season for crops. The growing season for crops in the mid-twentieth century on level unshaded surfaces was 222 days at Kelso (Muir 1956). Being temperature dependent, reductions of around 17 growing days per 100m increase in altitude (Harrison & Harrison 1988) imply that the growing season at Primside Mill, low down on the valley floor, might be 205 days, and deep in the valley at Cocklawfoot, about 180 days. In valleys shaded by east to west trending ridges the growing season is dramatically shorter.

The Cheviot Hills are considerably drier, up to 60%, than hills farther west (Harrison 1997), the product of a rain 'shadow' from westerly frontal depressions. Average annual rainfall recorded at Sourhope Farm (1952 to 1958) was 894mm, ranging from 676mm to 1100mm (King 1962). Within the valley, average values vary from around 750mm in the lower, northerly part of the valley to 1400 to 1800mm on the flanks of

Auchope Cairn (Muir 1956; Archer 1992). Harrison (1997) suggests a rule is for an increase of 1mm of precipitation per 1m altitude. Most rain falls in the depths of winter, and April is the driest month, but late summer convectional rainstorms can be extreme (Archer 1992). Snow is most common in east winds, and is twice as common in winters with a dominant easterly circulation (Harrison 1997), though it rarely lies for any length of time.

1.6 Landscape elements within the Bowmont Valley

Many, though not all, of the factors discussed in the last section are constant features that define landscape elements at all times. All but a few parts of the landscape were in place before the present interglacial. The distribution of slopes and surfaces has not changed significantly in the last 11 500 years. This is not to assume that these slopes and surfaces have always looked as they do now, but that slopes and surfaces have been where they are now throughout the Holocene period. It is not assumed that the types of soil mapped at the present day formed 11 500 years ago: this will be disproved in the analyses presented in this report. But it is assumed that gradients in soil formation, e.g. from wet to dry, from alkaline to acid, from cold to warm, have been maintained: environmental gradients were probably constant, but the steepness of environmental gradients will have changed.

The physical setting, the valleys and hills, determine the subtleties of climate and soil at local scales, and thus the ecological components, the distribution of plant and animal communities. However, although the physical setting has not changed significantly, the present day ecological patterning has been determined by events that are the subject of this study. Therefore, evidence for landscape change in the last 11 500 years, gathered prior to or during the present work, cannot be used to define landscape elements: this would introduce interpretative circularities.

Contrasts in geology, glacial history, soils and current land uses are striking between the *lower valley*, north of Primsidemill, and the upper valley. Within the upper valley the wet, occasionally waterlogged but readily accessible gentle lower slopes and gravel *valley floor* of the Bowmont Water from Primsidemill to Belford are together the focus for modern farms (Figure 1.3). The low gradient of the main valley floor, its width compared to the narrow defile of the Calroust Burn (Figures 1.3, 1.4) and its northerly alignment mean that pedological, ecological and climatic constraints are comparable.

The Bowmont Water north of Belford, and *tributary valleys* to the Bowmont Water, are different. The extent of gleyed soils on gentle slopes is substantially less, and steeper slopes are often closer to the river channels. Many side valleys run east to west, and the great depths of valleys created during preglacial and glacial incision mean that high ridges severely reduce sunlight and the growing season. Within the deeper valleys of the interior, contrasts emerge at all scales, between north-facing and south-facing slopes, between slopes and the plateau surfaces and across single hillsides. The limitations of moving modern farm machinery make current land use capabilities similarly intractable throughout the upper valleys, but extensive *low level plateau surfaces* supporting well drained podsols and brown forest soils would make agriculture more attractive with easier access or less advanced technology. It is these surfaces that, with the greater investment available for tracks and machines, have recently been made more accessible to conifer planting. Above these, the *summit ridges and high level plateaux* represent a distinctive landscape element. Not all are covered in blanket peat, and all are accessible by foot, horse, Argocat or 4WD vehicle across the many tracks of the watershed. Four of these five landscape elements are analysed in this report: the Bowmont Water valley floor between Primsidemill and Belford could not be characterised by the techniques used here because of the absence of appropriate sites.

1.7 Approaches to environmental reconstruction in the Bowmont Valley

Particular patterns of settlement and land use need not have been confined to particular landscape elements. Topographic and edaphic controls can be overridden by human choice. The imposition of a single farming system over a naturally heterogeneous landscape is one example: we do not always behave in ecologically predictive ways, but are driven as much by economic and social behaviours. In using the framework of landscape elements, then, there is no supposition of environmental determinism in the analysis: the framework is only a way of simplifying an inherently complex system.

Human societies have a complex but poorly understood relationship with uplands. The hills are often seen as marginal, environmentally, economically and socially, but these views are judgmental and relative, defined from the standpoint of a regional, and increasingly global, integrated economy (McNeill 2000). More positive views of the stimulation to people provided by these landscapes are possible (Fernadez-Armesto 2000; Tipping 2002b). A frequently used model has seen populations fully utilising upland areas at certain periods in the past but driven by environmental stresses to abandoning them at others (e.g. Parry 1978; Burgess 1984; Lamb 1985; Barber 1997; Coles & Mills 1998; Fagan 2000; Simmons 2001), but rarely has this model been rigorously tested (Young & Simmonds 1995; Tipping 1998, 2002b). Testing of this requires the description and interpretation of the many different components, natural and anthropogenic, in this web of linkages. To examine change in only one component is unsatisfactory, and the intent in this report is to develop a multidisciplinary approach to its resolution.

Chapter 2 considers in detail the key techniques employed. The principal technique used in this report is pollen analysis (palynology). Pollen analysis aims to reconstruct past vegetation patterns by identifying and quantifying the proportions of pollen and spores collecting and preserved in continually accumulating sediment stratigraphies. Behind this simple statement lies an array of assumptions and interpretative biases (Birks & Birks 1980; Huntley & Webb 1988; Faegri & Iversen 1989; Delcourt & Delcourt 1981; Moore, Webb & Collinson 1991). Nevertheless, palynology has proved to be one of the most robust and most sensitive methods of investigating past environments (Pennington 1969; Walker & West 1970; Godwin 1975; Lowe & Walker 1984; Ingrouille 1995; Simmons 2001), and has proved particularly successful in exploring the presence, activities and impacts of humans in the landscape (e.g. Evans, Limbrey & Cleere 1975; Limbrey & Evans 1978; Simmons & Tooley 1981; Birks *et al* 1988; Chambers 1993; Tipping 1994; Whittington & Edwards 1994, 1997; Edwards 1999). However, there are complexities in the representation of plant communities in pollen diagrams that are critical for understanding whether different landscape elements can be understood at the spatial scales attempted in this report, evaluated in Section 2.2, before the application of specific palynological techniques can be explained in Section 2.3.

Many slopes, soils and river valley floors have been affected by erosion in the past. Slope instability and soil loss is of great significance in interpreting the archaeological record, in potentially providing a proxy measure of the intensity of settlement and/or cultivation, identifying the consequences of anthropogenic activity, determining the types of soil available for cultivation, the nature of stresses faced by settlers, and in recognising the potential for eroding archaeological traces of human settlement (Brown 1997; Howard & Macklin 1999). It is difficult to determine rates of soil erosion directly (Kirkby 1967), and for the past, a proxy measure of soil instability needs to be sought. This was sought in the deposits on valley floors left by former fluvial activity (e.g. Gregory 1983; Starkel, Gregory & Thornes 1991; Neeedham & Macklin 1992; Benito, Baker & Gregory 1998; Brown & Quine 1999), described in Chapter 7. Water and sediments falling from valleyside slopes will destabilise the river system, and eroded sediments may persist to be stored on the valley floor (Brown 1987a). Rivers have not always appeared or behaved as they do now, but have experienced episodes when they were more active as well as periods of greater quiescence. Periods of accelerated fluvial activity relate to phases of increased landscape instability (Needham & Macklin 1992; Howard & Macklin 1999), although the cause of this instability has to be identified in other proxy data, such as pollen records (Tipping 2000a).

1.8 The structure of the report

Daniel Defoe reached the summit of The Cheviot after much apparent trepidation. On reflection, questioning his own fear of the unknown, climbing the mountain, and using metaphor to show that fear of the union between Scotland and England was also false (Browing in Defoe 1974), he surmised, 'And thus it is in most things in nature; fear magnifies the object, and represents things frightful at first sight, which are presently made easy when they grow familiar' (Defoe 1974 (1724), 357). It is the ambition of this report to make the comprehension of a complex subject easy and familiar. So the intention of this report is to make the scientific techniques of environmental reconstruction understandable to non-specialists, because they are critical to our understanding. In learning more about the hills, we make them comprehensible, and make the supposedly hostile world of these hills and valleys less fearful.

Chapter 2 explains the purposes and interpretative principles of the different techniques employed. The following five chapters then consider the data collected from sedimentological and pollen analytical investigations. Chapter 3 describes the landscape evolution of the lower Bowmont Valley, the extension to the study area. The last 11 500 cal years, all of the Holocene period, can be described from analyses at the infilling Yetholm Loch. These lake sediments and fen peats, receiving silts and sands periodically from eroded soils as well as pollen from surrounding slopes, provide a very detailed description of all the major landscape shaping processes. In Chapter 4, an almost complete Holocene basin peat stratigraphy within the large tributary valley of Sourhope provides insights into the climatic, vegetation and land use history of the deep cold valleys of the interior of the upper valley. Chapter 5 integrates palaeoecological data from two peat sequences, at Swindon Hill and at Quarry Knowe, in discussing how the most extensive of the low level plateaux within the upper valley developed in the last 5000 cal years. The peat at Swindon Hill began to form in the Later Neolithic period; that at Quarry Knowe only within the last 400 years. In Chapter 6 the focus turns to the summit ridges and high level plateaux. An almost complete Holocene blanket peat at Cocklawhead, analysed by Astrid Schweizer in collaboration with the present author (Schweizer 1997), describes the long term development of climate, vegetation, soils and land uses high on the ridge between Windy Gyle and Auchope Cairn. Away from the blanket peat, the plateau of Mow Law has supported small accumulations of peat for only the last several hundred years, but two sites here provide complimentary scientific data to archival records (e.g. Winchester 2000) on the use of the highest ground in the historic period. Chapter 7 then explores the Holocene development of the river systems in the upper Bowmont Valley and others in the northern and eastern Cheviot Hills, in the Halter Burn, Breamish Valley and the Milfield Basin (Figure 1.2).

Finally, Chapter 8 synthesises these data in presenting an environmental history of the Bowmont Valley and the northern Cheviot Hills. Rather than provide a discussion in this introduction of comparative analyses and interpretations from work prior to this study, Chapter 8 describes the existing paradigms of landscape evolution and human activities, provides the regional context, links the results of archaeological survey (Mercer & Tipping 1994; Mercer in prep.) to landscape change, and explores the major themes developed from the work in the northern Cheviot Hills.

Chapter 2

METHODS OF ENVIRONMENTAL RECONSTRUCTION

2.1 Introduction

Two principal approaches to environmental reconstruction were employed in the Bowmont Valley. These were (a) the reconstruction of vegetation change through pollen analysis at a network of sites in different landscape elements, and (b) an understanding of geomorphic instability and soil erosion in northern Cheviot valleys from the construction of a chronology of riverine sedimentation and fluvial dynamics (Section 1.7). The few methods specific to geomorphic reconstructions are described at the beginning of Chapter 7, but since pollen analyses are used throughout the report, this chapter will describe for the archaeologist and historian the principles of the different approaches needed in a modern standard analysis, and for the pollen analyst detailed discussions of the techniques used. This chapter also describes the different ways developed to establish a secure chronology for environmental change.

2.2 The representation of plant communities in landscape scale pollen analysis

Given the scale and natural diversity of a single but moderately large drainage basin such as the Bowmont Valley (Figure 1.4), with its many landscape elements (Section 1.6), there is the need to depict this variability from an interrelated network of pollen sites. Single sites cannot describe spatial heterogeneity because they are point sources. Spatial reconstruction requires a number of sites in a landscape to be linked. However, since pollen analyses are labour intensive, costly and time consuming, frequently taking months to build, these sites need to be well chosen. The analysis of landscape elements in Chapter 1 (Sections 1.5, 1.6) is a way of defining the minimum number of points in the network needed to explain the landscape.

A network approach to environmental reconstruction requires that each pollen site reflects only the landscape element it is part of. Each pollen site should reflect vegetation patterns through time at a definable and restricted distance around the site. This requirement is difficult to establish, and defining where pollen comes from to accumulate in a sediment has remained one of the central problems in pollen analysis (Oldfield 1970). This section briefly explains why.

Pollen sites have pollen recruitment or source areas around them, but pollen of different plants will travel to the site by very different mechanisms and from contrasting distances (Tauber 1965; Janssen 1973; Randall, Andrew & West 1986; Jackson 1994; Brayshay *et al* 2000). For example, the pollen recruitment area for heath plants and grassland herbs is probably measured in metres (Bunting 2002, 2003); that for many tree species can be tens or even hundreds of kilometres (Tyldesley 1973; Jackson 1994). All other things being equal, this should bias what is depicted at a single pollen site to local plant communities, those within a few metres of the site, but pollen production is vastly greater in trees than for herbs, so that in a wooded landscape it can be difficult even to identify the pollen of herbs growing at the pollen site. This problem of the over-representation of tree pollen is widely recognised.

The conditions in which pollen analysts have successfully modelled pollen recruitment to a site are limited. Quantitative models demonstrating the distance most pollen travels to a site work only for completely wooded landscapes because the productivity and dispersal of tree pollen are more easily understood (Prentice 1985; Jackson 1994; Calcote 1995, 1998). In such landscapes, it has been shown that the size of the pollen recruitment area, the distance from which most pollen comes to a site, is dependent on the size of the pollen site itself (Jacobson & Bradshaw 1981; Jackson & Wong 1992; Bradshaw 1994). Patches of open water infilling with sediment vary in diameter from very small hollows that one can step across to very large lakes. Small hollows receive pollen from a few to only tens of metres around. Pollen from greater distances will still be received, but in a small and insignificant proportion. Small hollows thus characterise local or extra-local stands of vegetation *sensu* Jacobson and Bradshaw (1981), a few metres to a few tens of metres around. At the other extreme, very large lakes such as

Loch Lomond or Loch Ness will receive pollen from local plants fringeing the lake, but also from much farther away, because the surface area of the water is large and fringeing vegetation that can contribute pollen distant from the lake centre. The proportions of far-travelled pollen grains are great, and they can potentially travel hundreds of kilometres to the site.

In the Bowmont Valley, the scale identified as most critical to understanding vegetation and land use dynamics is that of the landscape element (Sections 1.5, 1.6). Topographically, these are constant in size through time. They differ from each other in area and relative relief, but the narrowest element in the Bowmont Valley, the Bowmont Valley floor north of Belford, is 1 to 2km across. The optimum pollen site to characterise this landscape element most efficiently, then, can have a pollen recruitment area several hundred metres in diameter (pollen analysts tend wrongly to visualise pollen recruitment areas as circular), but not greater than several kilometres. A small hollow, one that you could step across, would describe a part of the landscape too small and potentially untypical to be coherent in this context. For more extensive and uniform landscape elements, such as the high plateaux, pollen recruitment areas can be larger than several hundred metres, and the interpretation would still be assured that only the single landscape element was being characterised. Theoretically in a wooded landscapes the pollen analyst can select a pollen site most appropriate to the problem (Jacobson & Bradshaw 1981), although a practical limitation is that invariably not all sizes of pollen site are equally available, particularly in the comparatively dry eastern side of southern Scotland.

It has proved very difficult, however, to resolve pollen recruitment characteristics for pollen sites when the landscape is not fully wooded. This is still a fundamental problem for analysts concerned with human impacts, because much of that impact is in deforestation and the creation of treeless landscapes. When woods are absent or have been removed, shrubs and herbs dominate pollen recruitment, but the pollen production and dispersal characteristics of these plants is so complex and variable that pollen recruitment is far less well understood than for trees (Sugita, Gaillard & Brostrom 1999). It is certain that the pollen recruitment area around a sampling site changes when the landscape shifts from wooded to open. It is much less clear, however, whether the area described gets larger or smaller. If a visual analogy is appropriate, then in one sense the analyst can see further from the pollen site, and the pollen recruitment area might get very much larger, but in another sense the detail of the ground flora nearby becomes more noticeable, and the pollen recruitment area might get much smaller. We do not currently know which view is correct, but it is increasingly likely that, even when trees are absent, pollen diagrams from small hollows and small diameter peat bogs depict landscapes specific to the scale of landscape element within the Bowmont Valley. Brayshay *et al* (2000) suggested that on the windy and exposed Outer Hebrides, present day plant mosaics dominated by heath and herb taxa were well characterised by surface pollen samples in that mosaic, suggesting limited lateral transfer of pollen. In northern Scotland, Bunting (2002, 2003) has recently suggested, developing techniques that successfully characterised wooded landscapes (Calcote 1995), that in open heath landscapes dominated by acid grasses and heather communities, the pollen recruitment areas to peat bogs are very small. Bunting suggested that most pollen diagrams from peat bogs may reflect the vegetation only a couple of metres around, although there are grounds for thinking this an underestimate. Unpublished data by Tipping and Long demonstrated that for heath and grassland landscapes in the upper Tweed Valley, a landscape closely comparable to the Cheviot Hills, pollen recruitment areas to soil surfaces can be measured in tens of metres. Long *et al* (2000) could also demonstrate that woodland growing only a kilometre or two downwind contributed very little pollen to peat sequences and soils in upland grass and heath communities. Randall *et al* (1986), Gearey and Gilbertson (1997) and Bunting (2002) also showed in largely treeless landscapes that abundant tree pollen is restricted to short distances away from extant woods: the odd tree pollen grain is capable of travelling hundreds of kilometres (Tyldesley 1973), but significant proportions of tree pollen grains do not travel farther than several hundred metres.

These new models of predominantly localised pollen transport, particularly for plants of open ground, are adopted in the analyses that follow in later chapters. They can also be argued to be correct from the contrasting patterns of past vegetation identified in Chapters 3 to 6 at the comparatively closely spaced pollen sites within the Bowmont Valley, as they have at more exposed sites in the Scottish highlands (Davies & Tipping 2004), although this is a potentially circular argument. Individual pollen sites analysed throughout the valley are thought to have pollen recruitment areas that do not overlap with others (Figures 1.4 and 1.6 to

1.8 inclusive). Likely pollen recruitment areas around each pollen site in this study are depicted on Figures 3.1, 4.1, 5.1 and 6.1 as circles of different diameters. The different sizes are derived from the evaluation of site and sediment characteristics at each site, discussed when each site is introduced in Chapters 3 to 6. The circles need to be regarded as probabilistic estimates: they are loose, fuzzy areas around each sampling site from which most, but not all, pollen is likely to have arrived. They should not be regarded as anything more than a guide to visualising the landscape.

There are several major caveats in the employment of pollen recruitment areas. The first is that sediment type in a pollen site determines pollen recruitment characteristics perhaps as much as the size of the site. Sediments forming in open water have depositional processes that distinguish them from peat accumulations (Moore *et al* 1991). Pollen diagrams from peat bogs, which have plants growing directly on the sampling site and forming the sediment, can be dominated by such plants, distorting the representation of plants, even trees, away from the peat (Janssen 1973; Dumayne-Peaty & Barber 1995). Strictly, pollen sequences derived from lake sediments cannot be compared with adjacent peat stratigraphies (Hirons 1988). In the Bowmont Valley, all but one pollen site, at Yetholm Loch (Chapter 3), are from peat bogs, and all but this site are considered directly comparable. The second caveat is that pollen recruitment characteristics will vary not only through vegetation structure and composition but also through topographic and climatic controls. The effects of wind speed and exposure with increasing altitude have not successfully been accounted for in quantitative pollen recruitment models. Data from very exposed Hebridean islands suggest that for most herb and heath plants these do not distort pollen recruitment processes (Randall *et al* 1986; Fossitt 1994; Gearey & Gilbertson 1997; Brayshay *et al* 2000; Bunting 2002, 2003), but it is likely that lowland and montane pollen sites, even when of comparable size and sediment type, will differ in how far pollen travels to them. Finally and most critically, a pollen recruitment area around a site will change through time as the site changes (Bunting & Tipping 2004). A small diameter lake such as Yetholm Loch (Chapter 3) will have grown smaller as sediments infilled from the edge. The pollen recruitment area may also have changed radically as lake sediments were replaced at the sampling site by a fen advancing from the edge. Conversely, as small basins filled with peat and their surface area increased the pollen recruitment area would have grown progressively larger through time. These issues are best evaluated at individual sites in Chapters 3 to 6.

Pollen analyses describe the vegetation cover of an area, whether natural or anthropogenic. In detail, the pollen analyst records the pollen or spores from individual plants. It is then a matter of interpretation as to how the analyst combines the pollen types into assemblages or communities of plants. The analyst does this by a process comparable to the archaeologist employing ethnographic parallels. Present day plant communities, such as heather moorland or types of woodland, can be classified in terms of the constancy of species, preferred soils, etc. (McVean & Ratcliffe 1962; Rodwell 1991). The recognition of past plants as belonging to clearly defined modern communities (Ingrouille 1995) is dangerous, however, because plant communities are not constant (Birks 1996): they are invaded and selectively destroyed (Burrows 1990). For this reason, past plant assemblages recognised in this study are only loosely identified with classifications of extant plant assemblages. Describing a past plant community as heather moorland is not to imply that all the species recorded today were present in the past: plant communities, like human communities, are highly malleable and adaptive.

Within a landscape like the Bowmont Valley, individual plant communities, loose assemblages of plants that tolerate similar environments, grazing pressures and each other, are at present irregular mosaics only tens or hundreds of metres in diameter (e.g. Hunter 1962; King 1962). The areas covered by plant communities are likely always to have been smaller than landscape elements. Each pollen diagram in this report sets out to describe the landscape element, and individual plant communities were and are too small from the analyses in this report to be spatially defined. The ecological landscape is more patchy and diverse than the physical landscape. Equally, at times in the past the impacts of human beings in the landscape may have been comparably small in scale (Edwards 1982; 1991), and their activities may have been outside the pollen recruitment area of a site.

2.3 Pollen analytical techniques

2.3a Site selection

Each landscape element within the Bowmont Valley was identified and defined in Chapter 1. Discussion of pollen recruitment characteristics (Section 2.2) allows the assumption that single pollen sites with pollen recruitment areas of several hundred metres can successfully characterise these landscape elements in broad terms. From this position, the major constraint on the structure of the work is the availability of pollen sites of appropriate size. Small hollows were not sought, although a number were located, because the pollen recruitment characteristics of such sites are too detailed for the scale of the physical and cultural landscape to be reconstructed. Sediment accumulations at peat bogs, ponds and lakes with diameters of tens of metres throughout the surveyed area were examined. There are few such sediment accumulations in the Bowmont Valley that have not been analysed and described in this report. All but one site, at Yetholm Loch, were peat, although the origins of these peat sequences are different.

2.3b Sediment descriptions

Sediments were recorded in the field, and from retained sediment cores were then described in more detail in the laboratory. Descriptions generally follow the code for inorganic and organic sediments outlined by West (1977), which is largely a genetic classification, making some assumptions of origin, hydrological relations and depositional environment in the classification. Plant remains in peats were rarely preserved in abundance to make more critical identifications of peat type (e.g. Barber 1981) valuable. Humified or highly decayed peats could be distinguished from poorly humified peats on criteria developed by Troels-Smith and modified by Aaby and Berglund (1986). On the water shedding slopes of the summit ridge at Cocklawhead (Chapter 6) the degree of humification in the peat was quantified according to the methods of Blackford (1990) and Blackford and Chambers (1993). Peat breakdown in the presence of air is characterised by the production of humic and other acids as well as colloidal particulate matter. This is the brown-stained liquid generated when some peats are squeezed in the hand. The amount of this material can be quantified in peat subsamples after extraction and concentration by a simple technique called colorimetry, which measures the proportion of light passing through a measured volume of an extract of peat. Cloudy peat is more decayed, probably because it formed on a dry surface or was decomposed after formation. It is more highly humified, and has lower light transmission values (percentages) than poorly humified peat, which is less cloudy and has higher light transmission values from peat formed under wetter conditions. Humification (% light transmission) was measured on 2cm thick contiguous slices at Station 7 at Cocklawhead (Chapter 6) with a DR/2000 Spectrophotometer with a wavelength of 540nm.

Particle sizes of mineral grains were estimated in the field, and Munsell colours determined on wet sediment. Thicknesses and descriptions of sediment stratigraphic units in the interpretation of sediment sequences are generalised from individual cores. From the lacustrine sediments at Yetholm Loch (Chapter 3) and the blanket peat on Cocklawhead (Chapter 6), sediment types, mineral and organic contents varied more markedly. To refine sediment descriptions at these sites, estimates of dry matter and organic contents were made according to the loss on ignition method of Ball (1964). Fluctuations in dry matter are products of different water contents in the sediments. Contiguous 1cm or 2cm thick slices of sediment were removed from cores, weighed wet, oven dried at 105 °C for twelve hours and reweighed; the percentage differences between wet and dry sediment represent the dry matter content of the sediments. Samples were then ignited in a muffle furnace at 550 °C for four hours and reweighed after cooling in a desiccator; the percentage differences by weight serve as reliable proxy measures of organic content (Dean 1974). At Yetholm Loch the percentages of sediment ignited and lost, the organic content, are depicted; at Cocklawhead the percentages of sediment retained, the mineral content, are depicted.

2.3c Sediment sampling

At each pollen site, the sediments were first probed to establish depth to impenetrable substrate, sediment thickness and sediment stratigraphy, with a lightweight Eijelkamp gouge sampler, essentially a 1m long, 2.5cm wide metal gutter with extension rods that allows the recording of sediments. Surface heights were defined by theodolite survey. Each peat basin and the blanket peat at Cocklawhead were entirely accessible and could be probed in a series of transects to determine basin morphology and identify the thickest available sediment accumulation. The sediments accumulating at Yetholm Loch were recorded in one section parallel to the loch edge (Chapter 3).

The thickest sediments at each site were located because these often provide the point where sediments accumulated most rapidly, and so provide the best resolved sequences. The thickest sediments often lie towards the basin centre, and habitually pollen analysts sample the part of a peat bog furthest from the edge, although this is also most distant from the drier parts of a landscape usually of most interest. As we come to identify the short distances most herb and heath pollen move (Section 2.2), this habit may prove an insensitive strategy, but is not thought to impact adversely on sites presented in this study.

Sediments were sampled with a range of closed chamber corers which provide stratigraphically secure, uncontaminated sediment stratigraphies. These were either 100cm long, 5cm diameter Russian corers, 60cm long piston corers of diameter 7.5cm (West 1977), or for shallow sediments, monolith tins of dimensions 50 × 15 × 15cm hammered into cleaned sections in excavated pits. Sediments are sampled in stratigraphic order but in 100cm or 60cm lengths, and to obtain the full pollen stratigraphy several cores at different depths from overlapping cores have to be subsampled. Narrow diameter cores were preferred to limit the number of overlaps needed to construct a complete pollen stratigraphy (see Section 2.4 for the implications of this). At sequences in the Bowmont Valley except the shallowest, sample depths were surveyed to the ground surface by theodolite. Samples were placed in clean plastic guttering, wrapped in aluminium foil or plastic sheeting, labelled and stored flat in a cold store at 4 °C.

2.3d Subsampling strategies and temporal resolutions

From the cores retrieved and kept in the cold store, sediment slices of between 0.4 and 0.5cm thickness and known volume (measured by displacement in distilled H_2O) were subsampled with scalpel and tweezers. Each sediment slice represents a duration of time which will, in the following processing, be homogenised into one analysis. The choice of subsample thickness has necessarily to be a compromise between the desirability of highly temporally resolved analyses (Turner & Peglar 1988), the cost of analysing many subsamples at one site and the need to understand vegetation dynamics at the landscape scale.

Dating controls applied to all the sediment sequences (Chapters 3 to 7) allow the calculation of approximate sediment accumulation rates, so that an estimate of how much time represented by each 0.4 to 0.5cm slice can be calculated. This can be called the sampling resolution of a pollen sequence (Tipping & McCulloch in press). It is possible in sediments that accumulate annually or faster to achieve a sampling resolution of less than one year (Peglar *et al* 1984; Peglar 1993), but clearly the research questions have to be very specific to permit such an investment in time and money. In the Bowmont Valley, the questions did not require such an approach (Chapter 1). It is very unlikely, in addition, that peat sequences such as those available in the northern Cheviot Hills can be subsampled at annual resolutions because processes involved in peat growth and rootlet penetration will mix together several years' pollen deposition. Sampling resolutions are defined for different depth increments at each site in later chapters.

Equally critical in subsampling strategies is the estimation of temporal resolution, the time interval between subsamples (Tipping & McCulloch in press). Again, many pollen analysts define a subsampling strategy in terms of depth intervals (e.g. Moore *et al* 1991). Subsamples are removed at, for example, 2 or 4cm intervals. However, a better practice is to be flexible, and adjust the subsampling strategy to accommodate the almost inevitable changes in rate of sediment accumulation or to focus on specific periods of most rapid change. The temporal resolutions are defined for each site in later chapters. Particularly when human activities are being measured, it is helpful also to think of temporal resolutions in human terms, in measuring time as passing generations. This is attempted in later chapters, assuming one generation to be around twenty-five years.

2.3e Chemical treatment of pollen subsamples

Pollen grains and spores have to be concentrated from the surrounding sediments in subsamples by different physical and chemical treatments. For sediments in the Bowmont Valley, standard methods were followed (Moore *et al* 1991). These included the use of hydrofluoric acid on most subsamples to remove detritus such as mineral particles made of silica. However, at most sites the use of this acid also removed the remains of siliceous microfossils such as diatoms. Subsamples were sieved through 10µm nylon sieves (Cwynar, Burden & McAndrews 1979) to remove fine particulate detritus. *Lycopodium* spares (Stockmarr 1971) in tablet form were added to subsamples to determine pollen concentrations (see Section 2.3h) at the earliest stage of treatment (Tipping 1985), broken down with 10% hydrochloric acid (Tipping 1987a). The residues remaining after these treatments were stained with an organic stain, safranin, which renders organic matter more easily identifiable under the microscope. Residues were embedded in a viscous medium, silicon oil of ×1200 centistokes viscosity, which allows the analyst to manipulate particles on the microscope slide and permits their easier identification. Residues were spread on microscope slides and sealed with cover slips.

2.3f Pollen counting and identifications

Microscope slides were analysed on a Prior binocular microscope at magnification ×400, and at magnification ×1000 for problematic grains and all determinations of the sizes of pollen grains. Traverses across microscope slides were analysed uniformly over the entire slide (Brookes & Thomas 1967). Pollen identifications were made by reference to type material and from several keys (Andrew 1984; Faegri & Iversen 1975; Moore & Webb 1978), and special keys when necessary. Microscope slides were analysed until 300 land pollen grains (see Section 2.3g) had been counted.

Pollen types are also called pollen taxa; both terms are used in this report. A pollen taxon often cannot be directly related to a particular plant. There is an imprecision in the identification of pollen taxa that is probably the single most important interpretative hurdle for pollen analysts to overcome (Birks 1994). As will emerge in the reconstructions in following chapters, there are many highly significant anthropogenic plant assemblages that cannot satisfactorily be differentiated because analysts cannot distinguish between indicator plants from their pollen. The names of pollen taxa in this report follow the convention established by Birks (1973) in indicating the level of taxonomic precision, from pollen taxa which unambiguously refer to one plant species (e.g. *Plantago lanceolata* (ribwort plantain)) to pollen taxa which incorporate all species within a family (e.g. Cyperaceae (sedges)). These conventions are explained in Table 2.1 with examples.

The names of pollen taxa in the diagrams in Chapters 3 to 7 are generally those used by Moore and Webb (1978) unless otherwise stated, because this was the principal key used. For the pollen analyst, Table 2.2 describes those pollen taxa that do not conform to the definitions of Moore and Webb (1978). This terminology may seem outmoded to some analysts. Botanical taxonomy has changed since publication of Moore and Webb's (1978) key (e.g. Stace 1991), and some workers have recommended changing palynological taxonomy accordingly (Bennett, Whittington & Edwards 1994). However, because pollen taxa are not directly synonymous with plant names, there is no direct translation of some pollen taxa in this scheme, and it is preferred in this report to allow the reader to understand what pollen grains were being recorded as unambiguously as possible. In the chapters that follow, when described initially, the latin (Linnaean) nomenclature for a taxon is accompanied by its common English equivalent. Plant names follow the definitions of Clapham, Tutin and Moore (1987).

The identification of pollen grains of cereal type has absorbed much time and debate among palynologists, summarised and reviewed by Dickson (1988). One of the most successful attempts is that of Andersen

Table 2.1

Definitions and usages of the terms employed to define the degree of taxonomic precision in pollen identifications (from Birks 1973).

Cyperaceae (sedges):	determination to family assured;
Papaver (poppies):	determination to genus assured;
Plantago lanceolata (ribwort plantain):	determination to species assured;
Avena/*Triticum* (oat/wheat):	one of two plant taxa possibly represented;
Hordeum type (barley):	one of three or more plant taxa possibly represented – the taxon named is no more likely to be represented than others in the type: e.g. in Table 2.1, ten species of grass (Gramineae >8µm anl-D) are included in *Hordeum* (barley) type – in some types, particular species can be dimissed on ecological grounds, but uncertainties remain as to the likely species represented;
Rosaceae undiff.:	taxon generally not capable of further differentiation except in some cases. In the pollen diagrams, taxa within this final category are grouped together; e.g. Rosaceae undiff. are undifferentiated members of the Rosaceae (rose family), but some pollen taxa within the family can be differentiated further, such as *Filipendula* (meadowsweet or dropwort) and *Potentilla* (tormentil) type.

Table 2.2
Notes on particular pollen taxa.

The following comments relate to particular pollen types distinguished in the counts:

Sorbus (rowan) and *Crataegus* (hawthorn) types:	these two types were distinguished on the criteria of Boyd and Dickson (1987a).
Ericaceae undiff. (heathers):	some grains were substantially larger than most, and these were measured and identified further using Oldfield's (1959) key (see comments in Chapters 3, 4, 5). The majority of these grains could be keyed to either *Andromeda polifolia* (bog rosemary) or *Arctostaphylos* (bearberry), or *Andromeda/Arctostaphylos*. Two grains of *Vaccinium* (bilberry) were also tentatively identified at Swindon Hill (Chapter 5).
Gramineae (grasses):	grass pollen grains are balloon shapes with single pores emphasised by a thickened ring called an annulus. The long and short axes and annulus diameters (anl-D) of grains significantly larger than average were measured (Andersen 1979). Four groups were defined: Gramineae <8μm anl-D (wild grasses): Andersen's Type I, all belonging to uncultivated grass species. Gramineae >8μm anl-D undiff.: grains with annulus diameters >8μm could be separated from wild grasses, but unless well preserved, such grains could not be classified further. *Hordeum* (barley) type: Andersen's (1979) Type II includes wild grass species in addition (in bold) to some cultivated grasses: *Ammophila arenaria* (marram grass); *Hordeum murinum* (sea barley); *Elymus repens* (couch grass); *E. farctus* (sand couch grass); *Leymus arenarius* (lyme grass); *Glyceria fluitans* (floating sweet-grass); *G. plicata* (plicate sweet-grass); ***Hordeum vulgare*** (barley); ***Secale cereale*** (rye); ***Triticum monococcum*** (einkorn). *Secale cereale* (rye): these grains have a distinctive prolate shape as defined by axial ratios (Andersen 1979). *Avena/Triticum* (oat/wheat)): Andersen's (1979) Type III includes *Avena fatua* (wild oat); ***A. sativa*** (oat); ***Triticum aestivum*** (naked wheats); ***T. polonicum*** (Polish wheat); ***T. spelta*** (spelt); ***T. dicoccum*** (emmer); ***T. compactum*** (club wheat). In some grains an as yet unpublished modification of Andersen's work (Section 2.2f) allowed the tentative identification of genera or groups of genera (Chapters 3–6).
Alismataceae (water plantains):	Punt and Reumer's (1981) key was used in distinguishing the three species.
Cannabis/Humulus:	numbers of grains were too few at most sites to successfully apply Whittington and Gordon's (1987) quantitative technique to differentiate *Cannabis sativa* (hemp) from *Humulus lupulus* (hop). At Yetholm Loch (Chapter 3) pollen grains were sufficiently abundant to apply this test. The mean of the polar axis of the 38 grains between 57 and 97cm is 25.5±3.2μm. 81.6% of the grains (31) had pores raised >1μm above the exine. 85.3% of the sample thus tentatively assigned to *Cannabis* (hemp), 14.7% of the sample to *Humulus* (hop).
Linum (flax) type:	grains could not be separated using Punt & den Breejen's (1981) key; this taxon thus includes several *Linum* species, but not *L. utissitatum* (common or cultivated flax).

(1979), based primarily on size characteristics. Each species of Gramineae produces pollen grains which vary in size around mean values (Andersen 1979), but with extensive size overlaps between species. Andersen defined four groups within the family Gramineae; (I) wild grasses, (II) *Hordeum* Group, (III) *Avena-Triticum* Group and (IV) *Secale cereale* (Table 2.2). Most Gramineae pollen grains can be from many species. However, using box diagrams summarising the variability of pollen size, pollen index and annulus diameter it is tentatively possible to refine Andersen's classes with particular well preserved pollen grains. For example, *Secale cereale* (rye) has a distinctive shape, and in size overlaps only with *Avena sativa*. In addition a Gramineae pollen grain with pollen size >46μm and annulus diameter >13.1μm must, according to Andersen's data but not discussed by him, be of *Triticum* (wheat) spp. Other separations are possible, and have been used in Chapters 3 to 6 to define possible cereal taxa.

2.3g Percentage calculations and the presentation of percentage data

Pollen counts are presented most commonly as percentage-based diagrams depicting proportional changes in pollen taxa through time. The basis of percentage calculations is called the pollen sum. The pollen sum employed in this report is that of total land pollen (tlp). This is an increasingly standard sum (Tipping 1994) and means that these analyses are directly comparable with nearly all other pollen analyses from southern Scotland and northern England (Chapter 8).

Pollen diagrams published before the later twentieth century are commonly based on a different sum, that of total tree or arboreal pollen (Durno 1956; Godwin 1956; Newey 1967; Hibbert & Switsur 1976). This calculation was devised to emphasise the proportions of trees in pollen diagrams since woodland history was an important research issue. This sum calculates all pollen types from trees as 100%. Taxa that are not trees are calculated on a basis that distorts their proportional significance. The analyses at Yetholm Loch (Chapter 3) provide an example of how different the arboreal and total land pollen sums depict the same data, because Figure 3.5 describes early to mid-Holocene tree populations on an arboreal pollen sum and Figure 3.7a describes the same taxa calculated as tlp. Arboreal pollen-based diagrams can readily give the false impression of a densely wooded landscape. As analysts became interested in understanding landscape history and the more precise description of open ground, a different pollen sum had to be introduced (Wright & Patten 1963).

The total land pollen sum includes all pollen taxa nominally growing or capable of growing on terrestrial soils. Accordingly, the percentages of dryland shrub, heath and herb taxa can be directly compared with the proportions of tree taxa. Taxa that are demonstrably of aquatic origin are excluded from this sum, and their proportions are calculated as percentages of land pollen taxa and aquatics. This diminishes their significance in pollen diagrams, but it can be argued that the growth of aquatic taxa at the pollen site inflates their palynological occurrence. Also excluded from direct comparison with dryland plant communities are spores produced by gymnosperm plants because the mechanisms of spore production and dispersal are not directly comparable to those in pollen grains produced by angiosperm plants.

All pollen sums are arbitrary. Using a total tree pollen sum, for example, debate centred on the assignation of hazel (*Corylus/Myrica* pollen) as either a tree or a shrub because this choice introduces a gross difference in its percentage representation (Godwin 1975). In defining pollen types as growing on dry soils or permanently wet ground, equally difficult choices have to be made, particularly when the pollen diagram is obtained from semiterrestrial peat. These difficulties are compounded by the taxonomic imprecision of many pollen types (Section 2.3f). There are, for example, both dryland and wetland species of grass, but these cannot be distinguished from pollen analyses. These issues are evaluated in later chapters.

The pollen diagrams in this report follow a convention in which vertical axes represent depth below ground surface and horizontal bars represent the percentage representation of individual pollen taxa in each subsample, as % total land pollen (% tlp) or, for taxa outside this sum as % tlp plus their life form group (e.g. tlp + aquatics). The taxa are placed in conventional life form groups (trees, shrubs, heathers, herbs, aquatics, ferns and mosses), and within these groups are listed in alphabetical order; where a major taxon contains several pollen types, these are grouped with the more general taxon (e.g. species within the Compositae or Rosaceae).

Each pollen diagram is subdivided, for convenience in discussion, into a number of local pollen assemblage zones (lpaz). These are units of time (chronostratigraphic units) in which the pollen stratigraphy is broadly unchanged; boundaries separating lpa zones are placed where the pollen stratigraphy changes significantly. Zonation is by visual assessment rather than statistical analysis (Gordon & Birks 1972; Bennett 1996), based on observations of fluctuations in major land pollen taxa, those represented on average at percentages >5% tlp. Every lpaz at each site is prefixed by the site name, and this serves to emphasise that the pollen zonation scheme relates only to that site.

2.3h Pollen concentration and influx values

Interpretations of percentage-based pollen diagrams are hampered by uncertainties in defining the direction of change in taxa. If the percentages of a dominant taxon increase, others must decrease, but it will remain unclear whether the one taxon is in real terms increasing. The calculation of pollen concentration and influx values allow 'absolute' changes in the abundance of pollen grains to be measured independent of proportional fluctuations. This is done by adding a known number of distinctive markers to the subsample (usually *Lycopodium clavatum* spores, a spore producing moss native to Britain but found naturally in very low numbers) in tablet form to a known volume of sediment, and recording the numbers of both *Lycopodium* spores and subfossil pollen (Stockmarr 1971). The calculation can be made for any taxon or all (total pollen), and is expressed as the number of grains per cm^3. Pollen concentrations are strongly dependent on the rate at which the sediment accumulated because these are measures of the numbers of grains per volume of sediment. To correct for differing sediment accumulation rates, pollen concentrations can be calculated as pollen influx, the influx of pollen grains per cm^2 of the sediment surface per year, by estimating from dating controls the annual rate of sediment accumulation. However, pollen concentration and influx values vary between subsamples due to a number of factors, not all of which can be controlled, and although pollen influx values were determined at all sites, they are used in describing change only at Yetholm Loch (Chapter 3) and at Cocklawhead (Chapter 6).

2.3i Pollen preservation analyses

Subfossil pollen grains accumulating in a sediment sequence need not be well preserved. A number of influences will deteriorate the shape and structure of pollen grains, from production in the anther, during dispersal from the plant, transport by different mechanisms to the site, to incorporation into the sediment and post-depositional changes long after the grain comes to rest (Tipping 2000c). An understanding of pollen preservation is important in assessing the interpretative value of a pollen diagram; intensely deteriorated pollen grains distort the original assemblage, through removal of taxa susceptible to deterioration, and by the enhanced representation of pollen types resistant to decay (Tipping *et al* 1994; Bunting & Tipping 2000; Tipping 2000c). More sophisticated analyses can allow a fuller understanding of the processes of pollen recruitment (Konigsson 1969; Tipping 1987b), sedimentological processes (Cushing 1964, 1967; Birks 1970; Lowe 1982) and post-depositional changes within sediments (Delcourt & Delcourt 1980; Tipping 1995a, d).

Each land pollen grain in this study was assessed as to its preservation state, and assigned to one of four categories defined by Cushing (1967). Pollen grains were assigned to one form of deterioration on the dominant state of the grain (Tipping 1987b). Deterioration can be physically induced, when a grain is crumpled, broken or split open, or induced by biological activity when aerobic microorganisms partially ingest pollen, leaving grains that are corroded or thinned (Elsik 1963; Havinga 1964, 1984). Amorphous or degraded grains have their origins in biochemical changes to the pollen wall structure, but these are inadequately understood. Grains recognisable as pollen or spores but rendered indeterminable to taxon by their extreme deterioration were also recorded, and assigned to one of three categories (crumpled/broken, corroded, amorphous); grains hidden by organic or mineral detritus were classed as concealed.

The presentation of these data in each chapter is by summary diagrams showing the changing preservation states of all determinable land pollen grains as % total land pollen (tlp). This is a comparatively unsophisticated analysis. Pollen taxa yield differentially to different forms of deterioration, and changes in summary deterioration trends can reflect only the increasing changing importance of particularly susceptible pollen types. At some sites in this study the contributions of different pollen taxa to preservation trends are explored, but by and large, at these sites there appear to be no interpretative advantages to depicting and analysing changes in individual taxa.

2.3j Microscopic charcoal analyses

Of increasing significance in palaeoecological analysis is the depiction of fire because it is regarded as a key driver of vegetation change, either naturally occurring or purposefully created by human activities (Tolonen 1986; Patterson, Edwards & Maguire 1987; Scott, Moore & Brayshay 2000). In this study, microscopic charcoal was recorded on microscope slides during pollen counting. It was identified through being entirely black (excluding partially charred material which still retains the reddish tinge of stained organic matter), completely opaque and generally angular. Occasional fragments showed cellular structure, but no attempt could be made from this material to define what types of organic matter (e.g. wood, herbaceous material) were being turned to charcoal.

Charcoal fragments were recorded from the subsamples homogenised for pollen analyses. Because these have sampling resolutions of several years and temporal resolutions of many decades (Section 2.3c; Chapters 3 to 6), each subsample will contain charcoal of either single or, most likely, many fires, so that it is only possible to establish broad temporal patterns (Swain 1973). It is in addition not at all clear which of the two factors, frequency or intensity, is being measured in these types of data. Increased fire frequencies should contribute more charcoal, but so might individual fires close to the sampling site, or particularly intense fires, or those that burn particular vegetation types, or any number of other factors, so that the data can only be interpreted as representing either fire frequency or intensity.

Numbers of charcoal fragments were recorded according to the length of the longest axis rather than by the area of the fragment under the microscope slide (Clark 1982). Tinner and Hu (2003) have shown that there is no advantage to the latter method. Fragments were recorded in four size fractions (10 to 25μm, 26 to 50μm, 51 to 75μm and >75μm) on the length of their longest axes. Fragments <10μm could not readily be recognised as being charcoal, and were not counted. Fragments >75μm long were individually measured. Macroscopic charcoal fragments in sediment sequences were not quantified, although they were noted in sediment descriptions. The reason for recording size fractions of charcoal fragments is that changes in proportions may indicate different sources of fires. Larger fragments may originate from fires closer to the sampling site, provided that processing of sediment subsamples (Section 2.3d) does not distort the proportions of these brittle particles, an assumption unlikely to hold true (Clark 1984; Paterson *et al* 1987). Clark's (1988) theoretical model of charcoal production and dispersal suggested that microscopic charcoal falling on sediments had very large source areas, many hundreds of kilometres, because many very small charcoal fragments are uplifted into the atmosphere by convectional processes during burning. This wide dispersal might tend to render microscopic charcoal fragments comparatively insensitive to source (see also Carcaillet *et al* 2001). However, Sugita (1993), Morrison (1994), Clark and Royall (1995), Clark and Paterson (1997) and Blackford (2000) have maintained that size differentiation of fragments preserves some component of spatial patterning, and that microscopic charcoal in sediments tends to reflect recruitment areas comparable to those of pollen (Section 2.2). The size distributions of microscopic charcoal fragments are used in this report as a way of defining local and more distant fires, but with the recognition that these terms are not well defined.

There is no standard calculation or presentation of microscopic charcoal records in the way that the total land pollen sum allows for standardisation of pollen records. This is a severe difficulty when comparing analyses produced by different workers (Tipping 1996b). Methods of recording and presentation were standard for all sites analysed in the Bowmont Valley, however, which makes these analyses comparable with each other. Total numbers of charcoal fragments per subsample are depicted as (a) percentages of land pollen grains, (b) as charcoal concentrations per cm^3 and charcoal influx per cm^2 per year (see Section 2.3h for explanation of concentrations and influx values) and (c) as ratios of charcoal concentrations to total pollen concentrations. The size fraction data are presented as percentages of the total numbers of charcoal fragments. Because it is highly likely that sediment processing shatters larger charcoal fragments (above; Clark 1984), a measure of the original amount of charcoal deposited per subsample (before presumed further fragmentation) was obtained by multiplying the numbers of fragments per size fraction by the mean length of the fraction (e.g. 17.5, 38, 63μm + the sum of individual fragments >75μm), called charcoal length (Tipping 1995d).

2.3k Opaque spherules

Different types of microscopic opaque spheres on microscope slides have received varying amounts of attention by palaeoecologists in recent years (Rose 1994). Some identified at sites in the Bowmont Valley are spheroidal carbonaceous spherules (SCPs), containing vacuoles or pores (Griffin & Goldberg 1975; Wik, Renberg & Darley 1986; Battarbee *et al* 1988; Wik & Natkanski 1990). They are a chronological control on recent sediment accumulation, evaluated in Section 2.4d.

Several types of non-porous spherule were recorded during pollen counting, presented in pollen diagrams in later chapters, but their significance and meaning remain unclear. Two types were defined:

(a) scabrate types have a rough surface, tending to microechinate (by comparison with pollen grains; Moore & Webb 1978): they seem to correspond to the pyrite spherules of Wiltshire, Edwards and Bond (1994), the scabrae under scanning electron microscope identified as framboidal (cubic) mineral structures. These are thought to originate at the sediment surface in aquatic environments by microbial decomposition of organic matter under reducing conditions, and so may represent sediments that accumulated in stagnant water (Wiltshire *et al* 1994; Ellis & Brown 1999);

(b) psilate types are perfect or near perfect spheres. Two size categories were recorded: <10μm and >10μm. Their origins are unclear, but they appear to resemble the magnetite spherules described by Puffer, Russell and Rampino (1980), and if correct can originate from a number of sources, industrial, volcanic and extraterrestrial.

2.4 Chronological controls on sediment sequences

In any analysis of temporal change at the landscape scale, it is fundamental that temporal correlation between sites and sequences is as rigorous and precise as possible. Radiocarbon dating (^{14}C) remains the best method of constructing chronologies for individual stratigraphies at the timescales analysed in this report. Nevertheless, the imprecision and many sources of error make it a problematic technique (Pilcher 1991; Lowe & Walker 1997). Few independent tests of the veracity of such chronologies exist, particularly for the prehistoric period: tephrochronology (Dugmore 1989) had not been defined as a technique applicable in northern Britain when the sediments considered in this report were analysed. Radiocarbon assays are supported at some sites in this study by a number of other dating techniques for the later historic period. These include the radiometric ^{210}Pb technique with a half life of twenty-three years, the identification of microscopic industrial pollutants and known age exotic tree pollen marker horizons, with the intention of allowing all in combination to constrain uncertainties in one particular technique (Oldfield *et al* 1994; Tipping 1999).

2.4a Radiocarbon (^{14}C) dating

Radiometric ^{14}C techniques were employed throughout the work because AMS techniques were not readily available at the time. Radiometric assays require a much larger sample of organic matter. Sediment slices submitted for ^{14}C assay obtained from monolith tins excavated into cleaned sections were of sufficient size to be obtained from the same sediment stratigraphies used for pollen analysis. However, because narrow diameter cores were preferred for pollen analyses (Section 2.3b), insufficient sediment was available from these cores for ^{14}C assays. This is a particular concern when maintaining high temporal precision of the assay, comparable to the sampling resolution of pollen subsamples. Large diameter (10cm) closed chamber Russian cores of 30cm length (Barber 1984; Plate 2.1) were sampled from immediately adjacent to pollen core samples and used to obtain single sediment slices of sufficient size for ^{14}C assay. The depths of these cores were also surveyed by theodolite, so correlation between cores is very close, but ^{14}C assays from cores do not date directly the sediments providing the pollen stratigraphies. Details of the subsamples taken for ^{14}C assays are provided in Chapters 3 to 6.

Subsamples from the pollen sites were assayed at the Radiocarbon Dating Laboratory, Scottish Universities Research and Reactor Centre, East Kilbride. All subsamples from river sediments were assayed at the NERC Radiocarbon Dating Laboratory at East Kilbride. These facilities both measure radiocarbon activity by liquid scintillation methods. All samples are digested in hydrochloric acid at 80 °C for twenty-four hours, to remove the acid soluble fulvic acid fraction, and then treated with 0.2M sodium hydroxide at 80 °C to separate the alkali soluble material (humic acid fraction) from the acid/alkali insoluble (humin) fraction.

Peats and lake sediments comprise a range of organic components, introduced to the sediment from different sources (Ficken, Barber & Eglinton 1998), and not all necessarily of the same age (Boyd 1986; Bartley & Chambers 1992; Kilian, van der Plicht & van Geel 1995; Shore, Bartley & Harkness 1995). The most abundant chemical components extracted in fractionation are humic acids, humin and fulvic acids. All of these have complex chemistries, can still be of mixed age, and are far from being single entities (Ashmore 1998). The ^{14}C assay of defined fractions is, however, better than former practices of not separating fractions or not defining which fraction was assayed. At the Scottish Universities Research and Reactor Centre (GU- laboratory numbers; Chapters 3 to 6) the humic acid fraction was assayed. At the NERC facility both humic and humin fractions were assayed when sufficiently plentiful (SRR- laboratory numbers; Chapter 7). For some samples dated at the NERC facility, sufficient material was available to allow separation of the sediment into two size differentiated fractions, 'coarse' and 'fine', by washing through a 3mm mesh (D D Harkness pers. comm.).

Radiocarbon assays in this study have been calibrated to calendrical years using the University of Washington CALIB program (Rev. 3.3A; Stuiver & Reimer 1993), using a curve based on bidecadal data, and employing sample age spans calculated from the sediment accumulation rates relevant to each sediment slice. Throughout the text, all ^{14}C ages are calibrated. Radiocarbon and other ages are reported as years BC/AD rather than years BP (Before Present). For prehistorians and early historians, it is of little significance that 'the present' is defined by radiocarbon specialists as 1950 cal AD, but for events in the later historic period, it is becoming critical that this baseline is now over fifty years short of the present day. Dates given as cal BC/AD avoid this irritation.

2.4b Lead 210 (^{210}Pb) dating

Radiocarbon assays are inappropriate chronological controls within the later historic period because of distortions introduced by industrial activities in the proportions of isotopes of carbon within the atmosphere. Combined with the difficulties that calibration introduces into assays of this period, ^{14}C assays have very little meaning in the last three centuries or so (Dumayne *et al* 1995). A second radiometric technique, ^{210}Pb assay, has allowed this most recent period to be dated with more precision than by radiocarbon (Clymo *et al* 1990; Oldfield *et al* 1994; Oldfield, Richardson & Appleby 1995). Rather than define the ages of individual sediment slices as in ^{14}C dating, this technique defines a rate of sediment accumulation from the dating of many contiguous thin sediment slices below the currently forming peat surface. Most commonly applied to lacustrine sediments (Appleby & Oldfield 1983), the application of the technique to peats is less assured because of the potential mobility of lead isotopes in sediments formed under a fluctuating water table (Urban *et al* 1990). In this study, ^{210}Pb data on sediment accumulation are used in conjunction with other techniques as recommended by Oldfield *et al* (1995).

^{210}Pb dating was undertaken at some peat sequences in this study by Dr A Mackenzie at the Scottish Universities Research and Reactor Centre, East Kilbride. Dried peat samples of 2cm thickness were taken from monolith tins, dried and turned to powder, and pressed into discs of constant geometry using a 20 tonne press. These were wrapped in plastic film and placed on a high purity low background (35% n-type crystal or 20mm LEGe) Ge gamma photon detector. Samples were counted for at least two days, to attain several thousand ^{210}Pb 46.5 keV photopeak counts; if present in detectable quantities, ^{226}Ra (radon 226) was assayed *via* photopeaks at 295, 352 and 609 keV. Detection efficiencies for ^{210}Pb and ^{226}Ra were determined by 'spiking' parts of the core too deep to have natural radiometric activity with known quantities of each, preparing and counting these discs. The concentration of ^{210}Pb is derived from the observed counting rate and the defined detection efficiency. If ^{226}Ra is present in detectable levels, the unsupported ^{210}Pb concentration is calculated by subtracting the ^{226}Ra concentration (Bq kg^{-1}) from the total ^{210}Pb concentration (Bq kg^{-1}). The plot of the natural logarithm of the unsupported ^{210}Pb versus depth is drawn and, if linear, the sediment accumulation rate is calculated by multiplying the gradient of the depth of the graph by the ^{210}Pb decay constant. This yields a sediment accumulation rate for the sediments analysed, evaluated in later chapters. The age estimates are determined in calendrical years BP.

2.4c Pollen marker horizons

Marker horizons within pollen sequences, the recording of abrupt events or sharply defined transitions that are regionally synchronous, can be used as dating controls providing the age of the horizon can be independently verified. Interpretative circularities quickly develop if the marker horizon itself is diachronous. For example, the average age of the mid-Holocene decline in *Ulmus* (elm) pollen has been defined (Parker *et al* 2001) from many ^{14}C assays but this does not mean that all elm declines are of this age.

The chronology of two parts of the Holocene can with caution be understood using regionally synchronous pollen marker horizons. In the earliest Holocene, the processes of tree colonisation and spread appear to have been so rapid that events like the first appearance (empirical limit; Smith & Pilcher 1973) or expansion (rational limit) of tree pollen from *Betula* (birch) and *Corylus* (hazel) are in general synchronous across the British Isles within the limits of the ^{14}C technique (Smith & Pilcher 1973; Huntley & Birks 1983; Birks 1989; Tipping 1994). Subsequent events such as the colonisation of *Quercus* (oak) and *Ulmus* (elm) are far less likely to be synchronous within a region because migration and establishment are more often determined by soil specific competitive interactions between species (Bennett 1986).

Pollen stratigraphic events in later prehistory and most of the historic period are highly variable in time because effected by small scale human impacts. However, a recurrent feature of pollen records of the last 250 years in the Bowmont Valley and throughout southern Scotland is the occurrence of a range of tree types that are either not native to the region or are thought to have been long absent from woods. Non-native taxa include *Picea* (spruce), *Abies* (fir) and *Fagus* (beech). Trees that are native but which had become rare or absent in the region before this time include *Pinus* (Scots pine), *Ulmus* (elm) and *Quercus* (oak) (Dickson 1992; Bennett, K D 1984; Tipping 1995b, 1997a, b, c, d, 1999). The increased representation in pollen diagrams of these trees is related to planted woodland developed for commercial and aesthetic reasons in the Agricultural Improvements of the mid-eighteenth century (Anderson 1967; House & Dingwall 2003; Stewart 2003). Archival records show that plantations were established at different times over the period 1650 to 1850 cal AD depending on purpose and landowner. This marker horizon has been used as a dating control in southern Scotland for a number of years, but there is a tendency to apply already quoted age estimates from one region to another (Birks 1972; Clymo *et al* 1990; Tipping 1995b, 1999; Mauquoy *et al* 2002; Oldfield *et al* 2003). The distribution of new woodlands across southern Scotland was, however, patchy (House & Dingwall 2003), the pollen load of these trees in the air above southern Scotland was never high, and pollen recruitment (Section 2.3a) such that pollen grains were principally derived from areas close to pollen sites (Tipping *et al* 1997; Long *et al* 1998), so that it is not possible to assume a single age across southern Scotland for this marker horizon. Local chronologies need to be created. Smith and Charman (1988), for instance, suggest that the comparable increase in *Pinus* (pine) pollen in the Kielder Forest of northern England were as recent as *c* 1930 cal AD, very different to the mid-eighteenth-century date assumed in the same area by Mauquoy *et al* (2002).

Major plantations were created in lowland areas of old Roxburghshire, north of the Bowmont Valley, in the mid-eighteenth century (Douglas 1798; Sinclair (1791–9) 1979; Anderson 1967). Figure 2.1 depicts the contrasting scales of natural woodland and plantations for each parish in Roxburghshire described by Douglas (1798). The upper Bowmont Valley, the archaeologically surveyed area (Figure 1.4), is in the south-east of what was Roxburghshire. Equivalent data are not known for English parts of the Cheviot Hills. Almost no planting was undertaken in parishes in the Cheviot foothills (Figure 2.1). In the Bowmont Valley itself, only small shelter belts and avenues were constructed around the improved farms at and north of Belford (Figure 1.4). By far the largest plantations were along the Teviot and Tweed Valleys, and were commercial. It is very likely that these plantations contributed the major component of tree pollen arriving at sites in the study area. They are all some distance from the study area, and it is likely also that the deposition of comparatively high amounts of tree pollen was synchronous within the valley. These plantations commenced in Roxburghsire in the 1730s. However, high temporal resolution pollen analyses in the upper Tweed Valley, close to one of the earliest and most distinctive plantations at Lour (Tipping *et al* 1997), showed unsurprisingly that there was a lag between the date of planting and measurable impacts on local pollen deposition as the first generation of trees matured and new growth developed. Allowing for such a lag within the upper Bowmont Valley, a date of 1775 ± 25 cal AD is ascribed to this marker horizon at pollen sites in this study.

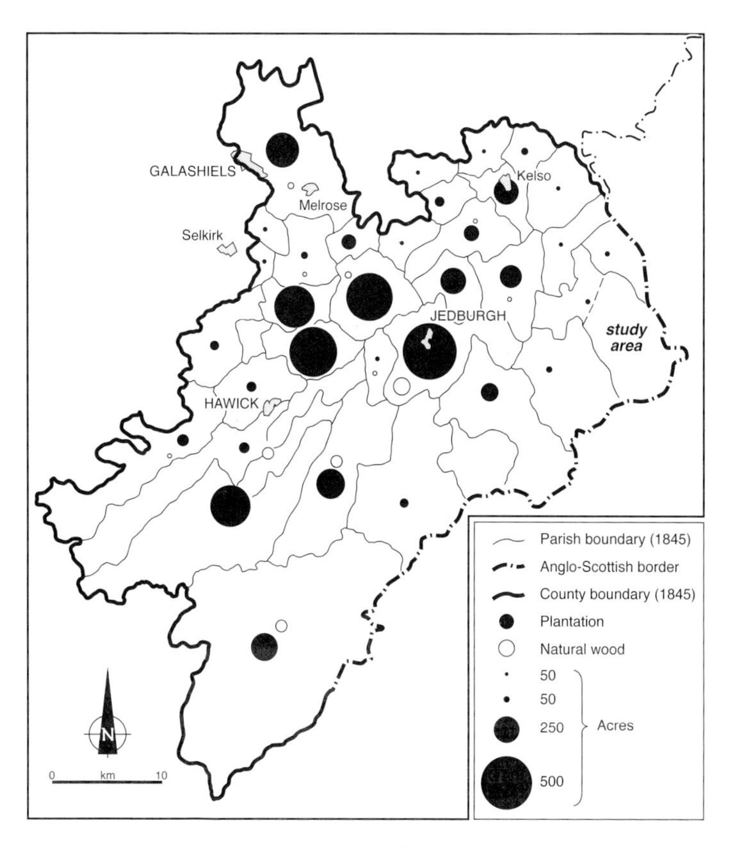

Figure 2.1
Map of the parishes of old Roxburghshire as they were in AD 1845, showing the acreage of woodland, planted and natural, in AD 1790–5, adapted from information in Douglas (1798).

2.4d Carbonaceous spheroidal particles (SCPs)

SCPs (see Section 2.3k) are generated through high temperature industrial fossil fuel (coal and oil) combustion. As such, they can only have been produced in industrial furnaces from the mid-nineteenth century (Rose *et al* 1995). Because of this origin, SCPs have been increasingly used as a dating technique for recent sediments. At lakes in south-west and north-west Scotland, Rose *et al* (1995) demonstrated using ^{210}Pb dating controls that the first appearances across the country occurred between 1830 and 1880 cal AD The first appearance at this time was demonstrated by Tyler *et al* (2001) for peat profiles in the upper Tweed Valley. In a landscape like the Cheviot Hills as distant from industrial sources as these others, it is likely that SCPs began to be deposited over this period and was synchronous at all sites.

Highly resolved lake sediment stratigraphies appear to be sensitive to twentieth-century fluctuations in soot production, and these may also act as regional chronological controls (Rose *et al* 1995). Although this refined chronology of twentieth-century change was utilised at the site of Quarry Knowe (Chapter 5), the stratigraphic records of SCPs from most sites in the Bowmont Valley proved insensitive to these fluctuations for several possible reasons. First, the concentration techniques employed by Rose (1990) were not developed: instead SCPs were recorded during routine pollen analyses after standard processing of sediments (Section 2.3d) and numbers of SCPs counted were therefore lower than might have been achieved. Second, rather than lake sediments, peat profiles provided the most highly resolved late historic sediment sequences, and although Yang, Rose and Battarbee (2001) report secure chronologies for recent peats, it is not clear whether SCPs are perfectly preserved in seasonally oxygenated sediments. Because of these limitations, the SCP records are used only to define their first appearance, though even this is uncertain.

2.4e Construction of preferred time-depth models

With the exception of the continuous sediment accumulation rates defined by ^{210}Pb dating (Section 2.4b), chronological controls provide age estimates for particular events. The interpolation of ages between directly dated events involves assumptions about how sediments accumulate (Birks 2003). The approach in this report is to use linear interpolation between dated events: in the construction of graphs plotting sediment depth against time in Chapters 3 to 6, straight lines join together dated depths.

There are rare exceptions to this, as in Chapter 3. Linear interpolation between dated points is the simplest approach to time-depth modelling, but is one that makes fewest assumptions. The method places too much emphasis on the precise depths of dating controls, and will inevitably introduce artificially abrupt changes in apparent sediment accumulation rates. However, the potential for abrupt changes in sedimentation in both lakes and peats is much higher than often assumed. Time-depth models employing different forms of polynomial equation to generate curvilinear age–depth relations (Bennett 1994; Bennett & Fuller 2002) make, it is thought, too many assumptions about the continuity of sediment accumulation.

Chapter 3

HOLOCENE LANDSCAPE EVOLUTION IN THE LOWER BOWMONT VALLEY – YETHOLM LOCH

3.1 Site location, description and pollen recruitment

Yetholm Loch lies 3km north of the archaeologically surveyed area (Figure 1.3), west of the village of Town Yetholm (Figure 3.1), at 101m OD. The site is more representative of the rich arable land of The Merse than of the deep recesses of the northern Cheviot Hills (Section 1.5).

Crookedshaws Farm lies on the low-lying watershed south of Yetholm Loch, a mass of fluvioglacial sands and gravels on the valley floor that separates the west-flowing tributaries of the Kale Water from a small unnamed stream draining north to Yetholm Loch from Primside Farm (Figure 3.1). The loch, a relatively small stretch of open water 630 by 250m has at its southern, upstream end, a deltaic sediment infill covered by a dense growth of willow (*Salix*) (Plate 3.1). The fluvial catchment of the loch is very small, at around 3.5km^2 (Plate 3.2). Below the loch the stream flows north and east through the once marshy valley of The Stank, drained in the late eighteenth century cal AD (Douglas 1798), to the Bowmont Water below Town Yetholm.

The sediments infilling the southern edge of Yetholm Loch were sampled for pollen and sediment analyses, at a point close to the present loch shore but beneath the dense willow carr (Figure 3.1). The sediments are described in detail below, but the location of the sampling site and sediment types define the pollen recruitment area and thus the character of the landscape described (Section 2.2). Until the last 2000 years the sediments were lacustrine, but the very limited extent of the sediment infill (Figure 3.2a) indicates that the sampling site has always been close to dryland plant communities. Most sediments arrived through fluvial transport, and such sites with inflowing streams receive very high proportions of pollen from sources within the fluvial catchment (Peck 1973; Bonny 1976, 1978; Pennington 1979). Most pollen to this site will, in the lacustrine sediments, have originated from at least several hundred metres away, but a significant component will have come from locally growing plants on the valley floor by the loch shore (Jacobson & Bradshaw 1981). Figure 3.1 attempts to depict the likely recruitment area for most pollen accumulating in lake sediments at the sampling site, the valley floor of the fluvial catchment and the slopes to either side of the valley. Fen peat encroached across the sampling site around 2000 years ago. This and the establishment of willow carr across the fen slightly later significantly reduced the pollen recruitment area from that depicted in Figure 3.1.

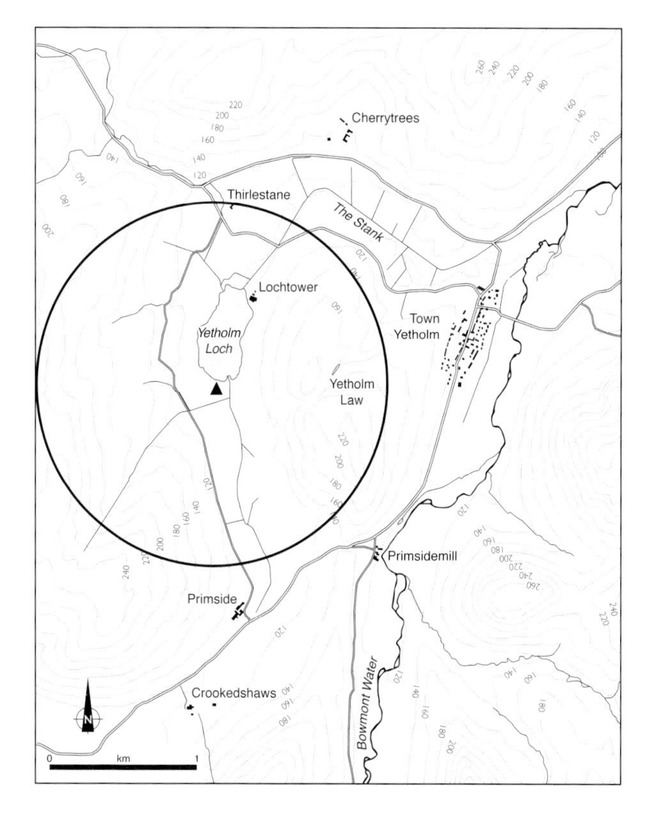

Figure 3.1

The physical and settlement geographies of the Yetholm Loch fluvial catchment in the lower Bowmont Valley, showing the farms and village of Town Yetholm and the drainage system. Contour intervals are 20m. The location of the sampling site within the sediment infill at the south of Yetholm Loch is indicated, as is the likely maximal pollen recruitment area around the sampling site.

Plate 3.1

From left to right, the southern upstream side of Yetholm Loch beneath the later twentieth-century conifer plantations and nineteenth-century enclosed fields of the steep western slopes of Yetholm Law, the deltaic sediment infill covered by dense willow carr and its fringe of pale coloured sedges bordering the loch and the valley sides, and the shallow valley south of the loch (Figure 3.1), looking from west of the loch east and south-east to The Curr in the background, within the upper Bowmont Valley.

Figure 3.2 depicts (a) the present soils mapped by the Soil Survey of Scotland (Ragg 1960) and current land use capabilities (Bown & Shipley 1982) for the pollen recruitment area outlined in Figure 3.1. The gentle to moderate slopes of the valley sides are of andesites and andesite rich till. These slopes support well drained brown forest soils of the Sourhope Series and, in less well drained gullies, Atton Series gley soils,

Plate 3.2

The small valley leading north to Yetholm Loch from the upper slopes of Wideopen Hill south of Crookedshaws Farm (Figure 3.1). In the middle ground below the recent plantation the shallow valley flows left to the Kale. Primside Farm is in the middle distance, and the valley also leads west of the slopes of Yetholm Law to Yetholm Loch in the distance to the left. The photograph illustrates the present highly organised enclosed landscape of pasture, arable and plantations, and shows the entire pollen catchment of the Yetholm Loch pollen site.

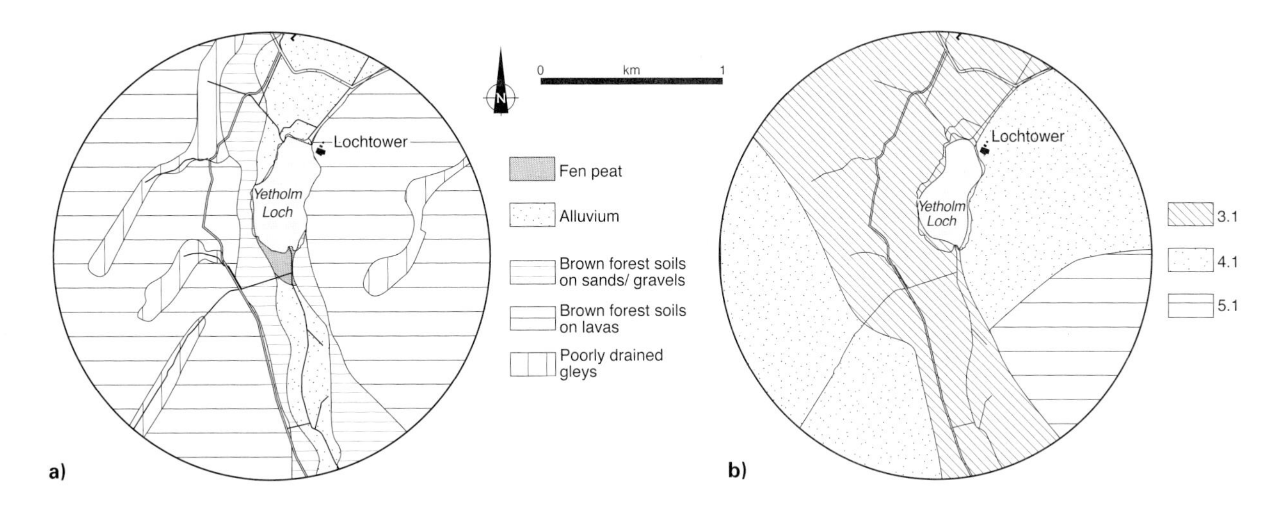

Figure 3.2
(a) Soil series mapped by the Soil Survey of Scotland (Ragg 1960) and (b) current land use capabilities (Bown & Shipley 1982) for the pollen recruitment area. See Table 1.1 for descriptions of current land use capabilities.

the higher ground today used most frequently as grass ley. The valley floor is choked with fluvioglacial sands, deposited in the Late Devensian glaciation, carried by the east-flowing Kale Water (Geikie 1876; Common 1953; Muir 1956). The watershed at Crookedshaws was created by the dumping of glacial sediments during deglaciation. These very well drained gentle slopes a few metres above the present valley floor support Eckford Series brown forest soils, and are the focus of arable cropping. Below the fluvioglacial sediments is a narrow strip of sandy alluvium, drained in the middle of the eighteenth century.

The distribution of archaeological sites is not known in detail since the valley lies outside the archaeologically surveyed area, and the records of stray finds cannot be compared with the upper valley (Chapter 8). The principal farms (Figure 3.1) are all recorded on Roy's Military Survey (1747–55), when the lower slopes were cultivated. In 1798, Douglas described the land use as by tradition arable land, and the valley was an enclosure landscape of hedged fields (Plates 3.1, 3.2).

3.2 Sediment sampling, subsampling and chronology construction

The sampling point is approximately 50m from the west edge of the sediment infill (Figure 3.2a), where the sediments are 315cm thick. The inset to Figure 3.3a shows the close proximity of the boreholes in plan, important in the correlation of stratigraphic events. A series of five 100cm Russian cores were sampled from Boreholes A and B for pollen analyses, fifteen wide diameter Russian cores for ^{14}C assays from Boreholes C–F, and four additional 100cm Russian cores for determination of dry matter and organic matter contents (Section 2.3b) from within this square, all depths controlled by theodolite survey. Figure 3.3a shows the correlations between major sediment units. Table 3.1 describes the simplified sediment stratigraphy obtained from descriptions of individual cores. Figures 3.3b and 3.3c show the fluctuating percentages from contiguous 2cm sediment slices of dry matter and organic content plotted against depth and related to the sequence of local pollen assemblage zones and subzones (A to H) defined in Section 3.3.

Eight ^{14}C assays were obtained on the sediments shallower than 200cm depth at Yetholm Loch (Table 3.2). Sediment slices were from single wide diameter Russian cores or were combined from either two or three wide diameter Russian cores to minimise the sediment thickness and maximise the temporal precision in individual assays from this comparatively shallow and slowly accumulating sediment sequence (Section 2.4a). These cores are listed in Table 3.2 and can be related to sediment cores drawn in Figure 3.3a. Sediment slices were, with the exception of assays GU-2515 and -2513, 4–6cm thick, excessive by modern AMS standards. Figure 3.4 suggests that sediments above 200cm are younger than 7000 cal BC. There is very good agreement in age between the

Table 3.1

The sediment stratigraphy at the sampled site at Yetholm Loch.

Unit G (0–22cm):	5YR 2.5/2 dark reddish-brown poorly humified, uncompacted, dry and blocky-structured amorphous peat with abundant fine filamentous monocotyledonous stems and occasional fresh fleshy grass-sedge stems, increasingly compacted below 6cm; sharp boundary to
Unit F (22–45cm):	10YR 3/2 very dark greyish-brown poorly humified grass-sedge peat, with a band of abundant black monocotyledonous remains between 34 and 36cm; sharp boundary to
Unit E (45–48.5cm):	10YR 3/2 very dark greyish-brown amorphous peat with common black monocotyledonous remains and abundant moss fragments; sharp boundary to
Unit D (48.5–125cm):	10YR 3/3 dark brown organic-rich clay with well-preserved and abundant monocotyledonous remains and rare medium-coarse fleshy stems and wood fragments, and a prominent layer of well-preserved and fresh coarse woody twigs and slender branches between 107 and 113cm; matrix becomes increasingly amorphous down-unit, with sand grains at 100cm depth, and between 122 and 127cm; sharp boundary to
Unit C_2 (125–128cm):	10YR 6/2 light brownish-grey structureless silty clay; sharp boundary to
Unit C_1 (128–138cm):	10YR 6/2 light brownish-grey structureless mixed coarse sand and silt in a clay matrix, colour ranging from 10YR 5/2 greyish-brown to 10YR 5/3 brown, with rare monocotyledonous remains and poorly preserved grass-sedge stems, varying in thickness from 2cm to 11cm; boundary varying from gradual to sharp, irregular and possibly erosive to
Unit B (138–160cm):	10YR 6/2 light brownish-grey clay with silt and rare sand, possibly exhibiting faint colour-banded laminae, increasing in organic content to 10YR 5/3 brown below 150cm, and with rare coarse fleshy grass-sedge stems; very gradual boundary to
Unit A_3 (160–235cm):	predominantly 10YR 4/3 brown to dark brown organic-rich clay with silt containing rare to common coarse woody fragments throughout, common to abundant between 164 and 167cm; amorphous matrix generally increases in proportion below 177cm as colour darkens to 10YR 4/2 dark greyish-brown, and to 10YR 3/2 very dark greyish-brown below 188cm; with sequence of alternating bands of organic-rich and organic-poor sediment, varying throughout in colour, organic matter content and thickness between cores, all separated by gradual boundaries: 170–185.5cm – grey clay with rare organic matter, but abundant charcoal flecks between 170 and 175cm; 185.5–187cm – thin band of darker brown, organic matter-rich clay; 187–201cm – lighter, more minerogenic clay; 201–216cm – predominantly more organic, but variable, with bands of markedly more organic clay, and with abundant monocotyledonous remains between 203 and 208cm, and between 211.5 and 215cm; 216–222cm – lighter grey, more minerogenic clay, but with common to abundant monocotyledonous remains; 222–226cm – more organic, with abundant monocotyledonous remains and rare grass-sedge stems; 226–235cm – lighter grey, more minerogenic clay; sharp boundary to
Unit A_2 (235–253cm):	light grey clay matrix containing dense layer of abundant wood remains, or mineral-rich wood peat, with diffuse bands of poorly preserved grass-sedge stems; gradual boundary to
Unit A_1 (253–315cm):	alternating bands of organic-rich and organic-poor sediment, varying throughout in colour, organic matter content and thickness between cores, all separated by gradual boundaries: 253–265cm – grey clay with very little visible organic matter; 265–283cm – grey minerogenic clay with common monocotyledonous remains and grass-sedge stems; 283–293cm – grey clay with very little visible organic matter; 293–315cm – 10YR 4/3 brown top dark brown organic matter-rich amorphous peat/fine detrial mud.

Table 3.2
Details of the radiocarbon assays obtained on the sediments at Yetholm Loch.

Lab. No. (GU-)	*Mean Depth (cm)*	*Sediment Depth (cm)*	*No. of Cores*	*Sample Weight (gms)*	*Organic Content (%)*	*^{14}C Age BP $\pm 1\sigma$ (‰)*	$\delta^{13}C$	*Calibrated Age BC/AD $\pm 1\sigma$ and Intercept Ages*	*Mean Calibrated Age BC/AD*
2518	19	21–17	3 (1,2,3)	261.4	n.d.	310±60	–24.4	1490 (1620) 1646 AD	1568 AD
2517	46.5	49–44	2 (3,4)	204.4	35	170±80	–28.1	1645 (1677,1749, 1782, 1937, 1950) 1952 AD	not determined
2516	71.5	74–69	8 (5,6)*	101.8	18	410±50	–29.1	1434 (1460) 1497 AD	1465 AD
2515	90.5	95–86	2 (6,7)	392	18	590±60	–27.2	1296 (1380) 1409 AD	1352 AD
2514	122	125–119	1 (8)*	984.5	20	1750±60	–28.9	204 (280) 346 AD	275 AD
2513	165.5	170–161	2 (10,11)	281.2	15	4690±110	–29.6	3600 (3459) 3350 BC	3475 BC
2665	197.5	200–195	1 (#)	596	17	6050±70	–28	5064 (4971) 4885 BC	4975 BC
2683	202.5	205–200	1 (#)	528.1	20	6180±100	–28.3	5260 (5139) 5000 BC	5130 BC

* resampled to increase original weight of subsample in July 1989; # sampled in December 1989

Table 3.3

Details of radiocarbon assays on early-mid Holocene sediments obtained by Hibbert and Switsur (1976) at Din Moss, the pollen-stratigraphic event dated and the suggested depth of the comparable event in the sediments at Yetholm Loch.

Lab. No.	*Pollen-stratigraphic event at Din Moss*	*Depth of event at Yetholm Loch*	*Proposed depth of event*	*^{14}C Age* BP *±1σ*	*Calibrated Age Range* BC *±1σ and Intercept Ages*	*Mean Calibrated Age* BC
Q-1062	end of *Ulmus* decline	50–54cm	168cm	5340±70	4315 (4224, 4187, 4141) 4040 BC	4178 BC
Q-1063	*Quercus-Alnus* zone begins	54–58cm	170cm	5390±70	4343 (4242) 4153 BC	4248 BC
Q-1064	Start of *Ulmus* decline	58–62cm	173cm	5440±70	4355 (4337) 4236 BC	4295 BC
Q-1067	*Quercus-Ulmus-Alnus* zone begins	184–188cm	200cm	6710±100	5649 (5622) 5489 BC	5569 BC
Q-1069	end of first *Alnus* rise	240–244cm	210cm	6860±100	5819 (5726) 5629 BC	5724 BC
Q-1072	*Quercus* values exceed *Ulmus*	286–290cm	230cm	7670±150	6673 (6473) 6399 BC	6536 BC
Q-1073	*Betula-Quercus-Corylus* zone begins	318–322cm	240cm	8680±170	7937 (7691, 7664, 7633) 7509 BC	7723 BC
Q-1074	*Ulmus* curve begins	368–372cm	258cm	8940±170	8086 (8003) 7733 BC	7910 BC
Q-1075	*Corylus/Betula* zone opens	372–376cm	264cm	9120±170	8343 (8088) 8007 BC	8175 BC
Q-1076	start of *Corylus* rise	376–380cm	270cm	9275±170	8479 (8338, 8303, 8267) 8085 BC	8282 BC
Q-1077	*Betula-Pinus-Corylus* zone begins	402–406cm	294cm	9810±190	9360 (9042) 8727 BC	9043 BC

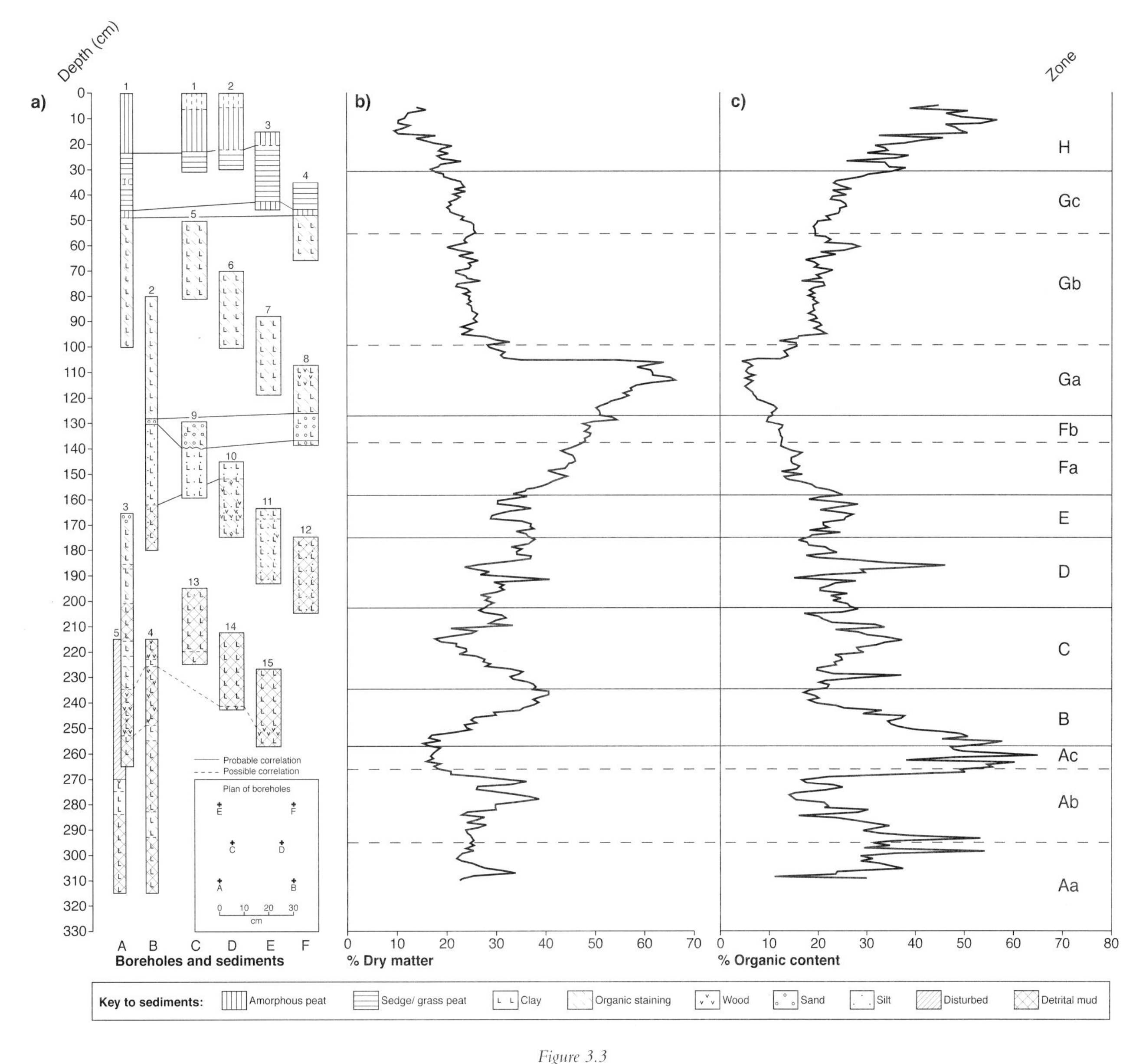

Figure 3.3

(a) The distribution in space and against depth of sediment cores making the sediment and pollen stratigraphies at Yetholm Loch; (b) percentages of dry matter in the sediments plotted against depth; (c) percentages of organic matter in the sediments plotted against depth. Local pollen assemblage zones are plotted to allow correlations to be made between the sediment and pollen stratigraphies.

two contiguous assays GU-2683 and -2665. Other ^{14}C assays are internally consistent except assay GU-2518. Although not demonstrably too old by comparison with the underlying assay GU-2517, which is anyway affected by distorted calibrations typical of recent sediments (Section 2.4b), assay GU-2518 is likely to be in error because its age estimate is not supported by the pollen marker horizon, and it is not used in the preferred time-depth model.

For the sediments between 315 and 200cm depth, pollen stratigraphic correlations were made between the Yetholm Loch stratigraphy and the robustly ^{14}C dated early to mid-Holocene pollen sequence at Din Moss (Hibbert & Switsur 1976; Birks 1993) 4km to the north. The Din Moss pollen stratigraphy was described using an arboreal pollen sum (Section 2.3g). To aid correlation the major tree taxa in the pollen sequence at Yetholm Loch between 315 and 160cm are

Table 3.4

Definitions of sediment accumulation rates between chronological controls used in the preferred time-depth model (Figures 3.4, 3.6) and the sampling and temporal resolutions of pollen and microscopic charcoal analyses at Yetholm Loch.

Depth between dating controls	*Cal ages* BC/AD	*Duration (cal years)*	*Accumulation rate (yrs/cm)*	*Lpaz*	*Depths (cm)*	*Pollen Analyses* (a)	(b)	(c)
0–71.5cm	1990 AD–1465 AD	525	7	H, G		4cm	3.5	28
71.5–90.5cm	1465 AD–1352 AD	113	6	G		4cm	3	24
90.5–122cm	1352 AD–275 AD	1077	34	G		4cm	17	136
122–165.5cm	275 AD–3475 BC	3750	86	G	122–127	2cm	43	172
				F	127–130	0.5cm	43	43
				F	130–138	1cm	43	86
				F, E	138–165	2cm	43	172
165.5–197.5cm	3475 BC–4975 BC	1500	47	E, D		4cm	23.5	188
197.5–202.5cm	4975 BC–5130 BC	155	31	D		4cm	15.5	124
202.5–210cm	5130 BC–5724 BC	594	79	D, C		4cm	40	316
210–230cm	5724 BC–6536 BC	812	41	C		4cm	20.5	164
230–240cm	6536 BC–7723 BC	1187	119	C, B		4cm	60	476
240–270cm	7723 BC–8282 BC	559	19	B, A		4cm	9.5	76
270–294cm	8282 BC–9043 BC	761	32	A		4cm	16	128
294–315cm	9043 BC–9300 BC	257	12	A		4cm	6	48

(a) sampling interval of analyses; (b) sampling resolution: time homogenised per subsample; (c) temporal resolution: time between subsamples

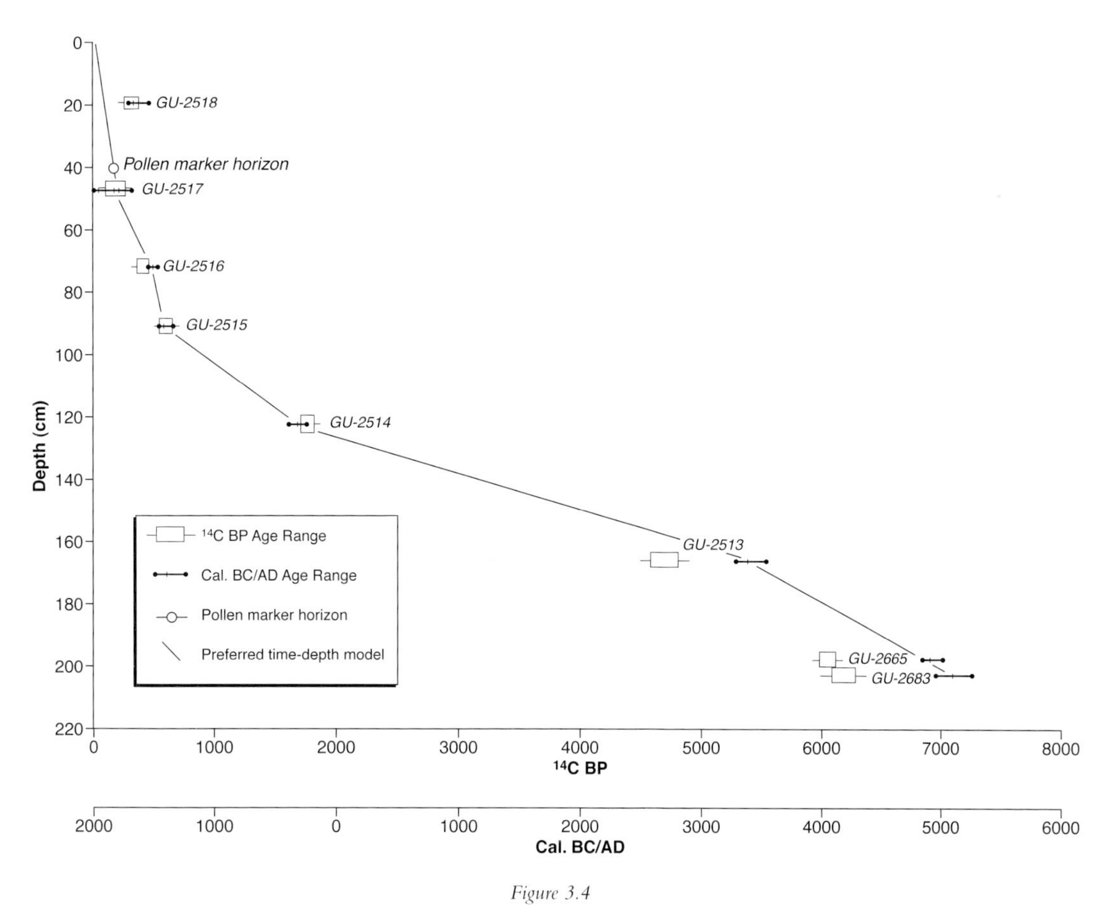

Figure 3.4
The preferred time-depth model for sediments directly dated at Yetholm Loch, showing ^{14}C ages BP at 1 and 2σ as cat-and-whisker plots and corresponding calibrated age ranges BC/AD at 2σ as dumb-bell plots (see Table 3.2). The only additional control obtained for these youngest sediments at Yetholm Loch is the pollen marker horizon at 40cm depth of Agricultural Improvement tree plantations (Section 2.4c).

drawn using this sum in Figure 3.5. Table 3.3 describes the eleven Holocene pollen stratigraphic events dated by Hibbert and Switsur (1976) and the age estimates of these together with the depths of the comparable events in the Yetholm Loch sequence (Figure 3.5). Figure 3.6 presents these eleven ^{14}C assays from the Din Moss sequence plotted against sediment depth at Yetholm Loch. At the base of the sequence, the first appearance of *Betula* (birch) pollen at *c* 10 000 ^{14}C BP (9200 cal BC) is used as a pollen marker horizon (Birks 1989; Section 2.4c).

This figure incorporates data on two pollen stratigraphic events that were independently dated at both pollen sites, (a) the first sustained rise to prominent percentages of *Alnus* (alder) (assays GU-2683 and -2665; Table 3.2: assay Q-1067: Table 3.3), and (b) at and near the first *Ulmus* (elm) decline (assay GU-2513; Table 3.2: assays Q-1062 to -1064; Table 3.3). When the ages of these two pollen stratigraphic events are compared between sites, assays at Yetholm Loch are 600 to 700 cal years younger than at Din Moss (Figure 3.6). There are no internal reasons to question the assays at Yetholm Loch since they lie (with one exception) in a conformable sequence (above; Figure 3.4). However, the assays at Din Moss are also internally in very good agreement (Figure 3.6) and have been considered reliable (Birks 1993). Several explanations for these differences are possible. Firstly, these two pollen stratigraphic events may not have been synchronous (Tipping 1996a). Differences between sites over short distances are known with both the alder rise (Smith 1984; Chambers & Elliott 1989; Bennett & Birks 1989; Tipping 1994) and the elm decline (Bonsall *et al* 1990; Turner, Innes & Simmons 1993; Tipping & Milburn 2002). Secondly, the middle Holocene peats dated at Din Moss are not comparable in sediment type with

TTable 3.5

Local pollen assemblage zones at Yetholm Loch, their characteristic pollen taxa and ^{14}C and calibrated age ranges.

Lpaz	*Depths (cm)*	*Characteristic taxa*	*Duration (^{14}C BP)*	*(cal BP)*	*(cal BC/AD)*
Yetholm H	31–0	Gramineae <8µm anl-D (grasses) – *Salix* (willow) – Cyperaceae (sedges)	n.d.	125-present	1830-present
Yetholm Gc	55–31	Gramineae <8µm anl-D (grasses) – Cyperaceae (sedges) – *Equisetum* (horsetails)	n.d.	350–125	1600–1830 AD
Yetholm Gb	99–55	Gramineae <8µm anl-D (grasses) – *Plantago lanceolata* (ribwort plantain) – *Rumex* (docks) – *Rumex* (docks) – Cyperaceae (sedges) – *Cannabis* (hemp)	860–350	900–350	1050–1600 AD
Yetholm Ga	127–99	Gramineae <8µm anl-D (grasses) – *Plantago lanceolata* (ribwort plantain) – *Rumex* (docks) – Cyperaceae (sedges)	1800–860	1900–900	50–1050 AD
Yetholm Fb	138–127	*Alnus* (alder) – *Corylus/Myrica* (hazel/bog myrtle) – Gramineae <8µm anl-D (grasses) – *Quercus* (oak) – *Ulmus* (elm) – Polypodiaceae undiff. (undiff. ferns)	2200–1800	2125–1900	175 BC–50 AD
Yetholm Fa	159–138	*Alnus* (alder) – *Corylus/Myrica* (hazel/bog myrtle) – Gramineae <8µm anl-D (grasses) – – *Quercus* (oak) – Polypodiaceae undiff. (undiff. ferns)	4875–2200	5100–2125	3070–175 BC
Yetholm E	175–159	*Alnus* (alder) – Gramineae <8µm anl-D (grasses) – *Corylus/Myrica* (hazel/bog myrtle) – Polypodiaceae undiff. (undiff. ferns)	5870–4875	5100–4250	3920–3070 BC
Yetholm D	203–175	*Alnus* (alder) – *Quercus* (oak) – *Ulmus* (elm) – *Corylus/Myrica* (hazel/bog myrtle) – *Pinus* (pine) – *Sphagnum* (bog moss)	6050–5100	7090–5870	5140–3920 BC
Yetholm C	235–203	*Corylus/Myrica* (hazel/bog myrtle) – *Ulmus* (elm) – *Quercus* (oak) – Cyperaceae (sedges)	8170–6180	9250–7090	7300–5140 BC
Yetholm B	251–235	*Corylus/Myrica* (hazel/bog myrtle) – *Betula* (birch) – *Ulmus* (elm) – Polypodiaceae undiff. (undiff. ferns)	9100–8170	10 100–9250	8150–7300 BC
Yetholm Ac	267–251	Cyperaceae (sedges) – Gramineae <8µm anl-D (grasses) – *Betula* (birch) – *Equisetum* (horsetails)	9325–9100	10 400–10100	8450–8150 BC
Yetholm Ab	295–267	Gramineae <8µm anl-D (wild grasses) – Cyperaceae (sedges) – *Betula* (birch) – *Pinus* (pine) – Polypodiaceae undiff. (undiff. ferns)	9725–9325	10 950–10400	9000–8450 BC
Yetholm Aa	315–295	*Betula* (birch) – *Salix* (willow) – *Dryopteris* (ferns)	10 000–9725	11 150–10950	9200–9000 BC

n.d. not determined

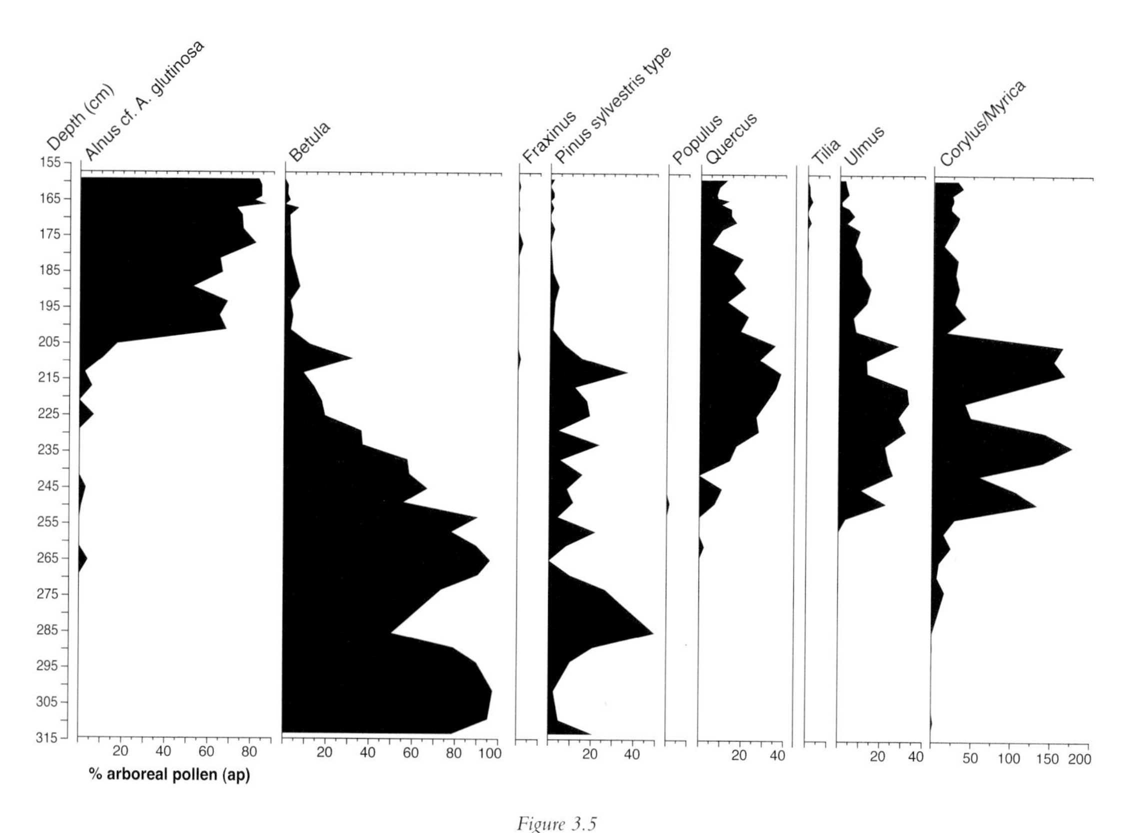

Figure 3.5
Major tree taxa (*Alnus* to *Ulmus*) and shrub taxa (*Corylus/Myrica*) between 315 and 160cm at Yetholm Loch, calculated using an arboreal pollen sum for comparison with the pollen stratigraphy at Din Moss (Hibbert & Switsur 1976).

the lacustrine muds dated at Yetholm Loch, and age differences may have been introduced through dating different proportions of mixed age organic matter (Section 2.4a): in this context, assays from events in the early Holocene from lacustrine muds at Din Moss agree well with other sites in southern Scotland (Birks 1989). Thirdly, there may be systematic differences in the results achieved by different radiocarbon dating laboratories (International Study Group 1982). Fourthly, differences may have been introduced through the homogenisation of thick sediment slices at both sites and from sampling sediments at Yetholm Loch with low rates of accumulation.

Accordingly, the application of radiocarbon dates from Din Moss to the Yetholm Loch sequence is tentatively made, but Figures 3.4 and 3.6 show the preferred time-depth model for the Yetholm Loch sediments. This is constrained also by the following observations: (i) basal pollen counts (Figure 3.7) record *Juniperus* (juniper) pollen but not *Empetrum* (crowberry), suggesting a likely age for these at around 9300 cal BC (Tipping 1987c); (ii) the good agreement between the rise of *Quercus* (oak) pollen at Din Moss (Q-1073) and a straight line projected through assays GU-2513 and GU-2665/-2683 at Yetholm Loch. Spheroidal carbonacaeous spherules were recorded too rarely to provide chronological controls for recent sediments (Section 2.4d; Figure 3.10).

Sediment accumulation rates fluctuated markedly, indicated by the changing gradients of the preferred time-depth model in Figures 3.4 and 3.6. Accumulation rates are high to very high until *c* 7700 cal BC, very low for over 1000 cal years after this and apparently sharply accelerating to very high rates after *c* 1350 cal AD Sediment accumulation rates between dating controls are calculated in Table 3.4; these are approximate (Section 2.4e). The subsampling intervals for pollen analyses also varied from 4cm to contiguous 0.5cm depending on the temporal resolution needed to explain events (Section 2.3d), and Table 3.4 defines what the variation in sediment accumulation and subsampling strategy means for the temporal resolution of pollen and microscopic charcoal analyses. This varies from the duration of a human generation (24 to 28 cal years)

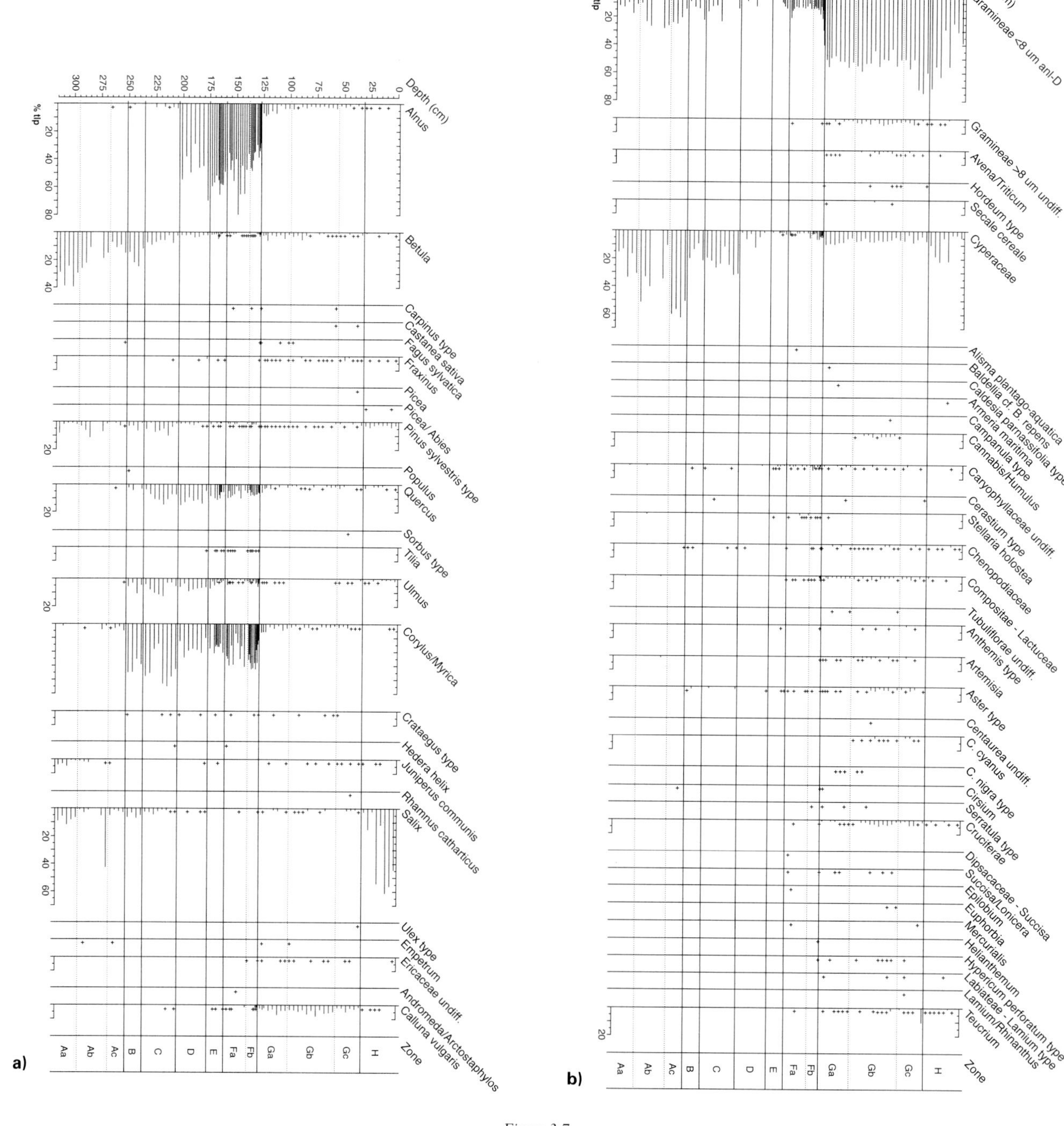

Figure 3.7

The complete pollen stratigraphy at Yetholm Loch plotted against depth (cm) and calculated as percentages of total land pollen (tlp) and tlp + group (Section 2.3g). Values recorded in a subsample at <1% are marked by a cross. Local pollen assemblage zone boundaries are plotted to permit correlation. See Appendix One for a glossary of English names for Linnaean taxa.

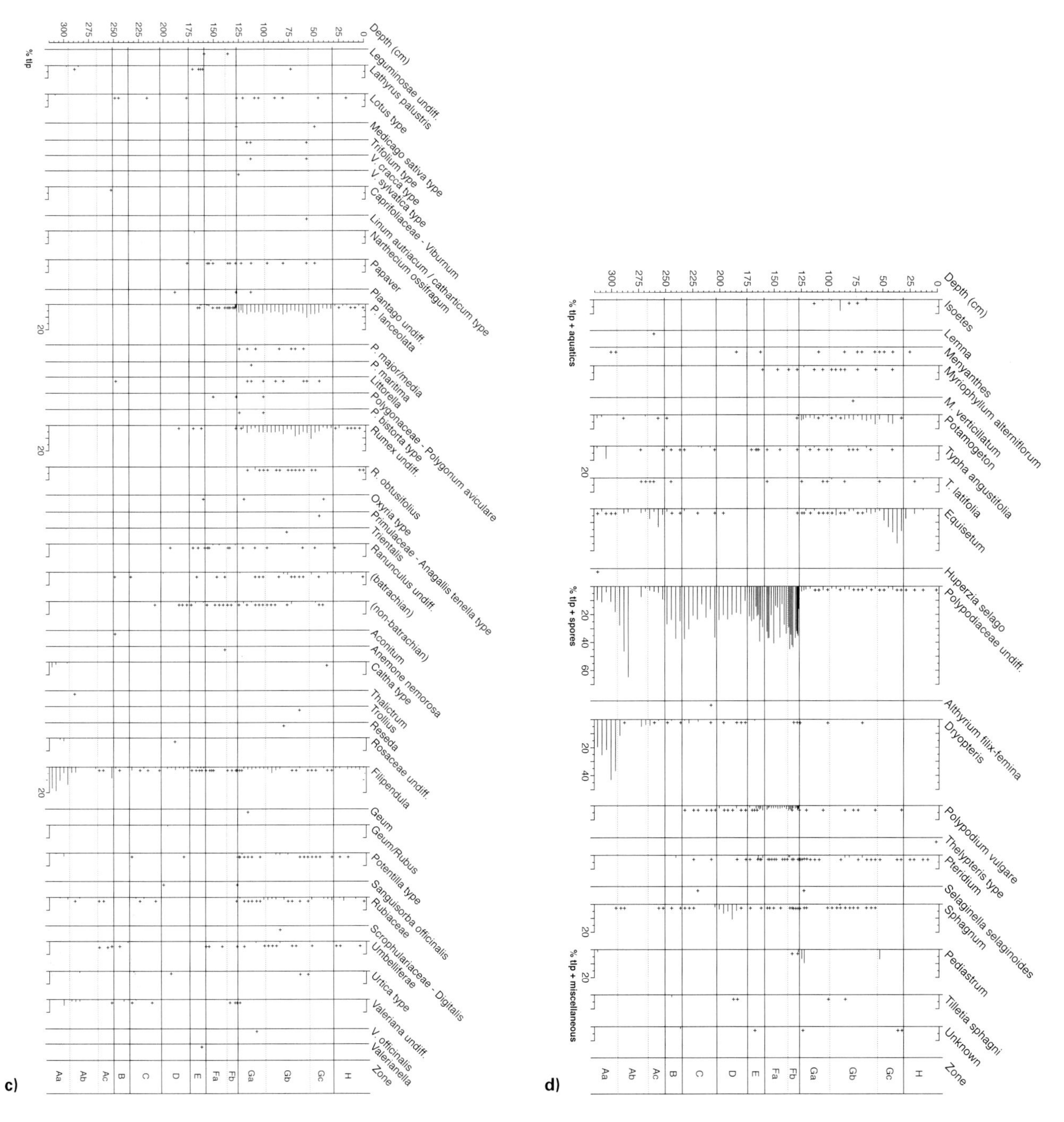

Figure 3.7 (cont.)

The complete pollen stratigraphy at Yetholm Loch plotted against depth (cm) and calculated as percentages of total land pollen (tlp) and tlp + group (Section 2.3g). Values recorded in a subsample at <1% are marked by a cross. Local pollen assemblage zone boundaries are plotted to permit correlation. See Appendix One for a glossary of English names for Linnaean taxa.

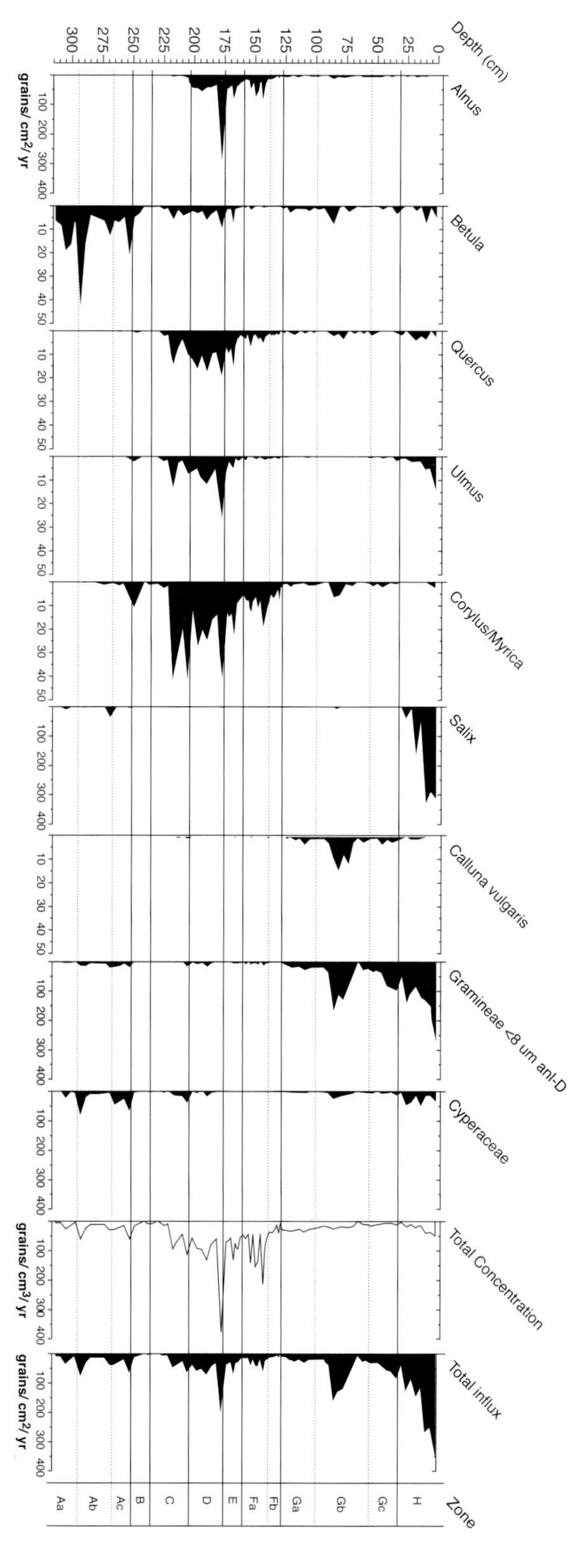

Figure 3.8

Pollen influx values (thousands of grains per cm^2 per year) for major pollen taxa and for total land pollen plotted against depth. Also plotted are total pollen concentration values (thousands of grains per cm^3) (see Section 2.3h). Local pollen assemblage zone boundaries are plotted to permit correlation.

greater productivity of aquatic organisms. The roots of plants are recorded in the sediments (Table 3.1) from a re-established sedge dominated fen (Figure 3.7). The abundance of local Cyperaceae (sedge) communities, probably including *Salix* (willow) in addition to those taxa recorded in lpaz Aa, probably reduced representation of dryland pollen. However, the absence of *Juniperus* (juniper) pollen may reflect the re-establishment of competitively superior *Betula* (birch) trees, and birch trees probably ousted open grassland communities. *Pinus* (pine) pollen is no longer recorded.

Lpaz Yetholm B (251–235cm): 8150–7300 cal BC

Sediment changes coincide with the pollen zone boundary, suggesting as in lpaz A that many apparent vegetation changes may be determined by sediment processes or *vice versa*. Sediment unit A_2 is a minerogenic clay (Table 3.1), with very low organic contents (Figure 3.3), possibly because of renewed soil erosion. However, except for increasing numbers of Polypodiaceae undiff. (fern) spores (Figure 3.7), there is little palynological evidence for this. Increases in the amounts of physically damaged pollen are not significant (Figure 3.9). Increases in corroded pollen are because of the large expansion of *Corylus/Myrica* (hazel/bog myrtle) pollen, which is highly susceptible to corrosion (Konigsson 1969; Havinga 1984).

Some evidence suggests that there was an hiatus in sedimentation. In combination the evidence might imply that the sampling site fluctuated in relation to the lake shore throughout the *c* 800 cal years represented by lpaz B, sometimes at the lake edge, suggested by the continuing representation of *Typha angustifolia* (lesser bulrush) and *Potamogeton* (pondweed), with the sampling site at least seasonally inundated (Figure 3.7), but sometimes within a drier fen. The clay rich sediment might in this context have been derived partly from *in situ* pedogenesis (mineralisation) of former lake sediment. The clay contains abundant wood remains (Table 3.1), and although not identified, probably included *Salix* (willow) in dense stands, perhaps enough to suppress pollen productivity of Cyperaceae (sedges). Other factors probably induced the abrupt losses in Cyperaceae at the lpaz A–B boundary also. There are synchronous abrupt increases of *Corylus/Myrica* (hazel/bog myrtle) and *Ulmus* (elm) pollen between adjacent subsamples (Figure 3.7), probably indicating an hiatus in sedimentation at the sediment boundary between units A_1 and A_2 (Table 3.1). How long this hiatus persisted can be defined from comparing pollen stratigraphies at Din Moss (Hibbert & Switsur 1976) and Yetholm Loch. At Din Moss the expansion of *Corylus/Myrica* (hazel/bog myrtle) pollen occurred stratigraphically before the continuous record for *Ulmus* (elm) pollen, estimated to have been *c* 400 cal years before. At Yetholm Loch the two taxa appear at the same time (Figures 3.4, 3.7). This might imply a break in sedimentation of this duration at the sampling site at Yetholm Loch.

Within lpaz B, the relative abundance of *Corylus/Myrica* pollen suggests that most of the grains are of hazel. However, if the identification of an hiatus is correct, it means that environmental conditions conducive to hazel colonisation cannot be precisely established at Yetholm Loch. It is possible that lake level lowering, and thus relative climatic aridity, was a factor in inducing the sedimentological hiatus, but this appears not to have influenced peat accumulation at nearby Din Moss (Hibbert & Switsur 1976). Fluctuating shorelines at Yetholm Loch need have had no vertical component in lake level because changing sediment inputs may have made the fen advance and retreat over the site. These fluctuations in sediment type continue in later pa zones.

Within lpaz B, numbers of charcoal fragments are again prominent (Figure 3.10). Fragments 10–25µm are more abundant early in the zone, and these smaller fragments account for cumulative charcoal length to be high as sediment accumulation resumed following the probable hiatus. Other measures of abundance (Figure 3.10; Section 2.3j) indicate that fire frequency/intensity rose during lpaz B, particularly above 245cm (7800 cal BC) and later than the expansion of *Corylus/Myrica* pollen.

Lpaz Yetholm C (235–203cm): 7300–5140 cal BC

Quercus (oak), inconsistently represented in lpaz B, has its rational limit at the lower zone boundary, and oak trees probably began to colonise the drier slopes of the catchment at this time, substantially after the first appearance of *Ulmus* (elm). The fern *Polypodium vulgare* (polypody) is closely associated with *Quercus*, growing as an epiphyte on trunks (Turner 1987). The gradual establishment of the oak and elm woodland between 7300 and 5500 cal BC (216cm) appears to have occurred at the expense, primarily, of *Betula* (birch) (Figure 3.7).

The smooth expansion of *Quercus* and *Ulmus* percentages is in contrast to the frequent fluctuations in sediment type at the sampling site (Table 3.1; unit A_3). This is taken to indicate that sedimentological fluctuations represent small scale events, local to the valley floor, and that dryland tree pollen sources on valley sides were undisturbed by these shifts. The sediment changes, alternating bands of organic mud and minerogenic clays (Table 3.1; Figure 3.3), probably represent further oscillations between organic rich lacustrine muds deposited in relatively deep water and semi-terrestrial minerogenic clays. Greater amounts of physically damaged pollen were introduced prior to 216cm (*c* 5900 cal BC), suggesting that eroded soils contributed some remobilised sediment and pollen. After *c* 5900 cal BC, pollen grains are most commonly corroded, but this pattern is influenced by the increased representation of *Corylus/Myrica* pollen, susceptible to corrosion. Fluctuations in sediment origin will have affected the recruitment of pollen from local sources and distorted the representation of taxa local to the site like Cyperaceae (sedges), Gramineae <8µm anl-D (wild grasses) and *Salix* (willow), and these probably explain the abrupt and very large shifts in abundances of pollen taxa (Figure 3.7). Short lived non-depositional or erosional hiatuses cannot be discounted: some sediment boundaries are also abrupt (Table 3.1). *Corylus/Myrica* percentages fluctuate abruptly, in contrast to those of *Quercus* (oak), *Ulmus* (elm) and *Betula* (birch), suggesting that hazel trees grew on the valley floor, affected by localised geomorphic change.

After *c* 5900 cal BC (216cm) were abrupt palynological changes to much higher *Corylus/Myrica* and Cyperaceae percentages, much lower proportions of Gramineae <8µm anl-D (wild grasses) and *Salix* (willow), the loss of *Sphagnum* (bogmoss) from close to the sampling site, and sharp reductions in percentages of both *Quercus* (oak) and *Ulmus* (elm). These are most simply explained by recognising the control on pollen recruitment of sedimentological processes, with an increase in organic matter content at this depth (Table 3.1; Figure 3.3) suggesting stability at the sampling site and probable closure of local woodland over the sampling site, reducing pollen recruitment from areas distant from the valley floor. However, the reductions in oak and elm were substantial and can be interpreted as representing the loss of trees: this is the first of several elm declines at the site though much earlier than the 'classic' early Neolithic event (Parker *et al* 2002). In addition, *Crataegus* type (cf. hawthorn) pollen is recorded: the pollen type is under-represented being insect pollinated. This small tree would have competed successfully in gaps with oak and elm on dry soils, and in part would have protected the slower

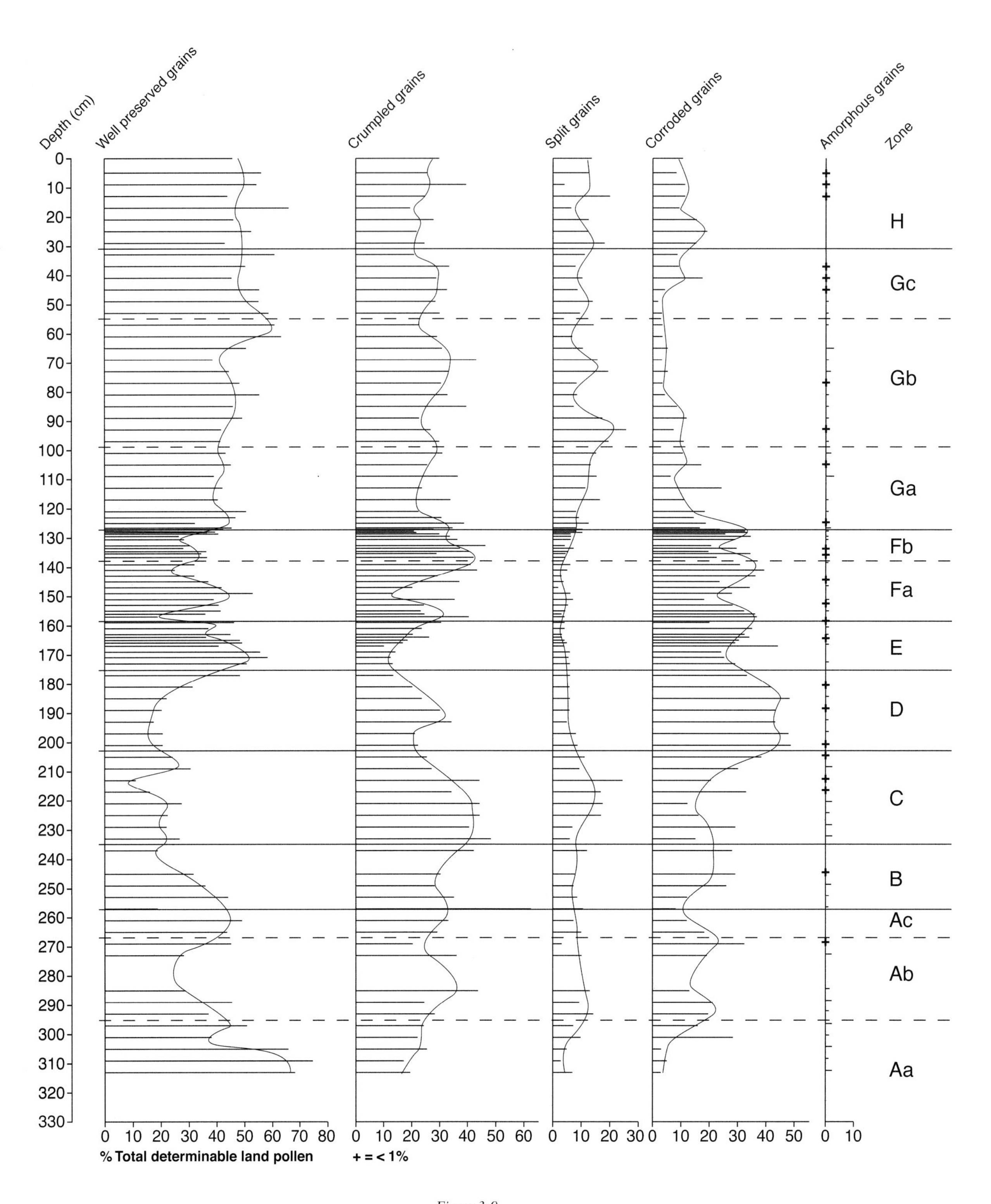

Figure 3.9

Pollen preservation states for all determinable land pollen grains plotted against depth and calculated as percentages of total land pollen (see Section 2.3i). Local pollen assemblage zone boundaries are plotted to permit correlation.

growing trees in a natural thorn hedge had they been partly grazed (Vera 2000).

The significance of the sediment changes is unclear. Towards the beginning of lpaz C, rates of sediment accumulation decreased significantly rather than accelerated (Table 3.4; Figure 3.6). Shifting stream courses across the fen, without severe soil erosion, may explain the changes. There is no reason to see more profound fluctuations in climate as causal because sediment changes occurred very frequently. Increasing fire frequency/intensity is not influential in inducing geomorphic change because the trend is to significantly reduced burning: numbers of microscopic charcoal fragments decline to low levels (Figure 3.10). There were very few fires, or only small ones, in the catchment after 220cm (*c* 6200 cal BC). One possible mechanism for geomorphic instability on the valley floor is the construction, abandonment and collapse of dams across the shallow river valley of The Stank, downstream but at no lower an altitude than the loch (Figure 3.1) by beaver (*Castor fiber*) (Coles & Orme 1982, 1983; Coles 1992, 2000, 2001; Sarmaja-Korjonen 2001). Such a proposal is not entirely hypothetical, as Wilson (1855, 1858) described the discovery of a beaver skull in the Kale Water valley at Morebattle, 5km south-west of Yetholm Loch, in a now infilled lake worked in the nineteenth century cal AD. This skull has been ^{14}C dated to 6170 ± 95 ^{14}C BP (Kitchener & Bonsall 1997; Conroy, Kitchener & Gibson 1998), around 5050 cal BC. Other ^{14}C dated beaver skulls from south-east Scotland show that beaver were present locally earlier than this (Conroy *et al* 1998). There is no requirement for such activity to have affected loch sediments only at this time since beaver survived in Scotland until the later historic period (Kitchener & Conroy 1997) and has been identified by Wells, Hodgkinson and Huckerby (2000) as initiating peat formation in later prehistory, but the sedimentological data for small scale fluctuations in lake position pertain at Yetholm Loch only to the later Mesolithic period.

Lpaz Yetholm D (203–175cm): 5140–3920 cal BC

Sediments with low organic contents became dominant, with sharply fluctuating dry matter contents indicating that short lived pulses of mineral sediment still pushed into the fen, seen also in sediment descriptions (Table 3.1, Figure 3.3). Sediment accumulation rates did not change significantly, however (Table 3.4; Figure 3.6). The sampling site is likely to have lain at or slightly above mean water level, given the virtual absence of aquatic spores and the high numbers of *Sphagnum* (bog moss) spores from peat (Figure 3.7), on the wet terrestrial valley floor. The site may indeed have been periodically dry because corroded grains are more common (Figure 3.9): reworking of pollen is unlikely to explain this as proportions of physically damaged grains decline. Grains of *Quercus* (oak), not readily prone to such decay, are corroded (unpublished data).

The sudden and substantial expansion of *Alnus* (alder) at *c* 5140 cal BC may, as with other abrupt pollen stratigraphic events at this site, be a product of an hiatus. It may also represent the very rapid establishment, over 200 years, of a tree suited to wet ground. Colonisation may have been aided by increased areas of wet ground resulting from beaver activity (Chambers & Price 1985). Dryland tree types like *Quercus* (oak) and *Ulmus* (elm) appear relatively unaffected by the dramatic colonisation of *Alnus*, but taxa growing on the valley floor such as *Betula* (birch), *Salix* (willow) and *Corylus/Myrica* (cf. *Myrica*; bog myrtle) suffered substantial reductions (Figure 3.7). *Betula* and *Salix* were rare plants in the catchment from this time.

Above 190cm (*c* 4600 cal BC) *Sphagnum* (bog moss) percentages decline. Oak and elm woodland is better depicted, with *Dryopteris* (ferns) and *Pteridium* (bracken) possibly representative of the ground layer of such woods. There are slight suggestions of a more open tree canopy cover at the sampling site, despite the dominance by now of *Alnus*. The pollen of dry ground species of buttercup (non-batrachian *Ranunculus*) is consistently recorded, and a single grain of the shade intolerant *Helianthemum* (rock rose) suggests dry grassland near the sampling site, the pollen being poorly dispersed (Proctor & Lambert 1961). The appearance of *Fraxinus* (ash) may also indicate limited openings in the woodland, the tree being relatively shade intolerant, although it is found in *Alnus* carr (Figure 3.7). Fire played no role in vegetation change given the very low counts of microscopic charcoal (Figure 3.10).

Lpaz Yetholm E (175–159cm): 3150–2300 cal BC

The deposition above 170cm (*c* 3800 cal BC) of organic rich sediment (Table 3.1; Figure 3.3) containing spores of *Typha angustifolia* (lesser bulrush), *Menyanthes* (bogbean) and *Myriophyllum alterniflorum* (alternate water milfoil) (Figure 3.7) shows that the sampling site was under water once more throughout this zone. Pollen grains are markedly better preserved in this sediment, suggesting environmental stability, limited geomorphic activity and sediment influx and a scarcity of reworked pollen (Figure 3.9). The lake shore was

Table 3.6

Size measurements (pollen size, pollen index: Andersen 1979) of well preserved Gramineae (grass family) pollen grains of annulus diameters >8μm at Yetholm Loch, and assessments where possible from these measurements of the probable cultivated grass (Tipping unpublished).

Depth (cm)	*anl-D*	*Size*	*Index*	*Group*	*Probable Taxon*
21	14	49.5	1.10	III	*Triticum*
33	8	40.5	1.13	II	
37	14	43.5	1.12	III	*Triticum*
45	14	47	19	III	*Triticum*
	12	48.5	1.15	III	
49	10	44.5	1.17	III	
	12	44	15	III	
	11	52.5	1.14	III	
53	12	45.5	17	III	
	13	51.5	1.10	III	
57	8	47.5	1.21	II	
	11.5	40	1.28	III	
	10	40.5	1.25	II/III	*Avena sativa*
61	10	43.5	1.35	II/III	
	10.5	41	15	II/III	
	12	47.5	1.16	III	
	13	44.5	1.17	III	
65	10	43.5	1.25	II/III	*Secale*
	12	44	1.31	III	*Avena sativa*
	9	41.5	1.44	II	*Secale*
	10	44.5	1.17	II/III	
	12	44.5	1.17	III	
	12	48	1.18	III	
	10	46	14	III	
	11	48	1.23	III	
	10	42	1.21	II/III	*Secale*
69	11.5	49	1.23	III	
	14	55	14	III	
	12	47	1.13	III	
73	10	50.5	1.19	III	
	10	46.5	1.26	III	
77	11.5	44	1.20	III	
	13	46.5	1.16	III	
	14	44.5	17	III	
	13	46.5	1.22	III	
	10	48.5	1.10	III	
	12	49	1.22	III	
81	11	43	1.20	III	
	11	44	1.44	III	
	10	44.5	1.40	III	*Avena sativa*
	9	42	1.47	II	*Secale*
	11	45	1.25	III	
	8	43	1.32	II	*Secale*
	10	43.5	1.29	II/III	*Secale/Avena*
85	12	48	1.18	III	
	10.5	46.5	1.11	II/III	
93	11	47.5	1.21	III	
	11	46	1.19	III	
	10	44.5	1.28	III	*Avena sativa*
125	11	44.5	1.17	III	
	9	40.5	1.53	II	*Secale*
	9.5	44	1.20	III	*Avena sativa*
127	10	43	1.20	II/III	

north of the sampling site, an unknown distance but close enough for *Lathyrus palustris* (marsh pea) to be common in pollen counts. This shift in valley floor environments appears to have been more substantive than earlier, more short lived oscillations, although the sediment accumulation rate did not significantly change (Figure 3.4).

Ulmus (elm) values decline above 173cm from 7 to 8% to <1% tlp for 8cm, over approximately 300 cal years from *c* 3825 to 3540 cal BC, directly ^{14}C dated by assay GU-2513 (Table 3.2). The dense valley floor *Alnus* (alder) carr was relatively undisturbed, as were associated fen communities. Above 167cm (*c* 3550 cal BC) *Quercus* (oak) percentages also decline for a short period. *Tilia* (lime) is consistently represented above 171cm (*c* 3750 cal BC): values of 1% tlp as at Yetholm Loch (Figure 3.7) can be regarded as indicating local tree growth (Pigott & Huntley 1980, Huntley & Birks 1983; see Section 8.7d for fuller discussion).

The continued or increased representation of shade intolerant trees and shrubs (*Fraxinus* (ash), *Juniperus* (juniper), *Crataegus* type (cf. hawthorn)), suggest that woodland openings developed further. Woodland loss appears to have occurred without the use of fire; total numbers of charcoal fragments are uniformly low (Figure 3.10). From *c* 168cm, coincident with the decline in *Quercus* (oak), Gramineae <8µm anl-D (wild grasses) percentages smoothly increase. An expansion of grassland communities on dry ground within the deciduous woodland is likely. Herb taxa are few or poorly represented but the difficulties of herb pollen reaching the sampling site through a dense screen of wetland trees must be borne in mind (Tauber 1965). Herb taxa such as dry ground (non-batrachian) *Ranunculus* (buttercups), Caryophyllaceae (pinks), *Pteridium* (bracken) and, for the first time, *Plantago lanceolata* (ribwort plantain) and *Rumex* (docks) are recorded (Figure 3.7). The latter two taxa are generally regarded as pasture indicators (Behre 1981). In the Bowmont Valley, *Plantago lanceolata* is restricted to species rich *Festuca-Agrostis* (fescue-bent) grasslands on neutral to base rich soils (King 1962).

Lpaz Yetholm Fa (159–138cm): 2300–175 cal BC

The steadily increasing amounts of clay in sediment unit B, with occasional silt and sand laminae (Table 3.1), represent very high proportions of sediment derived from upstream of the lake, probably from inflowing streams. Aquatic spores continue to be recorded (Figure 3.7) and the sampling site was probably under open water, but increasingly impacted

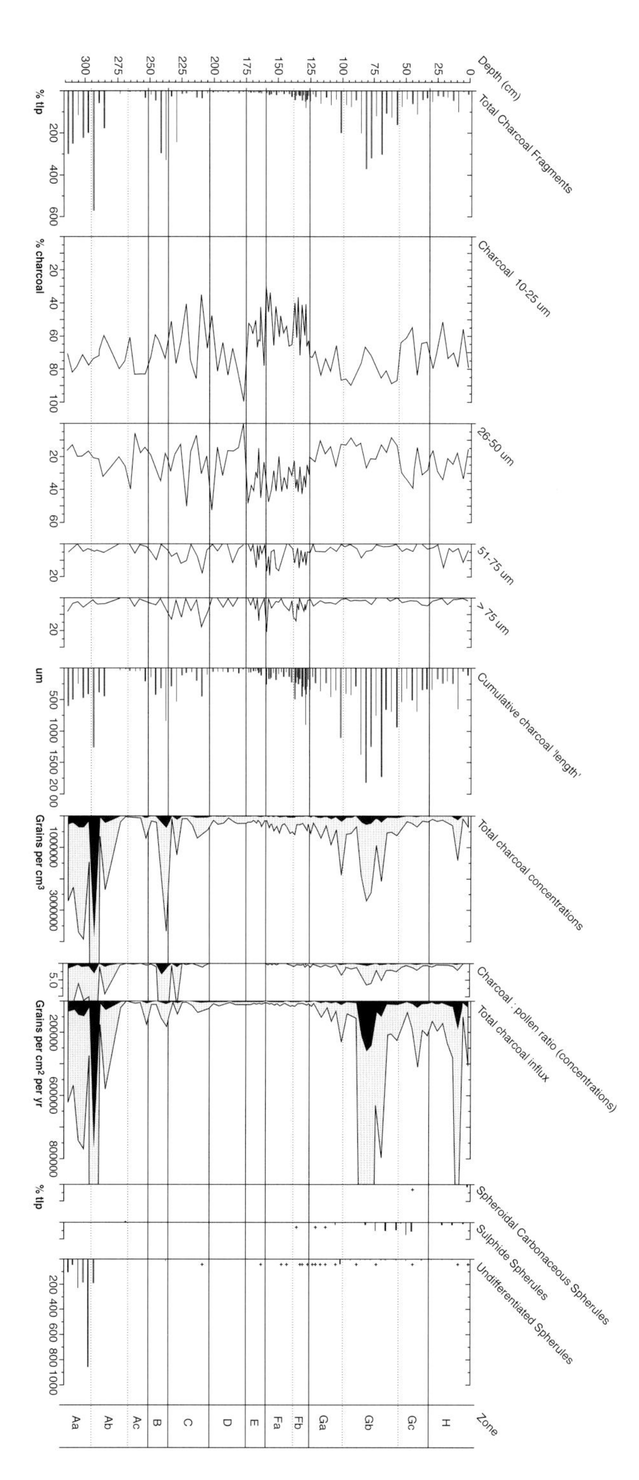

Figure 3.10
Measures of the abundance of microscopic charcoal fragments and opaque spherules plotted against depth (see Sections 2.3j, 2.3k). The pale shading of some curves represents an exaggeration of ×10 for values in black) that are generally small and difficult to see. Values of types of opaque spherule recorded in a subsample at <1% are marked by a cross. Local pollen assemblage zone boundaries are plotted to permit correlation.

by eroding stream sediment. Accelerated erosion and sediment transport are thought to be recorded rather than just the meandering of streams nearer the site. Stepwise abrupt reductions in organic matter content and matching increases in dry matter contents (Figure 3.3) between 153 to 150cm and 142 to 140cm suggest the input of sediment as pulses against a background of gradually increasing mineral inwashing.

Because much of the sediment was delivered as short lived pulses, it is very difficult to impose a timescale on events in this. The mean sediment accumulation rate of *c* 86 yrs per cm (Table 3.4), from which ages are estimated, is imprecise. Changes in the pollen diagram may also be affected by sedimentological changes, particularly above 146cm when a substantial amount of reworked pollen is probably implied by declining proportions of well preserved pollen and increases in numbers of crumpled and corroded grains (Figure 3.9).

An abrupt second decline in *Ulmus* (elm) percentages is apparent at 157cm, at some time between 2850 and 2550 cal BC (*c* 2640 cal BC) (Figure 3.7). A single cereal type (Gramineae >8μm anl-D) pollen grain is recorded at this depth, crumpled and so not classified in Table 3.6, but with an annulus diameter of 10μm (Table 2.2). This is the only good evidence that woodland clearings associated with this second elm decline were anthropogenic in origin. *Tilia* (lime) is not recorded for several subsamples above 151cm, and *Betula* (birch) is only inconsistently recorded. By 141cm, percentages of *Quercus* (oak) are halved. This single episode has a possible age between *c* 2100 and 1350 cal BC. These indications of clearance coincide with very high percentages of *Alnus* (alder), and may in part be induced by distortions in the representation of pollen taxa from slopes above the valley floor. Percentages of grasses and herbs show few changes and no cereal type pollen grains are recorded with the decline of oak.

Lpaz Yetholm Fb (138–127cm): 175 cal BC–50 cal AD

The ages of zone boundaries are unclear because the minerogenic sediment precluded ^{14}C dating. Interpolation between ^{14}C assays prior to this zone would imply that lpaz Fb has an age range from *c* 850 to 150 cal BC. Using assays after this zone the age range is much shorter because average sediment accumulation rates are higher, from *c* 175 cal BC to 50 cal AD. Because the coarse sandy silty clay of unit C_1 (Table 3.1) was probably deposited very rapidly, the latter estimate is used here (Table 3.4).

The sediments are almost certainly fluvial in origin, though from the presence of pollen and spores from aquatic plants and of the alga, *Pediastrum*, the sampling site appears to have remained lacustrine (Figure 3.7). The sediments represent high energy flows, and the stream above Yetholm Loch, though very small, was very active. It is likely that the alluvial deposits on the floodplain (Figure 3.2a; Section 3.1) were created during this period. Evidence for the reworking of pollen is abundant, in very high percentages of both crumpled and corroded pollen grains (Figure 3.9). To an extent, increased physical damage may have been derived from post-depositional abrasion within the sands and silts, but corroded grains probably imply transfer of pollen from aerobic soils, as suggested also by the consistently very high values of durable Polypodiaceae undiff. (undiff. ferns) spores (Figure 3.7). It is very likely that pollen grains were partly derived from eroding catchment soils, and that the pollen assemblage is of mixed age. An unknown proportion of the grains is older than the sediment itself (cf. Hirons 1988). Most of the pollen stored in soils eroding at this time will have been from tree taxa because the vegetation on these soils had been predominantly arboreal. Percentages of many tree types in this zone are thus inflated by this reworking. A corollary of this is that reductions in tree pollen percentages were actually more marked than is depicted in the pollen record.

Reductions in percentages of *Alnus* (alder) from lpaz Fa (Figure 3.7) probably resulted from population losses in valley floor woods, either as a consequence of accelerated fluvial activity or independent of it. However, removal of valley floor woods would have permitted increased stream bank erosion. Other palynological changes strongly suggest that this subzone is characterised by woodland clearance with erratic reductions in *Ulmus* (elm), *Corylus/Myrica* (hazel/bog myrtle) and *Quercus* (oak) pollen percentages (Figure 3.7). However, as a consequence of what must have been a very substantial contribution of reworked arboreal pollen grains, the loss of trees only becomes clear in the pollen record when soil inwashing ceased and pollen assemblages more closely reflected the contemporary landscape. So the changes in the pollen record above 130cm are thought to be a product largely of waning coarse sediment supply, seen in the deposition of sediment unit C_2 (Table 3.1). The evidence, scale and character of this agricultural activity is considered in discussion of lpaz Ga (Figure 3.7).

Lpaz Yetholm Ga (127–99cm): 50–1050 cal AD

Dry matter contents of the sediments fall sharply by 18% as the proportions of mineral matter were reduced. Organic matter contents rise, but more slowly. Prior to *c* 115cm (around 600 cal AD) small and decreasing amounts of clay were still being flushed into the lake (Figure 3.6), but after this time the sediment and pollen records indicate, from the pronounced increases in numbers of aquatic spores (*Potamogeton* (pondweed), *Myriophyllum alterniflorum* (alternate water milfoil), and later, *Isoetes* (quillwort) and *Littorella* (shoreweed)), that moderately deep, open, still and increasingly less turbid lake water lay over the sampling site. For a period lasting perhaps 500 years the high nutrient loads of sediments being flushed into the lake provided the conditions for abundant colonies of algae such as *Pediastrum* to grow in shallower waters. Herb rich fen and marsh communities flourished nearby, with Cyperaceae (sedges), *Filipendula* (meadowsweet), members of the Alismataceae family (water plantains), *Baldellia* (lesser water plantain) and *Caldesia* (parnassus leaved water plantain), with *Succisa* (devilsbit scabious) on acid peaty fen soils. A few *Salix* (willow) bushes may have survived on the fen.

Betula (birch) and *Fraxinus* (ash) pollen percentages increase, and these trees may have grown on the fen. Alternatively, both may have survived on steep rocky slopes protected from grazing with *Crataegus* (hawthorn) and *Juniperus* (juniper) (Figure 3.7). The re-establishment of juniper in the pollen record suggests that this shrub recolonised the catchment, although it may have persisted from the early Holocene (lpaz Ab) unrecorded when trees dominated pollen influx. The same problem of representation affects interpretation of *Calluna* (ling) growth. This heather, together with other species (Ericaceae undiff.), is recorded consistently from lpaz Ga, but heath may have grown before this, perhaps on steep slopes with scrubby birches, hawthorns and junipers, away from the valley floor and unseen palynologically. *Calluna* heath did not expand from this limited extent in later zones (Figure 3.7). All other trees and shrubs suffered profound reductions in woodland clearance within lpaz Fb. Both the dense valley floor *Alnus* (alder) carr and the dry woodland on the brown forest soils on slopes of *Quercus* (oak), *Ulmus* (elm), *Tilia* (lime) and *Corylus* (hazel) were completely destroyed. The scale of this clearance event cannot be underestimated. Although the event itself is poorly dated and the immediate effects are confounded by distortions introduced by reworked pollen, by lpaz Ga there were almost no trees remaining in the catchment, either on the valley floor or on the slopes around. There is no evidence of their persistence in the catchment in lpaz Ga.

The formerly wooded slopes were replaced during lpaz Fb by an intensively farmed landscape, both arable and pastoral, only detectable after the event (above). Cereal pollen grains are recorded throughout lpaz Ga, some sufficiently well preserved to classify further (Figure 3.7; Table 3.6). These are predominantly of *Avena/Triticum* (oat/wheat). One grain of *Avena sativa* (cultivated oat) was confidently identified, and one grain of *Secale* (rye) (Table 3.6). Weeds of arable fields probably included species of Caryophyllaceae (pinks), Chenopodiaceae (goosefoots), Cruciferae (cabbage family) and *Artemisia* (mugworts).

Grassland communities are also well represented. Several herb taxa that may have grown in unshaded fens are equally common in grasslands, including Umbelliferae (carrot family), *Galium* (bedstraws), *Potentilla* (cinquefoils) and *Lotus* (e.g. birdsfoot trefoil). It is incautious to be too assertive in defining grassland types, but the large numbers of herbs suggest a species rich grassland, possibly close to the present *Festuca-Agrostis* complex (King 1962, King & Nicholson 1964). There appears to be little evidence for increasing soil acidification to this time from the earliest anthropogenic grasslands recorded in lpaz E. Some herbs recorded (*Poterium* (burnet), *Trifolium* type (trefoils)) require a relatively high pH.

There is evidence for the development of hay meadows (Greig 1984, 1988; Hughes & Huntley 1988). In particular, *Centaurea nigra* (black knapweed) is thought to be a very good indicator of species rich, tall herb dominated meadow, together with *Vicia cracca* (tufted vetch), and other taxa are typical of ungrazed, mown grassland; *Cirsium* (thistle), some species of Compositae Liguliflorae (*Taraxacum* (dandelions), *Leontodon* (hawkbits)), *Trifolium* (both *T. pratense* and *T. repens*; red and white clovers), *Ranunculus* (*R. acris*, *R. bulbosus*; meadow and bulbous buttercups), *Potentilla* type *(P. erecta*; tormentil), *Geum* (*G. rivale*; water avens), and species of Umbelliferae. The majority of these indicate a form of traditionally managed, not overused, meadow (Greig 1988, Hughes & Huntley 1988). Conversely, the consistent occurrence of *Rumex obtusifolius* (broad-leaved dock) suggests that parts of the grassland system were being intensively managed, possibly overstocked (Hughes & Huntley 1988), as might the records for *Potentilla* type (Behre 1981) and *Plantago major/media* (Sagar & Harper 1964).

Lpaz Yetholm Gb (99–55cm): 1050–1600 cal AD

The rate of sediment accumulation more than doubled at some time around the lower zone boundary (Figure 3.4; Table 3.4) although the sediment remained an open water coarse detrital mud (unit D; Table 3.1). A step change to increasing organic matter contents and very much lower dry matter contents at 105cm (Figure 3.3) probably marks the time (*c* 1350 cal AD) at which sedimentation rates increased. The rate changed not because of a greater influx of mineral matter but because organic content was higher and the sediment much less compact as fen peat containing grass and sedge stems and the occasional wood layer (Table 3.1) advanced over the sampling site. The expansion of fen peat may have reflected the greater stability of the valley floor environment and increased nutrient flows from farmed valley sides to the loch. Sediment characteristics are very uniform (Figure 3.3), as are pollen preservation characteristics (Figure 3.9). Declining corrosion in pollen grains probably reflects the absence of eroded, reworked pollen and the contemporaneous high water table at the sampling site. Supporting evidence for high and stable water levels comes in the marked increases in opaque sulphide spherules formed in anaerobic conditions in the mud (Figure 3.10; Section 2.3k). The comparative abundance of *Isoetes* (quillwort) spores indicates lake water that was clear, not turbid. Aquatic and fen plant communities were otherwise stable (Figure 3.7).

Dryland vegetation changes were related to changing land use. Cereal pollen is more common, as also are herbs of disturbed ground (Figure 3.7). Cereal types identified (Tables 2.2, 3.6) are overwhelmingly of *Avena/Triticum* (oat/wheat), and a few are recognised as *Avena sativa* (oat). *Secale* (rye) was probably grown. *Centaurea cyanus* (cornflower), present in this zone, has been regarded as a plant of, predominantly, winter grown cereals, and particularly *Secale* (Behre 1981; Greig 1988). Pasture continued to be prominent (Figure 3.7).

One introduced crop was *Cannabis sativa* (hemp) (Table 2.2). Species of Compositae Liguliflorae (dandelion type) and Caryophyllaceae (e.g. *Scleranthus annuus*; annual knawel) have been linked to *Cannabis* cultivation in southern Sweden (Gaillard & Berglund 1988). Values of *Cannabis* at Yetholm Loch do not exceed 3% tlp, and it is therefore assumed that the pollen record reflects only the cultivation, and not the retting within the loch, of *Cannabis* (Bradshaw *et al* 1981; French & Moore 1986; Gaillard & Berglund 1988; Whittington & Edwards 1989; Edwards & Whittington 1990). *Reseda* pollen is recorded at 81cm (*c* 1420 cal AD). *Reseda luteola* (weld) is today found in Scotland as an escapee from cultivated land, and was probably introduced; the other possible pollen taxon, *R. lutea* (wild mignonette) is not recorded as native. Weld was commonly grown for dying wool different shades of yellow (Fraser 1983; Darwin 1996), and is recorded in the eastern Scottish Medieval burghs (Dickson & Dickson 2000). The plant was probably introduced to fields on the drier slopes above the loch.

Microscopic charcoal is much more abundant in this zone, particularly between 85cm and 69cm (*c* 1370 cal AD to *c* 1500 cal AD). By far the most common fragment sizes are those 10–25µm long, although fragments 25–50µm are more common in this phase (Figure 3.10). It is far from clear what the changes in size classes mean: the open ground around the sampling site may have allowed recruitment of charcoal from farther afield so that small fragments are better represented; fires may have been farther from the lake edge; fires burning the grass vegetation now dominant in the catchment may have generated smaller sized fragments. Woodland clearances were not likely sources of charcoal because all sizeable woodland patches in the pollen recruitment area had by then been cleared. The absence of trees makes it unlikely that a local charcoal industry developed. Domestic fires may have contributed a proportion, as might the burning of stubble (although cereals were cultivated in lpaz Ga when charcoal was not common). A much more tentative explanation would be to invoke the effects of scorched earth policies in warfare between Scotland and England (see Section 8.11).

Lpaz Yetholm Gc (55–31cm): 1600–1825 cal AD

Preceded by the deposition of an increasingly organic muddy peat rich in the shallow water alga *Pediastrum* (unit E; Table 3.1; Figure 3.3; Figure 3.7), a highly organic fen peat (unit F) with abundant matted grass and sedge stems had advanced over the sampling site by *c* 1750 cal AD (*c* 40cm). This resulted in the rapid replacement of open water aquatic plant communities including *Potamogeton* (pondweed) by *Equisetum* (cf. *E. palustre*; marsh horsetail) and then by Cyperaceae (sedges) fen communities in lpaz H (Figure 3.7). Conditions may have become too dry for plants like *Littorella* (shoreweed) but too wet for plants like *Succisa* (devilsbit scabious). The development of fen peat contrasts with earlier open water phases in the seasonality of water table fluctuations that affected the sediments, and the sharp but erratic increases in amounts of corroded pollen above 41cm (Figure 3.9) are probably the result of these. Opaque sulphide spherules become rare, again indicating the periodic, probably seasonal fall in water levels and the introduction of air to the peat (Figure 3.10). This sediment change need not have had regional significance; fens will advance into a lake by the accumulation of undecayed organic matter given environmental stability (Walker 1970). Because of the high rate of vertical growth of spongy, uncompacted fen peat, the sediment accumulation rate is very fast and the temporal resolution of pollen analyses good (Table 3.4). Perhaps because the peat was rapidly elevated above the lake surface, Cyperaceae (sedge) communities were probably invaded by wetland grasses, and some of the increases in Gramineae <8µm anl-D (grasses) pollen are probably related to this. *Rhamnus catharticus* (buckthorn) may have colonised the fen, but the few remaining individual wetland trees and shrubs of *Alnus* (alder) and *Betula* (birch) were removed or died.

Reductions in percentages of dryland and anthropogenic indicator pollen probably result from increasing numbers of Gramineae and Cyperaceae pollen grains growing on the sampling site (Figure 3.10), and from the pollen record there was no decline in the intensity of agricultural production. There are changes in the agrarian landscape, however. Above 46cm (*c* 1600 cal AD) the numbers of probable cereal pollen grains (Gramineae >8µm undiff.) are much fewer (Figure 3.7), suggesting a shift to more and permanent pasture. A proportion of the increase in wild grass pollen (Gramineae <8µm anl-D) probably came from wet and dry pasture. The grasslands remained species rich, and reductions in percentages of some grazing indicators such as *Plantago lanceolata* (ribwort plantain) and *Rumex* undiff. (docks, sorrels) may be a consequence of the relative abundance of grass pollen. The absence of *Rumex obtusifolius* (broad-leaved dock) and *Plantago major/media* (greater or hoary plantains) may suggest, however, that stock were being managed less intensively or more skilfully. Well preserved cereal pollen grains are, with one exception, all assigned to Andersen's (1979) Group III, but in three instances the grain was more specifically identified as *Triticum* (wheat), not *Avena* (oat) (Table 3.6). *Hordeum* type (barley type) pollen is recorded only once. *Centaurea cyanus* (cornflower) continued to flourish, but *Secale* (rye) itself may not have been grown. *Cannabis* cultivation probably ceased by *c* 1700 cal AD. Some evidence for landscape improvement and tree planting prior to the mid-eighteenth century cal AD (Section 2.4c) is recorded in the frequent occurrences of single pollen grains of *Ulmus* (elm) from *c* 1600 cal AD (Figure 3.7), probably for their aesthetic value close to farms, some 150 cal years before the more commercial planting of *Pinus* (pine) and other conifers: the presence of *Castanea* (sweet chestnut) pollen as single grains is not necessarily indicative of local growth but may accord with seventeenth-century practices (House & Dingwall 2003). The frequency and/or intensity of burning declined after *c* 1500 cal AD, and probably again at the start of lpaz Gc after *c* 1600 cal AD (Figure 3.10). Fragments 26–50µm long are much more common but it is not known why.

Lpaz Yetholm H (31–0cm): 1830 cal AD–present

On the surface of a fully organic peat which at the present day is some 50m from the lake edge but seasonally waterlogged, *Salix* (willow) colonised the peat surface, after *c* 20cm and within the last 100 to 150 years. It is the only tree or shrub growing on the fen, and was rapidly established as a very dense stand with few open spaces in the canopy. The rapidity of this event and the rarity of its pollen prior to *c* 1875 AD suggests this carr to have been established purposefully, perhaps for withies. With its growth, the pollen recruitment area of the sampling site effectively became a few metres around, and no estimates of vegetation or land use change on slopes above the loch can be gained.

3.4 Summary of environmental change at Yetholm Loch

The interpretation of events from the sediments at Yetholm Loch has not been straightforward. The formation of the record is complicated by a complex series of sedimentological fluctuations which have at times distorted the pollen stratigraphy. These fluctuations were induced by lake level changes, soil erosion, accelerated fluvial activity, fen expansion and even possibly the activities of beaver. Causal factors in many of these events can only be established when correlations are made with other sequences in Chapter 8.

Sedimentation commenced in the early Holocene at *c* 9200 cal BC. A scrub woodland of birch, willow and juniper grew on dry ground above a species rich fen and open water. The period may have been quite arid, resulting in a high frequency of fires, possibly leading to soil erosion.

A phase of lowered lake level at around 8150 cal BC may have led to a *c* 400-year hiatus in sediment accumulation, probably induced by climatic aridity. Hazel colonised the catchment during this period. Elm also colonised during this period, preceding the arrival of oak, which was established at around 7300 cal BC. Between *c* 6200 cal BC and at least 5150 cal BC oscillations in lake level may have been induced by beaver. The increased area of marshy ground following these fluctuations perhaps permitted the very rapid colonisation of alder at *c* 5150 cal BC.

Limited openings in the dry woodland are suspected from around 4600 cal BC or before. The early Neolithic elm decline at *c* 3825 cal BC (5775 cal BP) is actually the second such event at Yetholm Loch. This lasted for perhaps 300 years. Lime is thought to have become a component of the dry woodland as the elm population was reduced. There is little clear evidence for anthropogenic interference with the woodland until *c* 3525 cal BC when oak was cleared, grassland communities expanded, pasture established, and limited evidence of cereal cultivation recorded. The rate of woodland clearance appears to have been gradual, does not appear to have involved the use of fire, and could have been the product of grazing pressure alone.

Subsequent prehistoric clearance activity is difficult to discern through problems of pollen reworking during phases of soil erosion. A third elm decline is recorded at *c* 2850–2580 cal BC. The appearance of coarse stream sediment in the later Iron Age (*c* 250 cal BC) is associated with the contemporaneous widespread, eventually total woodland clearance, but only at *c* 150 cal AD can the true scale of this massive clearance be discerned. The woodland was replaced by a very intensively farmed landscape, with cereal cultivation and stock raising, the latter incorporating meadowland. Cereal agriculture became increasingly important after *c* 1100 cal AD, and specialised crops such as hemp and weld were grown. Crop rotations involving winter and spring sown cereals may have been introduced. Hemp cultivation ceased around 1700 cal AD.

Chapter 4

THE UPLAND TRIBUTARY VALLEYS – SOURHOPE

4.1 Site location, description and pollen recruitment

At the heart of the upper Bowmont Valley is a series of large deeply incised tributaries that flow to the Bowmont Water between Mowhaugh and Cocklawfoot (Section 1.5). The Sourhope subcatchment is one of these (Figure 1.3). The Sourhope and Kaim Burns drain the eastern summits of the Border ridge between The Curr and Auchope Cairn. These steep and very steep slopes fall rapidly some 300m to the Sourhope Burn and, to the south, the Dod and Kaim Burns. A large bowl-shaped basin (Plate 1.6) lies between Fasset Hill, Dod Hill and Bonnie Laws at around 260m asl (Figure 4.1). In a wide subglacial meltwater channel on the valley floor a peat mire some 300m long but only 50m wide (Figures 4.1, 4.3a) has accumulated nearly continuously since the early Holocene period. Because the peat mire is narrow it is also close to dryland soils and plant communities. The likely maximal pollen recruitment area (Section 2.2) is suggested to be within 1000m of the sampling site (Figure 4.1), reflecting the wet and cold basin beneath high ridges, sheltered from winds but seeing very little direct sunlight until late spring. The pollen recruitment area would have been smaller than this when the peat surface was colonised by trees (below).

Today the peat supports a grassy heath of *Molinia* (purple moor grass), *Nardus* (mat grass), *Calluna* (ling heather) with *Sphagnum* (bog moss). The andesite and till covered lower slopes of the hills have peaty podsol soils of the Cowie Series supporting *Festuca-Agrostis* (bent-fescue) grassland, often rich in *Pteridium* (bracken), and tussocky *Molinia* sward (Hunter 1962). The poorly drained valley floor has gleys (Atton Series) beneath bent-fescue grassland and rushes (Hunter 1962). Skeletal soils occur on the narrow channel floor where high rates of channel movement limit soil development (Figure 4.2a; Muir 1956). The valley floor and hillslopes are currently under permanent grassland of Land Use Capability classes 5.2 and 5.3 (Figure 4.2b; Table 1.1; Bown & Shipley 1982), and are managed by hefting for sheep (Hunter 1962).

Despite the current grasslands and rough grazing of the catchment, the peat mire is surrounded by a high density of prehistoric and historic settlements, and cultivation remains (Mercer in prep.; Mercer & Tipping 1994: Chapter 8). The overwhelming majority of remains are cultivation traces, of both cord rig type on the Bonnie Laws plateaux to the south and broad rig, of much later date, but hill forts and later Iron Age scooped settlements are found within the maximal pollen recruitment area (Figures 8.10 to 8.14; Plate 8.2). Sourhope is mentioned in a gift to the monks of Lindisfarne in 655 x 670 cal AD (Morris 1975). A farm at Sourhope is known from medieval documents (Jeffrey 1855) and one is on Blaeu's Atlas of 1634 cal AD, though not on Roy's survey of 1747–55 cal AD. However, the lower slopes of the Kaim and Sourhope Burns are shown on Roy's map as cultivated. The walled intake to the north of the peat (Plates 1.6, 4.1) is probably of nineteenth-century cal AD date. There is clear evidence of peat cutting on the peat surface (Plate 4.1) and this determined to some extent the sampling point within the mire.

4.2 Sediment sampling, subsampling and chronology construction

Figure 4.3a shows the shape of the valley mire wrapped round a large nineteenth-century walled intake (Plates 1.6, 4.1). A transect of boreholes A–B–C was recorded along the mire to determine stratigraphic variation and sediment thickness (Figure 4.3b). This shows that the base of the peat is very uneven, infilling hollows in the channel. Station 2 (Figures 4.3a) was sampled. Although not quite the thickest sequence of sediments, the area of visible peat cutting (Plate 4.1) contained a very fresh and uncompacted peat which had probably accumulated very rapidly following abandonment of peat cutting (Giller & Wheeler 1986). Pollen and ^{14}C samples were taken by Russian corer and by monolith tins (Section 2.3c) from both the infilled peat within the cut area, 16cm lower than the undisturbed surface

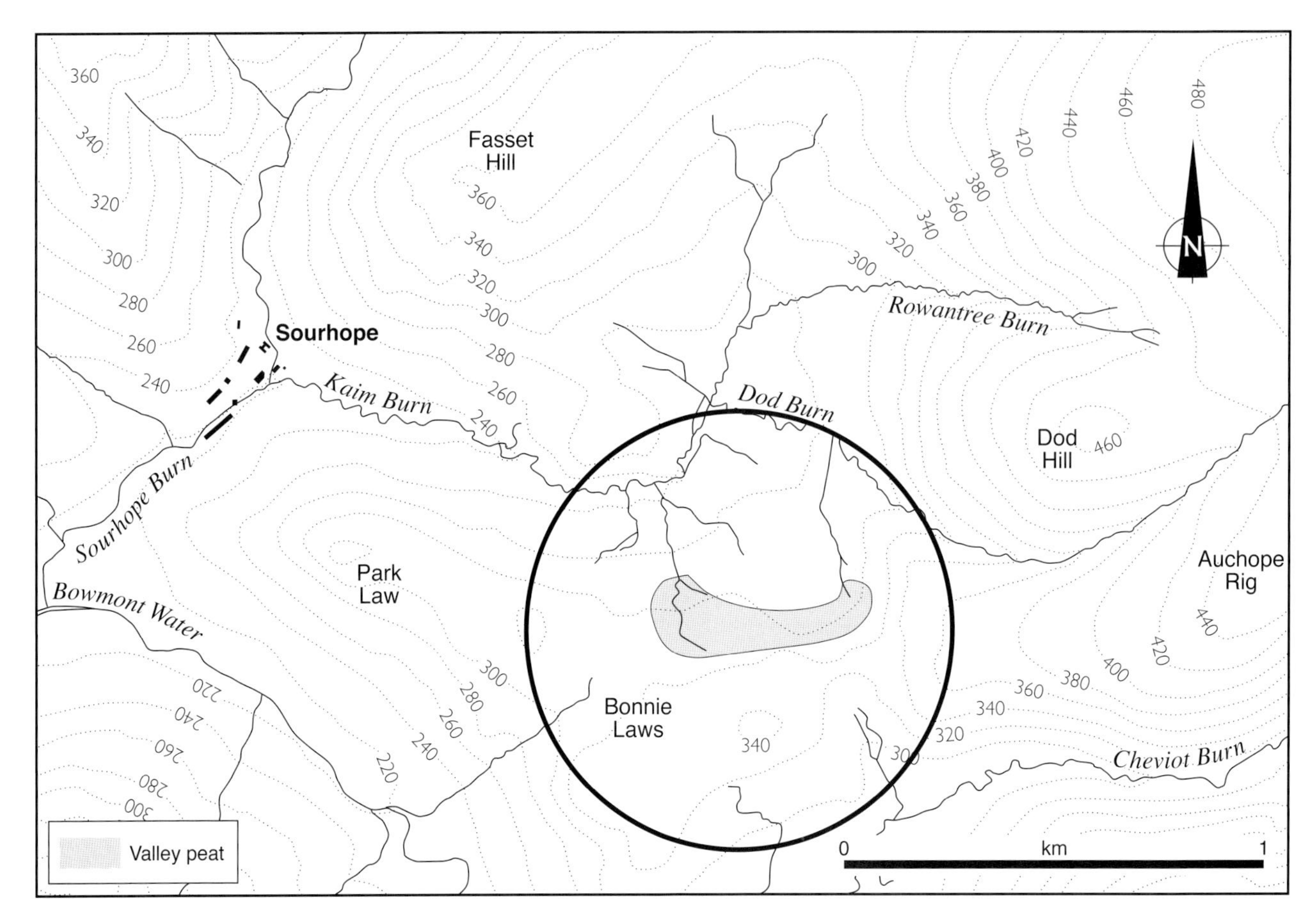

Figure 4.1

The physical and settlement geographies surrounding the Sourhope pollen site in the upper Bowmont Valley, showing the farm of Sourhope at the confluence of the Sourhope and Kaim Burns, and the location of the valley peat sampled. Contour intervals are 20m. A circles of 1000m diameter indicates the likely maximal pollen recruitment area around the sampling site.

of the peat bog at the baulk, and from the intact baulk itself (inset to Figure 4.3a), depths controlled by theodolite survey. It was hoped by identifying and dating the infilled peat in addition to adjacent undisturbed peat to (i) establish the age of peat cutting and (ii) analyse this most recent period with an unusually high temporal resolution (Figure 4.3).

The bulk of the analyses are from a sediment stratigraphy within the peat cut area (pollen sample stations a to c; inset to Figure 4.3a). The sequence is 330cm thick (Station 2: Figure 4.3b; Table 4.1). The sediment stratigraphy in Table 4.1 defines the depths recorded at the sampling site as well as indicating the 16cm difference in height with the baulk, necessary in subsequent sediment stratigraphic correlation. The development of the sequence is described in Section 4.3. The uppermost unit (F_3; Table 4.1) was identified as peat that had grown after peat cutting because of its fresh appearance, described as a 'recurrence surface' although anthropogenic, and despite it not having an abrupt boundary with the underlying unit F_2. This interpretation in part determined the ^{14}C subsampling strategy.

Thirteen radiocarbon dates were obtained on this stratigraphy (Table 4.2; Figure 4.4). The later eighteenth-century cal AD rise of non-native tree pollen types is the pollen marker horizon identified on Figure 4.4. Marked on this figure is the 'recurrence' surface at 53cm. All assays are conformable and internally consistent. Assays GU-2397 and -2398 have virtually the same radiocarbon age despite being separated by 27cm of peat. Peat accumulation may have been extraordinarily rapid, discussed in Section 4.3, but assay GU-2397 may be in error because sediment accumulation rates ignoring this assay are consistent. The preferred time-depth model does not use assay

Plate 4.1
From the lower slopes of Bonnie Laws, the valley mire can be seen filling the shallow meltwater channel between the track in the foreground and the improved and heavily grazed grasses of the walled intake in the mid distance. The square outline of the visible and most recent peat cut area on the mire can be seen (see Figure 4.3). A lone figure (Peter McKeague) stands by the dark patch of peat at Station 2. In the distance is The Schil, from where Plate 1.6 of the Sourhope Valley was taken.

GU-2397 (Figure 4.4). Assays GU-2399 and -2400 are on the same mean depth but from different sample locations (Table 4.2; inset to Figure 4.3a), and confirm that at *c* 60cm, age depth correlations between Monolith 1 and wide diameter Russian cores from Stations A–C are good. The mean of these two assays is used in the preferred time-depth model (Figure 4.4).

Assay GU-2401 dates the peat immediately below the 'recurrence' surface caused by visible peat cutting. Overlying this, assays GU-2402 and -2403 are from peats formed on abandonment of cutting. They are significantly younger than assay GU-2401, demonstrating an hiatus. Both these assays have large calibrated age ranges because they are on recent peats (Table 4.1) and cannot be used in the preferred age depth model (Figure 4.4), but non-native tree taxa (Section 2.4c) are abundant within peat above 20cm depth (Figure 4.5). Assuming a linear peat accumulation rate below this of 10.75 cal years per cm, peat began to grow again within the peat cut area after *c* 1450 cal AD.

To analyse peats forming and still preserved during this hiatus near Station 2, Monolith 2 was sampled from the baulk (Figure 4.3a). No ^{14}C assays were obtained, but pollen counts showed the representation of non-native tree taxa above *c* 10cm depth, assigned an age of 1775 ± 25 cal AD. Estimates of sediment accumulation through this point from the peat surface yield a rate of 17.5 yrs/cm for the topmost 60cm of peat in the baulk, comparable with assays beneath the 'recurrence' surface in the peat cut area.

Pollen analyses from the different contexts (Russian samples and Monolith 1 from within the peat cut

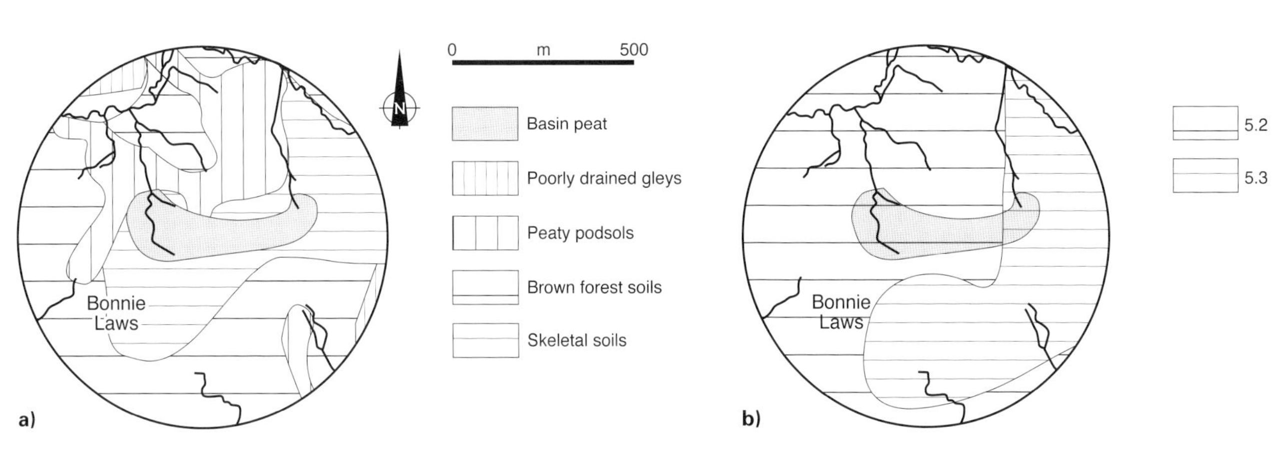

Figure 4.2
(a) Soil series mapped by the Soil Survey of Scotland (Muir 1956); (b) current land use capabilities (Bown & Shipley 1982; see Table 1.1).

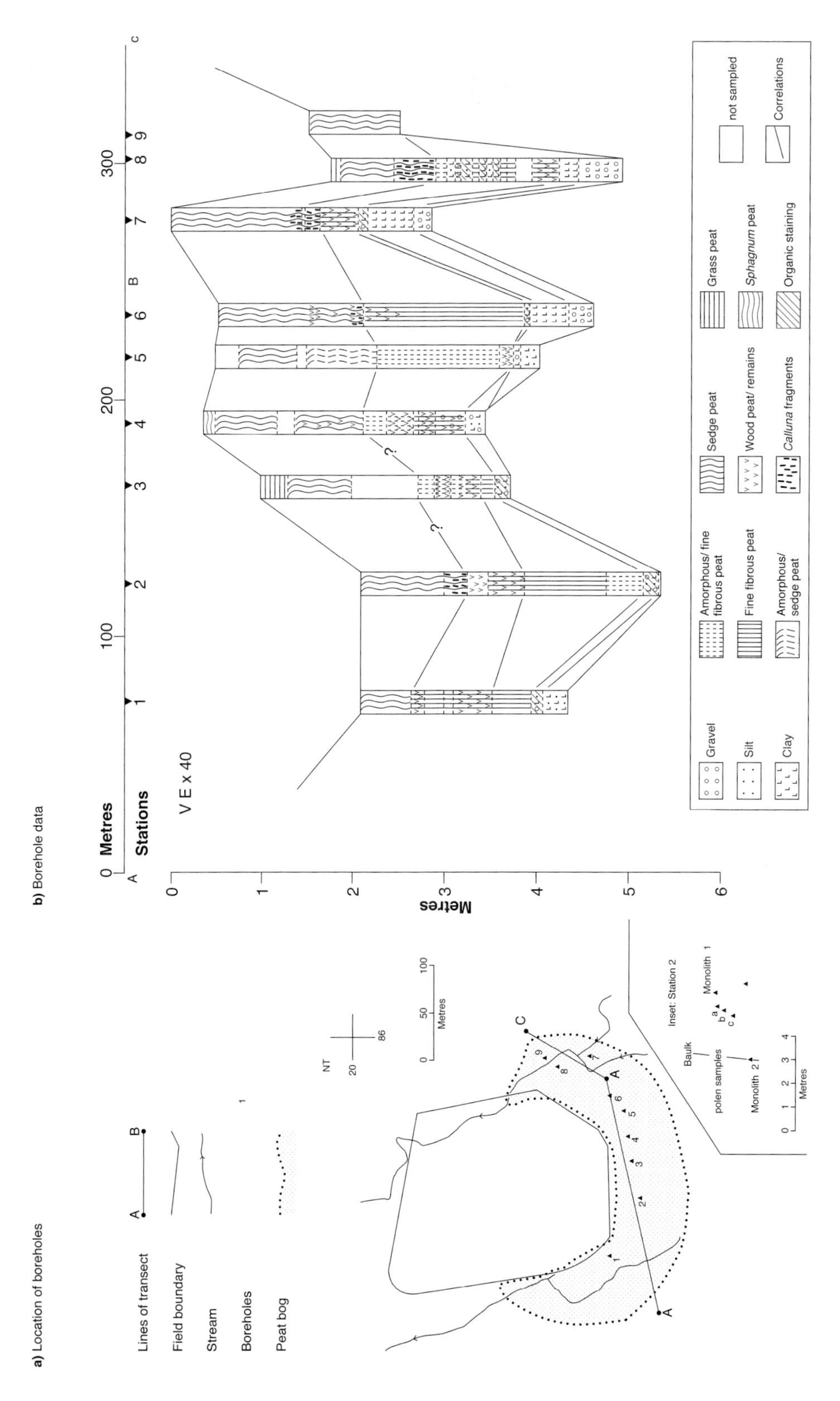

Figure 4.3
(a) The position of the sediment stratigraphic transect and boreholes recorded in Figure 4.3b in relation to the outline of the Sourhope Valley mire and the adjacent field wall, and, in the inset, a plan of the relative positions of samples taken for pollen analyses and dating controls; (b) the sediment stratigraphy of the valley mire along the transect.

Table 4.1
Sediment stratigraphy of the peat cut area at Sourhope.

Unit F_3 (0–53cm) [16–69cm]:	10 R 2.5/1 reddish-black poorly humified sedge peat; gradual boundary to
Unit F_2 (53–90cm) [69–100cm]:	5 Y 2.5/2 dark reddish-brown poorly humified sedge peat; gradual boundary to
Unit F_1 (90–125cm) [100–135cm]:	5 YR 2.5/1 black well humified sedge peat with very rare wood fragments; gradual boundary to
Unit E (125–186cm) [135–196cm]:	5 YR 2.5/1 black well humified sedge peat with rare to occasional wood fragments and occasional *Calluna* rootlets; gradual boundary to
Unit D (186–270cm) [196–280cm]:	5 YR 2.5/1 black well humified sedge rich wood peat, with common to abundant well preserved fine and coarse wood fragments; gradual boundary to
Unit C (270–310cm) [280–320cm]:	2.5 Y 2/0 black well humified structureless amorphous peat with occasional fine and rare coarse wood fragments, frequency of wood fragments increasing upunit; gradual boundary to
Unit B (310–324cm) [320–334cm]:	2.5 Y 2/0 black well humified grass and sedge peat and coarse detrital mud with rare to common fine wood fragments; sharp boundary to
Unit A (324–330cm) [334–340cm]:	2.5 Y 3/2 very dark greyish-brown, changing upunit to 10 YR 2/2 very dark brown structureless organic rich clay with coarse sand throughout and with lenses and bands of gritty coarse sand.

area and Monolith 2 from the adjacent baulk; Figure 4.3a) have been combined using the dating controls discussed above in Figure 4.5 to provide a pollen stratigraphy that is continuous, with no hiatuses caused by recent peat cutting. In this, the highly resolved pollen counts formed after *c* 1775 cal AD from the fresh peat within Monolith 1 replace the few counts from this period in the uppermost 10cm from Monolith 2: this means that the pollen stratigraphy is 10cm deeper than the sediment stratigraphy. Analyses from Monolith 2 in the 30cm representing the period between *c* 1775 and *c* 1250 cal AD are placed in Figure 4.5 above pollen counts from analyses below the 'recurrence' surface dated to *c* 1250 cal AD within the peat cut area.

However, there are additional stratigraphic complexities. The pollen stratigraphy of Figure 4.5 was zoned, and twelve local pollen assemblage zones defined, prefixed 'Sourhope' (Section 2.3g; Table 4.3; Figure 4.5). Part of the pollen sequence, from a 1m long sediment core at Station 2d, 75cm from stations a–c (inset to Figure 4.3a), does not correlate with the zones established in Figure 4.5. Figure 4.6 shows the suggested correlation of pollen assemblage zones between these sequences. This indicates that two lpa zones recognised from Stations 2a–c are not identified in sediment at Station 2D; these are lpaz G_2 and lpaz I. There are apparently two hiatuses at depth in the peats at Station 2d, and the likelihood is that peat cutting also affected mire formation earlier than that recognised in recent sediments. At Station 2d the peat immediately above these postulated hiatuses is notably better preserved (unpublished data), suggesting 'recurrence' surfaces as peat regrew after cutting. Not all hiatuses in peat growth need have been recognised in the vegetational history discussed in Section 4.3.

The dating controls (Table 4.1; Figure 4.4) allow estimates of the sampling and temporal resolutions of the pollen analyses (Section 2.3d) in Table 4.4. Temporal resolutions are low for much of the prehistoric period, up to *c* 300 years or twelve human generations between subsamples, but are much higher between the Iron Age and the early Medieval period. An uncertain but probably slower peat accumulation rate in lpaz Sourhope K means that much detail has been lost in the Medieval period, with subsamples every *c* 200 years or eight human generations, but rapid accumulation of peat on the floor of abandoned peat cuttings provided analyses from *c* 1450 cal AD at the scale of single human generations (Table 4.4). The preservation states of all determinable land pollen grains are recorded in

Table 4.2

Details of the radiocarbon assays obtained on the sediments in the peat cut area at Sourhope.

Lab. No. (GU-)	*Mean Depth (cm)*	*Sediment Depth (cm)*	*No. of Cores (gms)*	*Sample Weight* BP	^{14}C *Age* BP $\pm 1\sigma$	$\delta^{13}C$ *(‰)*	*Calibrated Age* BC/AD $\pm 1\sigma$ *and Intercept Ages*	*Mean Calibrated Age* BC/AD
2403	35.25	34.5–36	1 (Monolith 1)	280.2	180 ± 50	–27.3	1653 (1672, 1762, 1774, 1944, 1945) AD 1951	not determined
2402	510	50–52	1 (Monolith 1)	347.3	170 ± 50	–26.2	1656 (1677,1749,1782, 1937, 1950) AD 1951	not determined
2401	550	54–56	1 (Monolith 1)	333.9	760 ± 140	–25.3	1150 (1259) AD 1358	AD 1254
2400	62.50	61–64	1 (Monolith 1)	357.8	1300 ± 60	–28.1	656 (692) AD 769	AD 712
2399	610	56–66	1 (1)	117.5	1180 ± 60	–28.3	787 (857) AD 924 688 (777) AD 854	AD 855 AD 771
mean age of assays GU-2400 and GU-2399 (see text)					1240 ± 42		717 (782) AD 876	AD 796
2398	72.50	70–75	2 (1,2)	180	1450 ± 70	–28	547 (610) AD 647	AD 597
2397	1000	95–105	1 (3)	187.6	1440 ± 50	–28.5	564 (599) AD 634	AD 599
2396	1220	119–125	2 (4,5)	173.2	2570 ± 50	–28	827 (799) 745 BC	786 BC
2395	152.50	150–155	2 (6,7)	199.4	3430 ± 50	–29	1802 (1745) 1691 BC	1746 BC
2394	189.50	186–193	3 (8,9,10)	292.7	4100 ± 50	–28.9	2728 (2657) 2586 BC	2657 BC
2393	248.50	245–252	3 (12,13,14)	276	5750 ± 70	–29	4730 (4618) 4531 BC	5080 BC
2392	277.50	275–280	2 (14,15)	223.8	6250 ± 50	–28	5263 (5237) 5204 BC	5233 BC
2391	320.50	318–323	2 (18,19)	266.2	8630 ± 70	–28	7831 (7580) 7541 BC	7686 BC

Figure 4.7, together with measures of the total numbers of grains rendered indeterminable by deterioration. The quality of interpretations in lpa zones A–G_1 (Section 4.3) is adversely affected by pollen deterioration, a factor that determined the low temporal resolution of analyses in this period. Microscopic charcoal fragments were measured only on microscope slides above 230cm; Figure 4.8 depicts the different measures defined in Section 2.3j. Opaque spherules were recorded but were too few to have significance.

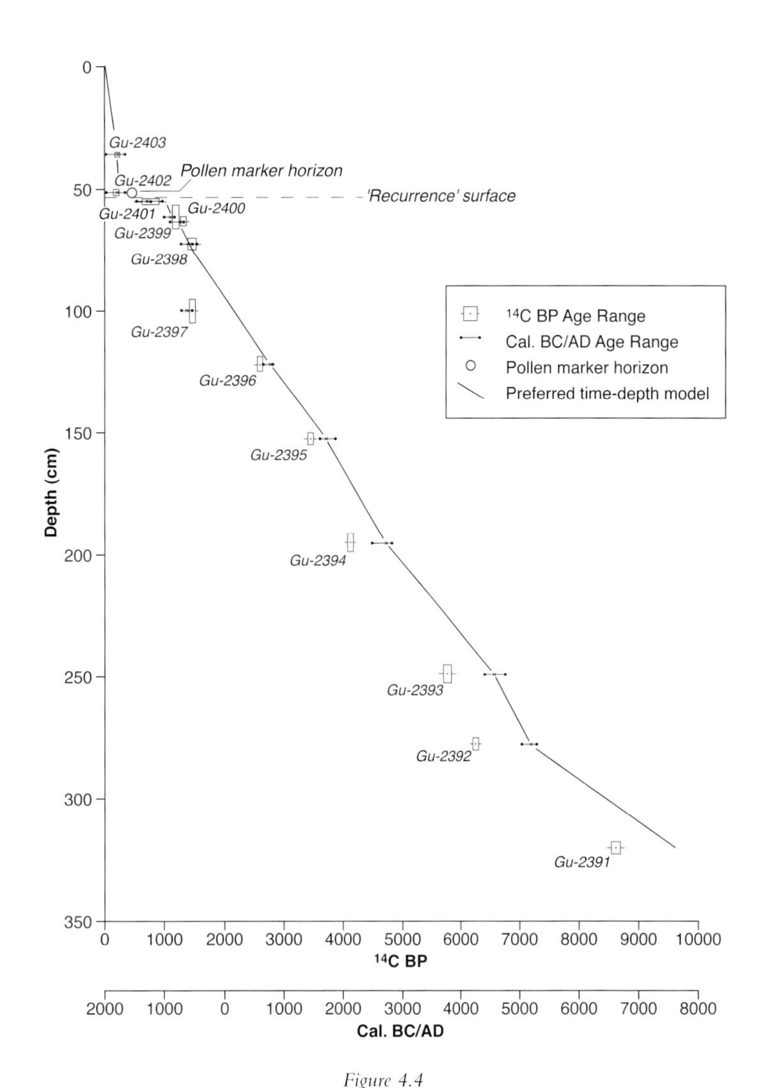

Figure 4.4
The preferred time-depth model for sediments within the peat cut area at Sourhope, showing ^{14}C ages BP at 1 and 2σ as cat-and-whisker plots and corresponding calibrated age ranges BC/AD at 1σ as dumb-bell plots (see Table 4.2) and the only additional control obtained from Agricultural Improvement tree pollen (Section 2.4c).

4.3 Landscape and environmental change at Sourhope

Lpaz Sourhope A (330–287cm): 7690–5237 cal BC

The peat sequence at Station 2 began to form some 1500 years after the beginning of the Holocene interglacial. Other parts of the mire may have formed earlier. Bedrock hollows between Stations 5–8 (Figure 4.3b) contain lacustrine sediments overlying fluvial gravelly clays, suggesting continuity in sedimentation from the last time water flowed in the channel, in contrast to the sharp boundary at Station 2 at *c* 7690 cal BC (GU-2391: Table 4.2; Figure 4.4), from lacustrine organic clays to well humified sedge and wood peat (Table 4.1). There need be no significance in the date of peat formation at the sampling site.

Pollen preservation is poor (Figure 4.7) with <30% of land pollen grains being well preserved, but there is no evidence from individual taxa to suggest differential preservation of resistant taxa (Section 2.3i). After *c* 6500 cal BC corrosion dominates the pollen assemblages until lpaz Gb. This appears to have occurred post depositionally since all taxa are affected to varying extents (unpublished data). Peat initiation was probably in shallow ponds in hollows on the channel floor, but increased growth elevated the peat to a point by *c* 6500 cal BC when water was able to drain laterally, maintaining a dry and comparatively free-draining surface for thousands of years.

Cyperaceae (sedges) were the most common peat forming plants, probably with Gramineae <8μm anl-D (wild grasses) and also *Filipendula* (? meadowsweet), *Potentilla* type (tormentil, cinquefoils), *Galium* type (bedstraws), *Succisa* (devilsbit scabious), Umbelliferae (carrot family) and ferns. Taxa typical of wetter ground, such as *Sphagnum* (bog moss) and *Equisetum* (horsetails), were common only in the basal spectra before the peat surface became drier (Figure 4.5). *Calluna* (ling) and other heathers seem not to have been locally present despite the apparent dryness of the peat surface.

Betula (birch) and *Corylus/Myrica* (cf. *Corylus avellana*; hazel) were probably both present in the valley at the onset of sediment accumulation, together with *Salix* (willow) and *Crataegus* type (*Crataegus*

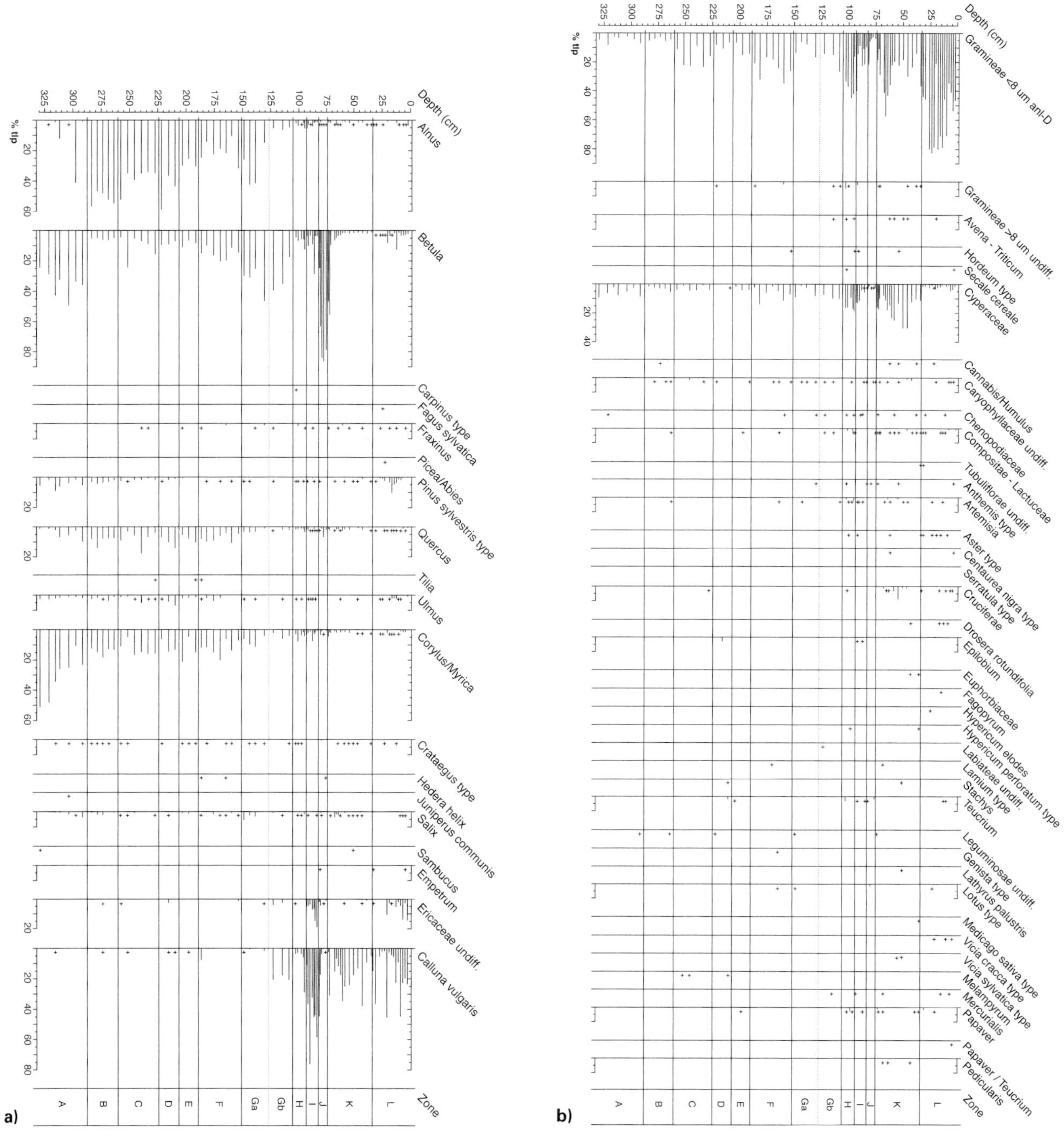

Figure 4.5

The complete pollen stratigraphy at Sourhope plotted against depth (cm) and calculated as percentages of total land pollen (tlp) and tlp + group (Section 2.3g). Values recorded in a subsample at <1% are marked by a cross. Local pollen assemblage zone boundaries are plotted to permit correlation. See Appendix One for a glossary of English names for Linnaean taxa.

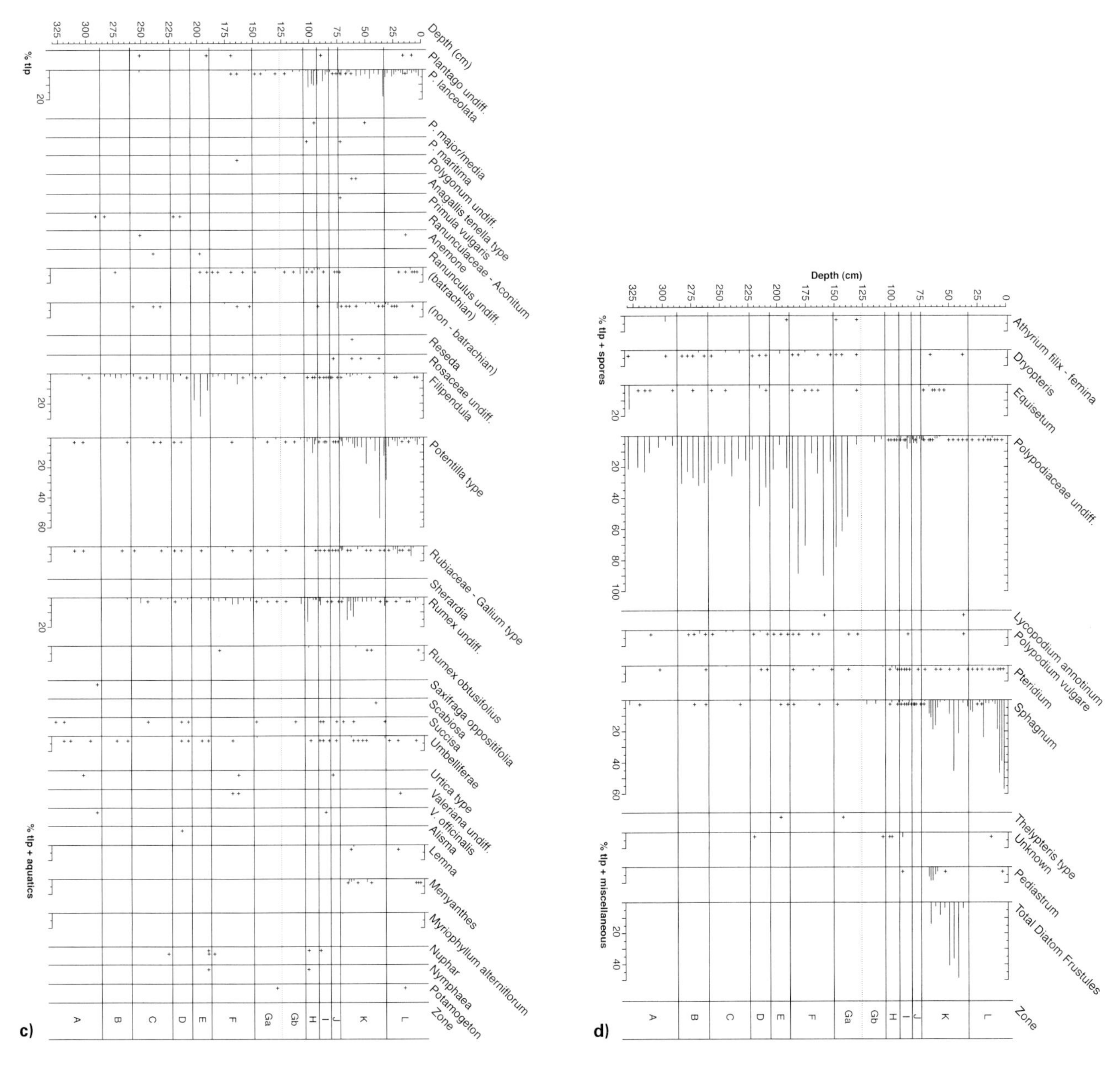

Figure 4.5 (cont.)

The complete pollen stratigraphy at Sourhope plotted against depth (cm) and calculated as percentages of total land pollen (tlp) and tlp + group (Section 2.3g). Values recorded in a subsample at <1% are marked by a cross. Local pollen assemblage zone boundaries are plotted to permit correlation. See Appendix One for a glossary of English names for Linnaean taxa.

Table 4.3
Local pollen assemblage zones at Sourhope, their characteristic pollen taxa and ^{14}C and calibrated age ranges.

Lpaz	*Depths (cm)*	*Characteristic taxa*	*Duration (cal BC/AD)*	*(cal BP)*	*(^{14}C BP)*
Sourhope L	33–0	Gramineae <8µm anl-D (wild grasses)	AD 1675–1985	275–0	
Sourhope K	74–33	Gramineae <8µm anl-D (wild grasses) – *Calluna* (ling) – Cyperaceae (sedges) – *Potentilla* type (tormentil, cinquefoils)	AD 875–1675	950–275	1025–275
Sourhope J	82–74	*Betula* (birch)	AD 710–875	1240–1075	1200–1025
Sourhope I	93–82	*Calluna* (ling) – Ericaceae undiff. (heathers)	AD 425–710	1525–1240	1475–1200
Sourhope H	105–93	Gramineae <8µm anl-D (wild grasses) – *Plantago lanceolata* (ribwort plantain) – *Rumex* undiff. (docks)	AD 50–425	1900–1525	1825–1475
Sourhope Gb	126–105	*Betula* (birch) – *Calluna* (ling)	550 BC–50 AD	2500–1900	2350–1825
Sourhope Ga	150.5–126	*Alnus* (alder) – *Betula* (birch)	1350–550 BC	3300–2500	3100–2350
Sourhope F	188.5–150.5	Gramineae <8µm anl-D (wild grasses) – *Betula* (birch) – *Corylus/Myrica* (hazel/bog myrtle) – Cyperaceae (sedges)	2050–1350 BC	4400–3300	3950–3100
Sourhope E	206–188.5	*Filipendula* (? meadowsweet) – Gramineae <8µm anl-D (wild grasses)	2890–2050 BC	4840–4400	4240–3950
Sourhope D	224–206	*Alnus* (alder) – *Quercus* (oak) – *Corylus/Myrica* (hazel/bog myrtle)	3480–2890 BC	5430–4840	4660–4240
Sourhope C	260–224	*Alnus* (alder) – Gramineae <8µm anl-D (grasses) – *Corylus/Myrica* (hazel/bog myrtle)	4618–3480 BC	6568–5430	5750–4660
Sourhope B	287–260	*Alnus* (alder) – *Quercus* (oak) – *Corylus/Myrica* (hazel/bog myrtle)	5237–4618 BC	7187–6568	6250–5750
Sourhope A	330–287	*Betula* (birch) – *Corylus/Myrica* (hazel/bog myrtle)	7690–5237 BC	9530–7187	8630–6250

(hawthorn) and/or *Sorbus* (rowan)). The very high percentages of *Corylus/Myrica* pollen suggest the taxon to have been hazel (Birks 1973; Godwin 1975). Birch may have grown closer to or on the sampling site, suppressing the representation of hazel from drier slopes after *c* 6500 cal BC as the peat surface became drier (Figure 4.5).

The very erratic representation of *Alnus* (alder) is difficult to interpret, but alder is not considered to have grown locally until lpaz B. Pine (*Pinus*) is not recorded at percentages high enough to confidently assert local presence (Huntley & Birks 1983; Bennett 1984) but isolated stands may have grown nearby. *Quercus* (oak) probably colonised the catchment after 315cm (*c* 6450 cal BC). The low *Ulmus* (elm) values suggest that this tree did not gain a strong foothold in this part of the valley (Figure 4.5).

Lpaz Sourhope B (287–260cm): 5237–4618 cal BC

Alnus (alder) was locally dominant from *c* 5240 cal BC (Figure 4.5). The peat surface continued to be relatively very dry, with high amounts of corrosion (Figure 4.7) and only infrequent occurrences of wetland pollen taxa (Figure 4.5). Nevertheless, colonisation of *Alnus* appears to have been very rapid. There is no evidence from the peat stratigraphy (Table 4.1) or rates of accumulation (Table 4.4) for an hiatus at the lpaz A–B boundary; indeed, for a time in the last quarter of the sixth millennium cal BC peat accumulation rates accelerated (Table 4.4). Lateral peat spread to further fill the channel is possible, increasing the wetter soils on which alder had competitive advantages. This was in turn probably driven by increasing peat surface wetness, which may have facilitated the establishment of alder on and close to the mire. *Alnus* (alder) probably replaced *Betula* (birch) on the mire but *Salix* (willow) was able to gain from the increasingly wet peat (Figure 4.5). On drier soils *Quercus* (oak) appears to have consolidated its presence, successfully competing with *Corylus* (hazel). The epiphytic *Polypodium vulgare* (polypody) again is closely linked to the increased representation of *Quercus*. Although declining, the initial high representation of *Pinus* (pine) pollen despite the dominance of *Alnus* (alder) might suggest that pine trees resisted invasion by deciduous woodland until *c* 4600 cal BC.

Lpaz Sourhope C (260–224cm): 4618–3480 cal BC

Clumps of pollen grains bound together as if just released from the anther can be an excellent indicator of a plant's local presence, and in this zone abundant clumps of *Alnus* (alder) pollen strongly suggest its growth on the peat surface (unpublished data). Despite this, *Alnus* percentages underwent marked reductions, and *Salix* (willow) became rare. *Betula* (birch) and *Corylus/Myrica* (hazel/bog myrtle), together with *Fraxinus* (ash), may have grown in more open dryland woods above the valley mire with *Quercus* (oak). *Quercus* (oak) values become more erratic, and *Polypodium vulgare* (polypody) is noticeably less frequently recorded, suggesting a change in woodland structure. Values of Gramineae <8μm anl-D (grasses) are substantially higher, accompanied by open ground herbs not previously recorded, including Cruciferae (cabbage family), Plantaginaceae (plantains, including *P. lanceolata*; ribwort plantain), non-batrachian (dry-ground) *Ranunculus* (buttercups) and *Rumex* (docks). Herbs more closely associated with the dry peat surface (above; lpaz A) continue to be well represented. Present for a short period around 250cm (*c* 4300 cal BC) is pollen of *Melampyrum*, a plant of open woodland, grassland and dry fen (Figure 4.5).

The apparently greater openness of both carr and dryland woods is suggestive of anthropogenic clearance, and a number of herbs (*Plantago*, *Rumex*) can be regarded as representing grazed grassland (Behre 1981), so that partial woodland clearance for grazing is, perhaps, the simplest explanation for these changes (but see Section 8.6e for fuller discussion). This phase persisted for around 1500 cal years, although the very low temporal resolution of analyses (Table 4.4) almost certainly conceals many short lived events. Subsequent gradually increasing proportions of *Betula* (birch) and *Quercus* (oak) (Figure 4.5) suggest that the initial impact was the most extensive or intensive, and woodland regeneration followed above 240cm (*c* 4050 cal BC).

Lpaz Sourhope D (224–206cm): 3480–2890 cal BC

Woodland regeneration continued, and *Quercus* (oak) values rise to a peak at *c* 3370 cal BC, accompanied once more by *Polypodium vulgare* (polypody). *Ulmus* (elm) pollen is recorded at >5% tlp, and the tree probably grew locally for the first time. *Fraxinus* (ash) is not recorded, Gramineae <8μm anl-D (grass) values are relatively low, and except for a single *Melampyrum* grain, and *Rumex* (docks) pollen at low frequencies, open ground herb pollen representation is limited (Figure 4.5). Fire frequency and/or intensity, able to be assessed from this zone, is very low and there is no evidence that fires occurred in the catchment (Figure 4.8).

Table 4.4

Definitions of sediment accumulation rates between chronological controls used in the preferred time-depth model (Figure 4.4) and the sampling and temporal resolutions of pollen and microscopic charcoal analyses at Sourhope.

Depth between dating controls (cm)	*Cal ages* BC/AD	*Duration (cal years)*	*Accumulation rate (yrs/cm)*	*Lpaz*	*Depths (cm)*	*Pollen Analyses* (a)	(b)	(c)
0–20	AD 1990–AD 1775	215	10.75	L		2cm	5.5	22
20–54	AD 1775–AD 1250	525	17.5	L, K	20–34	2cm	9	35
					34–54	4cm	9	70
54–62.5	AD 1250–AD 796	454	53.4	K		4cm	27	215
62.5–72.5	AD 796–AD 598	198	19.8	K		2cm	10	40
72.5–122	AD 598–786 BC	1384	28	J, I, H	72.5–102	2cm	14	56
				H	102–122	8cm	14	224
122–152.5	786 BC–1746 BC	960	29.5	G	122–138	8cm	15	236
					138–152.5	5.5cm	15	160
152.5–189.5	1746 BC–2657 BC	910	24	F		5.5cm	12	132
189.5–248.5	2657 BC–5080 BC	2423	41	E–B		5.5cm	20	225
248.5–277.5	5080 BC–5233 BC	153	5	B		5.5cm	2.5	27
277.5–320.5	5233 BC–7686 BC	2453	57	B, A		5.5cm	29	313

(a) sampling interval of analyses; (b) sampling resolution: time homogenised per subsample; (c) temporal resolution: time between subsamples

***Lpaz Sourhope E (206–188.5cm): 2890–2050 cal* BC**

A sharp reduction in *Ulmus* (elm) values occurred at *c* 2890 cal BC. Although the temporal resolution of analyses continues to be very low, there is only limited evidence of subsequent recovery. No other significant change in dryland plant communities is recorded. *Quercus* (oak) values decline but rapidly recover; *Polypodium vulgare* (polypody) is consistently recorded. On the mire, Cyperaceae (sedges) communities increased. Most noticeably, *Filipendula* (probably meadowsweet) grew profusely and many clumps of *Filipendula* pollen were recorded. *Alnus* (alder) carr appears to have given way to herb rich wetland plant communities. The peat contains noticeably fewer wood fragments (unit E; Table 4.1). The mire surface may have become drier. Proportions of corroded grains determinable to taxon are already very high, but increases in numbers of indeterminable grains are largely due to greater values of corroded grains (Figure 4.7). Fire frequency/intensity was, however, unchanged (Figure 4.8).

***Lpaz Sourhope F (188.5–150.5cm): 2050–1350 cal* BC**

Betula (birch) percentages rise, assumed to relate to recolonisation of the mire surface, indicated by clumps of *Betula* pollen. Birch trees appear to have ousted *Alnus* (alder). Cyperaceae (sedges) grew more vigorously, again seen in clumps of pollen, species of wetland

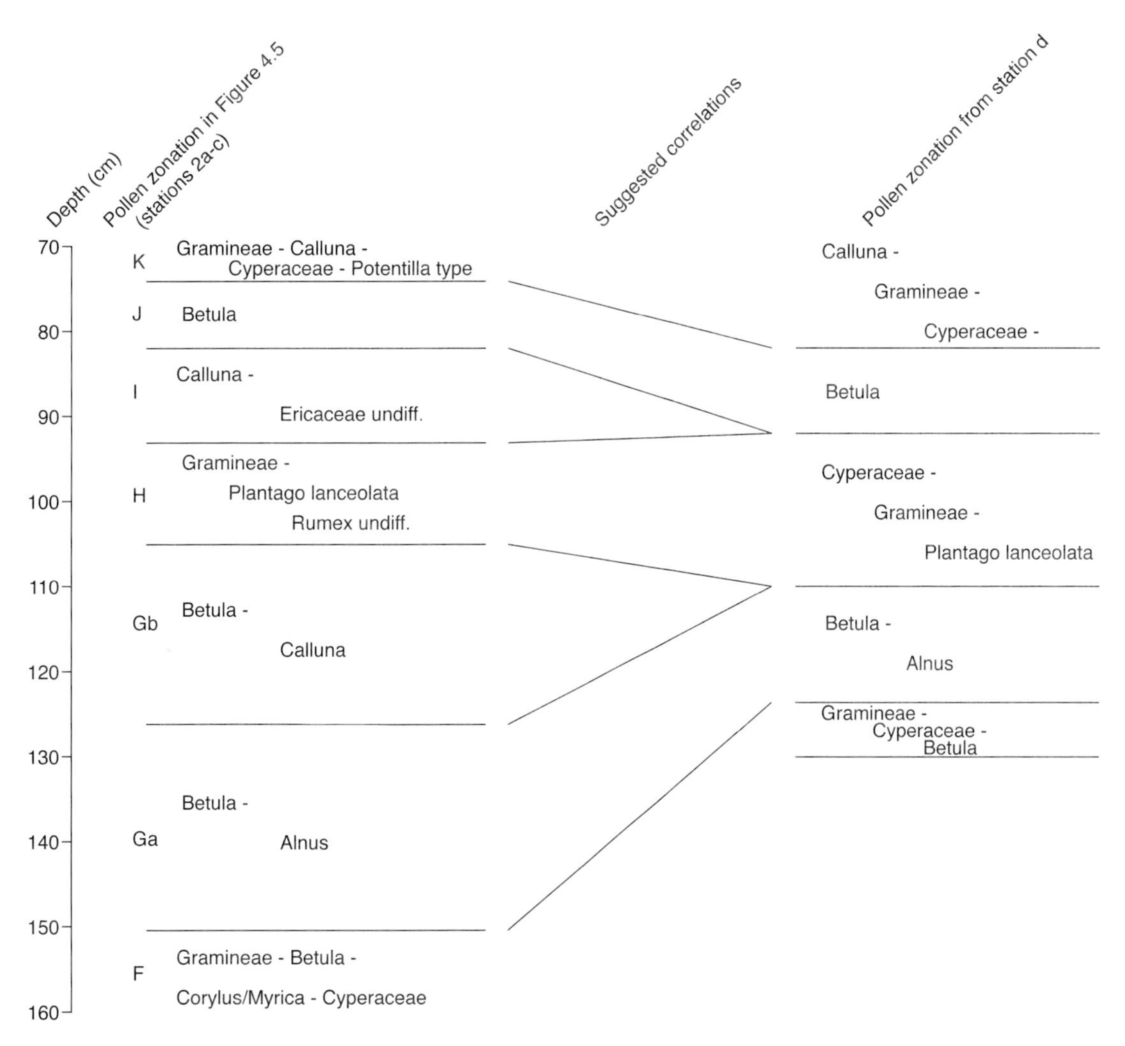

Figure 4.6

Correlation of pollen assemblage zones between the composite pollen stratigraphy constructed from cores at Stations 2a–c (Table 4.3; Figure 4.5) and a pollen diagram from Station 2d (unpublished data) showing the two periods of non-correlation and probable missing sediment at Station 2d.

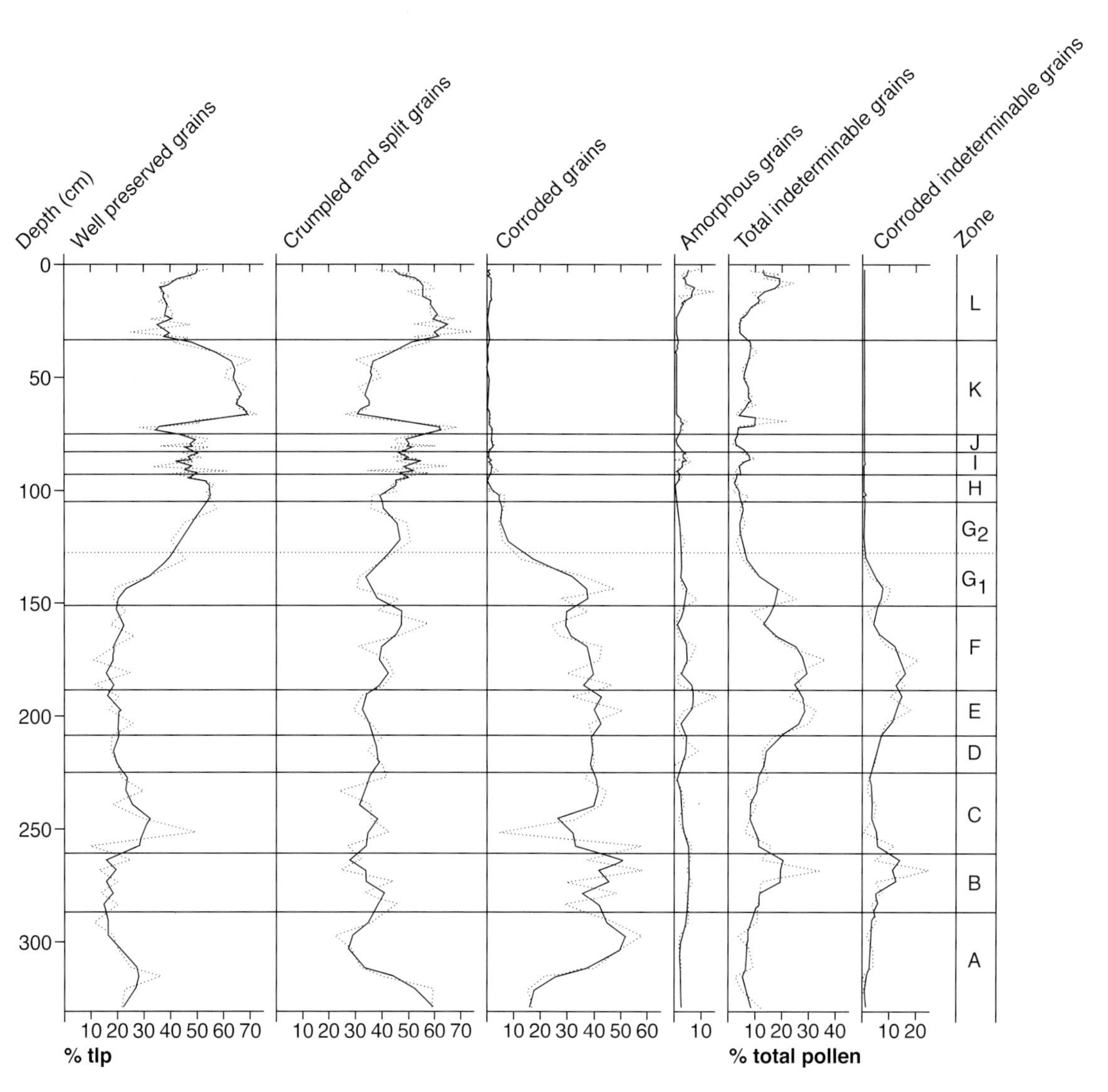

Figure 4.7

Pollen preservation states for all determinable land pollen grains plotted against depth and calculated as percentages of total land pollen (see Section 2.3I). Also depicted is the proportion (as % tlp + indeterminable grains) of grains rendered indeterminable by deterioration (see Section 2.3i). Local pollen assemblage zone boundaries are plotted to permit correlation.

buttercup (batrachian *Ranunculus*) were common, but the abundance of *Filipendula* (? meadowsweet) was less. Huge numbers of Polypodiaceae undiff. spores (undifferentiated ferns) strongly indicate that ferns grew on the mire surface, and very high numbers of clumps were recorded. Their abundance might reflect growth within open birch fen woodland, but their abundance may also imply that differential destruction by intense corrosion of the original pollen assemblages had occurred; Polypodiaceae are very resistant to such deterioration (Tipping *et al* 1994).

Quercus (oak) and *Ulmus* (elm) percentages show clear and strong reductions, with *Ulmus* almost certainly absent in the valley after *c* 1950 cal BC. *Corylus/Myrica* (hazel/bog myrtle) values declined *c* 150 cal years later. *Plantago lanceolata* (ribwort plantain) was present with some consistency after *c* 1950 cal BC; *Rumex* undiff. (docks, sorrels) had been comparatively abundant from the lower zone boundary at *c* 2050 cal BC. The coincidence with reductions in dryland tree pollen percentages suggests an intensification of grazing activities. Microscopic charcoal counts (Figure 4.8) do not suggest clearance to have been facilitated by burning. After *c* 1800 cal BC herb pollen taxa indicative of disturbed ground (Chenopodiaceae (goosefoots), *Artemisia* (mugworts)) are recorded, and late in lpaz F at around 1450 cal BC a grain of *Hordeum* (barley) type (Gramineae Type II) is recorded (Table 4.5), more convincing evidence for crop growing than the single grains of Gramineae >8µm anl-D undiff. recorded earlier at 221cm and 186cm.

Lpaz Sourhope Ga (150.5–126cm): 1350–550 cal BC

Sharp reductions in corroded pollen after *c* 1050 cal BC probably reflect a shift to an increasingly wet mire surface (Figure 4.7). Water levels within the peat may have been consistently at the peat surface after *c* 550 cal BC. The origin is probably climatic in increasing precipitation (Section 8.8f). Anthropogenic disturbance to slopes above the mire is not considered influential. There is evidence of intensified woodland clearance after *c* 850 cal BC but this occurred after the change to a wetter mire surface. Increases in percentages of *Alnus* (alder) and *Betula* (birch) may have resulted from the re-establishment of trees, together with *Salix* (willow), on the wetter mire surface. There is no expansion in numbers of wetland herbs, although a single spore of the aquatic *Potamogeton* (pondweed) is recorded (Figure 4.5).

After *c* 850 cal BC values of *Quercus* (oak) sharply decline, and oak trees are unlikely to have grown in the valley after this time. The same may be true of most hazel trees because *Corylus/Myrica* values fall abruptly at this time. Populations of *Alnus* (alder) and *Salix* (willow) were adversely affected also, though

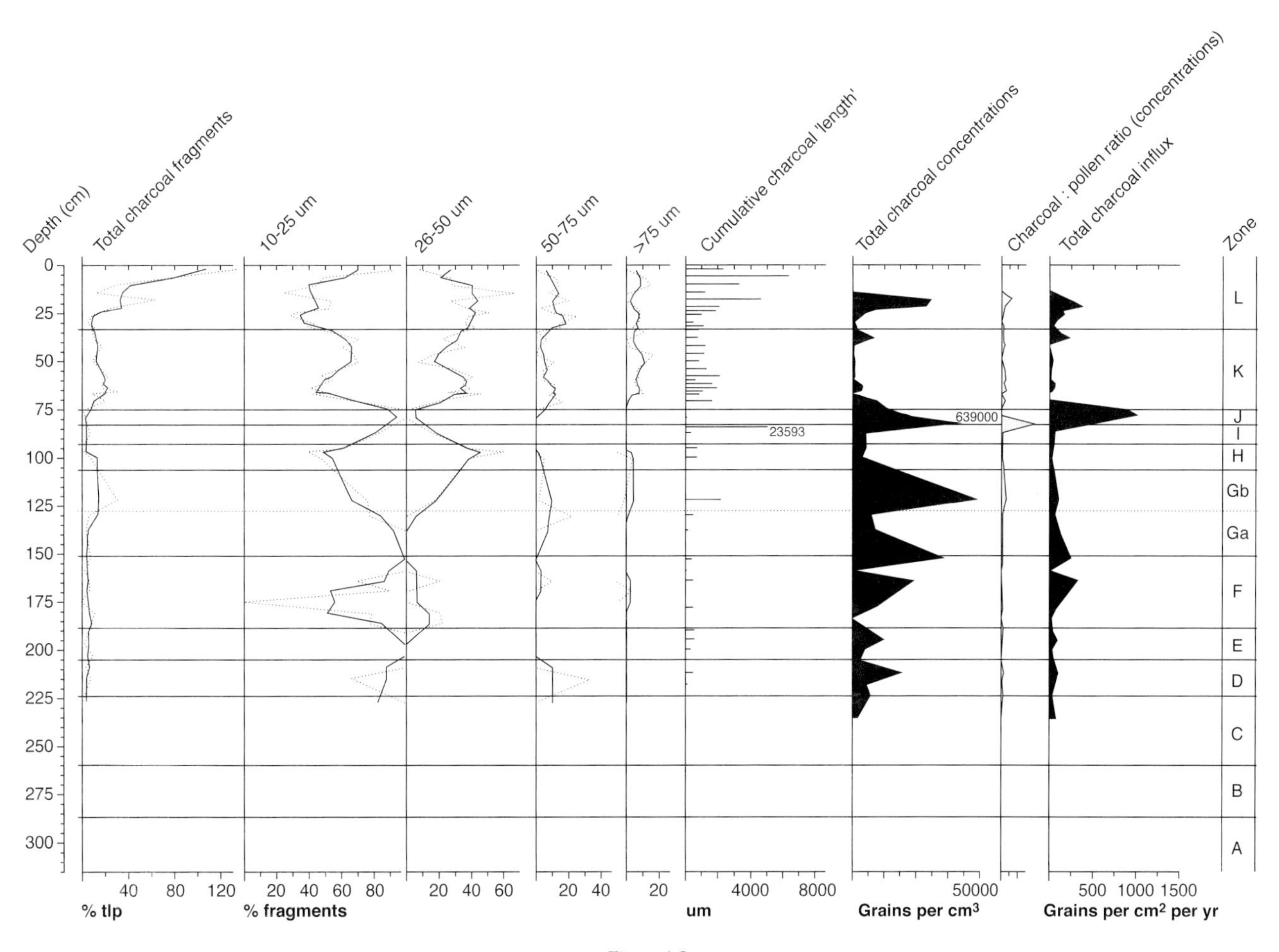

Figure 4.8

Measures of the abundance of microscopic charcoal fragments (see Section 2.3j). Solid outlines of some curves represent smoothed values; individual counts are marked by dashed curves. Local pollen assemblage zone boundaries are plotted to permit correlation.

Table 4.5

Size measurements (pollen size, pollen index: Andersen 1979) of well preserved and physically damaged Gramineae (grass family) pollen grains of annulus diameters >8µm at Sourhope, and assessments where possible from these measurements of the probable cultivated grass (Tipping unpublished). Grains are well preserved unless indicated by (c) crumpled, (sc) slightly crumpled, or (s) split.

Depth (cm)	*anl-D*	*Size*	*Index*	*Group*	*Probable Taxon*
4	10	40.5	1.53	II	*Secale cereale*
20	11	46.5	1.32	III	*Avena sativa*
34	>8	(c)	(c)	undiff.	
38	>8	(c)	(c)	undiff.	
46	12	42	1.10	III	
	11	(c)	(c)	undiff.	
	12	49	1.39	III	*Avena sativa*
50	10	40.5	1.15	undiff.	
	11	(c)	(c)	III	
54	10	40	1.10	undiff.	
	9	44	1.31(sc)	undiff.	
58	14	48	1.23	III	? *Triticum*
	12	44.5	1.12	III	
62	12	45.5	1.33	III	*Avena sativa*
	13	43	1.15	III	
66	14	41	1.21	III	*Triticum*
	14	44.5	1.28	III	*Triticum*
71	11	(c)	(c)	undiff.	
72	13	(c)	(c)	III	
91	8	35.5	1.62 (s)	II	
	8	37.5	1.14	II	
	10	41.5	1.30	undiff.	
	10	43.5	1.35 (s)	undiff.	
94	9	38.5	1.33	II	*Secale cereale*
102	8	(c)	(c)	II	
	10	44	1.66	II	*Secale cereale*
	>8	41.5	1.29	undiff.	
	>8	(c)	(c)	undiff.	
	12	41	1.34	III	*Avena sativa*
	12	45	1.72	III	*Avena sativa*
	12	(c)	(c)	III	
108	11	(c)	(c)	undiff.	
	11	(c)	(c)	undiff.	
114	12	48	1.34	III	*Avena sativa*
	10	(c)	(c)	undiff.	
153	8	38	1.30	II	
186	9	(c)	(c)	undiff.	
221	8	42	14	undiff.	

Betula (birch) appears to have been able to replace these plants, probably close to and on the mire surface. The scale of woodland clearance is difficult to define because of the increases in *Betula* pollen, but though dryland tree taxa were removed, clearance appears to have been of limited scale. There is, for example, no corresponding increase in wild grasses (Gramineae <8 µm anl-D) or herb types indicative of grazing pressure such as *Plantago lanceolata* (ribwort plantain) or *Rumex* (docks) (Figure 4.5). Cereal pollen is not recorded, and fire frequency/intensity was not increased (Figure 4.8).

Lpaz Sourhope Gb (126–105cm): 550 cal BC–50 cal AD

The comparisons of pollen assemblage zones at Station 2 in Figure 4.6, discussed in Section 2.2, suggest that hiatuses in peat accumulation were common in this period and subsequently. Corroded pollen grains become very rare in this zone (Figure 4.7) and it is very unlikely that peat ceased to grow because of increased aridity. The probability is that peat cutting occurred within the sampled area (inset to Figure 4.3a). A consequence of this pattern is that continuity of peat accumulation cannot be assured in the pollen stratigraphy (Figure 4.5). There is no suggestion that sediment accumulation was interrupted in the sediment stratigraphy (Table 4.1). Within this zone, however, ^{14}C assay GU-2397 is considerably younger than expected (Table 4.2; Figure 4.4), briefly evaluated in Section 2.2. The pattern of ^{14}C dating controls is comparable to that more conclusively defined as representing an hiatus above 55cm depth (Section 2.2), and suggests that an hiatus might exist also between 122cm (assay GU-2396) and 100cm (assay GU-2397), and that peat growth was exceptionally rapid between 100cm and 72.5cm (Figure 4.4), impossible to calculate (Table 4.2). The instantaneous growth of almost 30cm of peat is the principal reason for rejecting assay GU-2397, but short lived gaps may still exist within this zone.

Few pollen taxa show abrupt changes supportive of hiatuses, although the temporal resolution of analyses is very low (Table 4.4), but decreases in *Alnus* (alder) and increases in *Calluna* (ling) percentages are sharp at the lower subzone boundary. *Calluna* may have become established on the mire surface following partial clearance of *Alnus* (alder) and *Salix* (willow) in lpaz Ga after *c* 850 cal BC, accompanied by other heathers (Ericaceae undiff.). Small increases in lpaz Gb in *Sphagnum* (bog moss), Cyperaceae (sedges) and batrachian *Ranunculus* (wetland buttercups) percentages are also probable responses to removal of some shade casting trees from the mire (Figure 4.5). The limited increase in abundance of microscopic charcoal fragments suggests a small increase in fire frequency/intensity and the greater proportions of larger fragments suggest that fires were close to the sampling site (Figure 4.8). There may have been a causal link between the development of readily combustible woody heath vegetation on the mire and the frequency of local fires.

There is no evidence for the expansion of areas of pasture in lpaz Gb, although again this may partly be due to statistical distortions induced by the relative abundance of *Betula* (birch) and *Calluna* (ling) pollen from sources on the mire. Above 114cm (*c* 250 cal BC) cereal type pollen grains (Gramineae >8μm anl-D) are recorded (Figure 4.5), including one grain of demonstrable cereal origin (Gramineae Type III), possibly *Avena sativa* (oat) (Table 4.5).

Lpaz Sourhope H (105–93cm): 50–425 cal AD

Major reductions in *Betula* (birch) percentages, and sharply rising values for Gramineae <8μm anl-D (wild grasses) are seen after *c* 100 cal BC. The presence after this of any woodland in the pollen catchment is questionable. A limited cover of low scrub may have been maintained, perhaps within gullies on the steeper upper slopes, of *Fraxinus* (ash), *Crataegus* (hawthorn) and/or *Sorbus* (rowan) (*Crataegus* type pollen) with *Hedera* (ivy), *Ilex* (holly) and *Ulex* (gorse) (Figure 4.5). There are sharp increases in *Plantago lanceolata* (ribwort plantain) and, initially, *Rumex* undiff (docks). The floristic richness of this grazed grassland is suggested by the appearance of pollen of *Papaver* (poppy), *Plantago major/media* (greater or hoary plantain) and *P. maritima* (sea plantain), Umbelliferae (carrot family) and, possibly, *Potentilla* type (tormentil, cinquefoils). *Rumex obtusifolius* (broad-leaved dock) in this zone is taken to be an indicator of over grazing (Hughes & Huntley 1988). *Pteridium* (bracken), present from the earliest pa zone, became much more abundant. Cereal pollen (Gramineae >8μm anl-D) continued to be commonly recorded, including grains of *Avena/Triticum* (oat/wheat; possibly again *Avena sativa* (oat)), *Hordeum* type (Gramineae Type II, possibly barley) and, tentatively, *Secale* (rye) (Table 4.5). Pollen of disturbed ground plants, Chenopodiaceae (goosefoots), Compositae (including *Artemisia* (mugworts) and Cruciferae (cabbage family) is very common (Figure 4.5). Microscopic charcoal values decline, however (Figure 4.8).

Lpaz Sourhope I (93–82cm): 425–710 cal AD

Dramatic increases in the proportions of *Calluna* (ling) and other Ericaceae (heathers) (Figure 4.5) are taken to represent vegetation change on the mire surface, and may relate to the stratigraphic evidence at Station 2d for further phases of peat cutting (Section 2.2; Figure 4.6), as cutting led to drainage and local lowering of the water table, and colonisation of drier areas by heathers. There is little to suggest that a settled and intensively worked agrarian landscape was not maintained.

Lpaz Sourhope J (82–74cm): 710–875 cal AD

For a brief period of *c* 160 cal years, *Betula* (birch) was re-established as a dominant taxon (Figure 4.5). The abundant clumps of pollen (unpublished data) indicate that *Betula* once more grew on the mire surface. There is no requirement to see birch trees as having colonised other parts of the catchment. The rapidity of recolonisation, the selectivity seemingly only of *Betula* and its equally sudden decline at *c* 875 cal AD strongly suggest some form of management or at least protection from grazing, and within this intensively managed landscape it may have been that uses of the peat surface, in addition to its role in supplying fuel, was the intent.

Lpaz Sourhope K (74–33cm): 875–1675 cal AD

The abrupt reduction in *Betula* (birch) values (Figure 4.5) is very likely to have been through anthropogenic clearance, clear felling of all the trees that had grown on the mire surface. It is very probable that a single generation only of birch trees grew before being consumed.

After this event, at around 1450 cal AD from estimates of peat accumulation, further truncation of the peat affected the sediments at Stations 2a–c (Section 2.2). The preferred age depth model (Section 2.2) implies that the amount of peat removed was not great: estimates are that only *c* 10–12cm of peat were lost, given that the temporal hiatus is estimated at around 200 cal years, from *c* 1250 to *c* 1450 cal AD, and rates of undisturbed peat accumulation were *c* 17–18 years per cm (Table 4.4). This thickness of peat is substantially less than obtained by flauchter spade.

The stratigraphic evidence shows the growth of faster growing, poorly humified peat in a 'recurrence' surface. The newly formed peat had far fewer deteriorated pollen grains because it accumulated more rapidly, in wetter conditions and with greatly reduced sediment compaction (Figure 4.7). The mire surface at Station 2 was flooded on abandonment of peat cutting, with open water in pools supporting *Lemna* (duckweed), *Menyanthes* (bogbean) and *Myriophyllum* (water milfoils), the aquatic alga, *Pediastrum*, and abundant diatoms, with *Sphagnum* (bog moss) becoming established as a major mire surface plant together with *Equisetum* (horsetails) (Figure 4.5). Open water may have persisted for *c* 200 cal years. Rising values of Cyperaceae (sedges) may represent increasing terrestrialisation, associated with *Potentilla* type pollen (cf. *P. palustris* (marsh cinquefoil), *Menyanthes*, *Equisetum* (cf. *E. palustre*; marsh horsetail), *Pedicularis palustris* (marsh lousewort; *Pedicularis*), *Galium palustre* (marsh bedstraw; *Galium* type), and *Anagallis tenella* (bog pimpernel; *A. tenella* type). *Calluna* (ling) suffered temporary reductions in the face of this sustained wet phase.

There are few major changes within taxa growing away from the mire surface. Trees that still grew in the catchment (perhaps only *Fraxinus* (ash) and *Betula* (birch)) probably did so only in ungrazed ravines, or in managed woodland in other parts of the valley floor, with a few shrubs (*Corylus/Myrica* (hazel/bog myrtle), *Crataegus* and/or *Sorbus* (hawthorn/rowan), *Salix* (willow)) (Figure 4.5). Proportions of pastoral indicator herb types continue to be high, and pasture continued to be of major importance in the agricultural economy. The consistent presence of *Rumex obtusifolius* (broad-leaved dock) might again suggest high stocking rates, particularly after *c* 1600 cal AD. Cereal pollen and associated disturbed ground herbs are abundant. Size measurements (Table 4.5) suggest that some grains of *Avena/Triticum* (oat/wheat) may be of *Triticum* (wheat), but this is uncertain. *Secale* (rye) is not recorded. The *Cannabis/Humulus* pollen in this zone may represent *Cannabis* (hemp) (Table 2.2); the find of *Centaurea nigra* (black knapweed) may represent a weed of this crop (Gaillard & Berglund 1988). The low pollen percentages provide no evidence that retting was undertaken on the mire. Also recorded is a grain of *Reseda*, possibly weld (*R. luteola*), grown for its dye. Modest increases in microscopic charcoal (Figure 4.8) are likely to represent a generally elevated frequency or intensity of fires, and in the increased proportions of larger fragments, of fires that were closer to the mire.

Lpaz Sourhope L (33–0cm): 1675–1990 cal AD

Percentage reductions as well as losses from the pollen record of a number of previously important wetland indicators (above; Figure 4.5), may be related to continued peat infilling of the peat cut area at Station 2. The large expansion in Gramineae <8μm anl-D (wild grasses) is ascribed to increasing proportions of *Molinia* (purple moor grass) communities on the mire surface, related to drying of the peat surface with the cutting of artificial drainage channels, visible today. This activity also seems to have encouraged *Calluna* (ling) and other Ericaceae (heathers). It is not clear whether the expansion in *Calluna* is also representative of growth away from the peat, but moor burning would be an additional explanation for the concurrence of *Calluna* pollen increases and those of microscopic charcoal fragments in the last few hundred years (Figure 4.8). Pastoral activities were sustained to the top of the pollen record (*c* 1925 cal AD). However, with the exception of one *Avena/Triticum* (oat/wheat) grain at around 1775 cal AD, and one possible cereal grain in the late nineteenth century cal AD, there is little evidence for the area around the site to have been used for cereal cultivation (Table 4.5). With the exception of trees planted in and after the later eighteenth century the representation of woodland remains minimal.

4.4 Summary of environmental change at Sourhope

Peat deposition commenced at the sampling site at *c* 7690 cal BC, although this is not necessarily the earliest peat infilling the channel. Drainage within the valley mire exposed peat and contained pollen grains to aerobic decay after *c* 6500 cal BC. Birch and hazel were the major components of the early Holocene woodland, although oak was a subsidiary component of the woodland after *c* 6450 cal BC. Elm need not have grown in this valley until *c* 3500 cal BC. Alder colonised the catchment after *c* 5250 cal BC, perhaps encouraged by a short lived climatic change which promoted greater peat surface wetness and which accelerated peat growth, vertically and possibly laterally.

Initial disturbance of the woodland took place at about 4550 cal BC, seemingly to provide grazed grassland, and though poorly defined temporally, lasted for perhaps 1500 cal years. Woodland regeneration was probably complete by *c* 3150 cal BC. An elm decline is recorded at *c* 2890 cal BC. At this time, a change to an increasingly dry mire surface led to the temporary replacement of wet carr woodland by more open herb rich plant communities. After *c* 2450 cal BC, dryland woods were reduced, probably by grazing pressure, intensified after *c* 1950 cal BC after which elm was absent. The first evidence for crop growing was at *c* 1800 cal BC.

Between *c* 1050 and 550 cal BC there was a decisive shift to a much wetter mire surface, which encouraged the stronger growth of carr communities on the mire surface, in particular of alder. This is interpreted as a change to a much wetter climate. Areas of pasture seem to have been maintained, and further woodland clearance occurred at around 850 cal BC when oak was lost.

This increased anthropogenic activity is accompanied after *c* 550 cal BC by utilisation of the mire itself in peat cutting. This need not have been the first time the mire had been cut, but is the earliest recognised at the sampling site. Although there appear to be no further increases in the extent of pasture, cereal pollen grew sufficiently close to the mire after 250 cal BC to be more strongly represented. Agricultural activity was substantially intensified after *c* 50 cal AD. Remaining woodland, principally by this time of birch, was cleared except for a few areas possibly protected from grazing animals. Areas of pasture expanded considerably and cereal cultivation continued. Further episodes of peat cutting led to several transient vegetation changes over the next several hundred years, until at least the fifteenth century cal AD. In addition, between 700 and 875 cal AD managed birch woodland probably grew on the mire, the single generation of trees being clear felled. Activities diversified in the last 1000 years with the probable cultivation of hemp and weld.

Artificial drainage may have led to the expansion of grass and heath communities on the mire surface after *c* 1675 cal AD. It is probable that ling heather management, through burning, was established in the last 200 or so years. Cereal cultivation is not confidently recorded above 1775 cal AD, and pasture continued to be the principal land use.

Chapter 5

THE LOW LEVEL PLATEAUX OF THE UPPER BOWMONT VALLEY – SWINDON HILL AND QUARRY KNOWE

5.1 Introduction

Swindon Hill is in the centre of the upper Bowmont Valley. It is one of a series of broad, finger-like plateaux rising 140 to 160m above the tributary valley floors of Sourhope, Kelsocleugh and Calroust Burns and the Bowmont Water (Figure 1.3). The plateau of Swindon Hill itself is a 1.5km long level to very gentle bedrock surface stretching from The Castles and Swindon Hill in the north to the long gentle slope south of Quarry Knowe rising to the high level plateaux and the Border ridge (Figure 1.4). In this distinctive landscape element (Section 1.6) two small diameter valley mires were found during fieldwalking, filling bedrock hollows at Swindon Hill and Quarry Knowe, both analysed to characterise how these uplands were used in the past.

5.2 Swindon Hill: site location, description and pollen recruitment

The pollen site on Swindon Hill at 365m asl is 2km south-west of and 100m higher than the Sourhope pollen site (Chapter 4), and is 1km north of and at the same altitude as the site of Quarry Knowe (Figures 1.3; 5.1). At the head of the Outer Souter Cleugh is a small enclosed basin less than 100m long and a few tens of metres across (Plate 5.1), infilled with peat to a maximal depth of 1.5m (Figure 5.1; Table 5.1). The small size of the basin, with a mean diameter for the site of around 60 to 65m, suggests that the pollen recruitment area extends a few hundred metres only (Figure 5.1). The pollen record will have been dominated by pollen derived from the plateau. The pollen catchment has probably always been distinct from those at Sourhope and Quarry Knowe (Figures 4.1; 5.1). Radiocarbon assays show the peat at Swindon Hill to have formed around 5500 cal years ago (Table 5.2).

The mire has a vegetation cover of *Molinia* (purple moor grass), *Nardus* (mat grass), *Calluna* (ling heather) with *Sphagnum* (bog moss). The peat has no evidence of peat cutting although it has been drained. Across the plateau, andesitic bedrock is exposed in many glacially scoured rock knolls. Around the mire the gentle slopes have freely drained peaty podsols of the Cowie Series, with skeletal soil complexes on

Plate 5.1
The peat filled basin in andesitic bedrock at the head of the Outer Seuter Cleugh on Swindon Hill from the south, looking to the summit ridge at Cocklawhead. The small basin is surrounded by grazed acid grasslands.

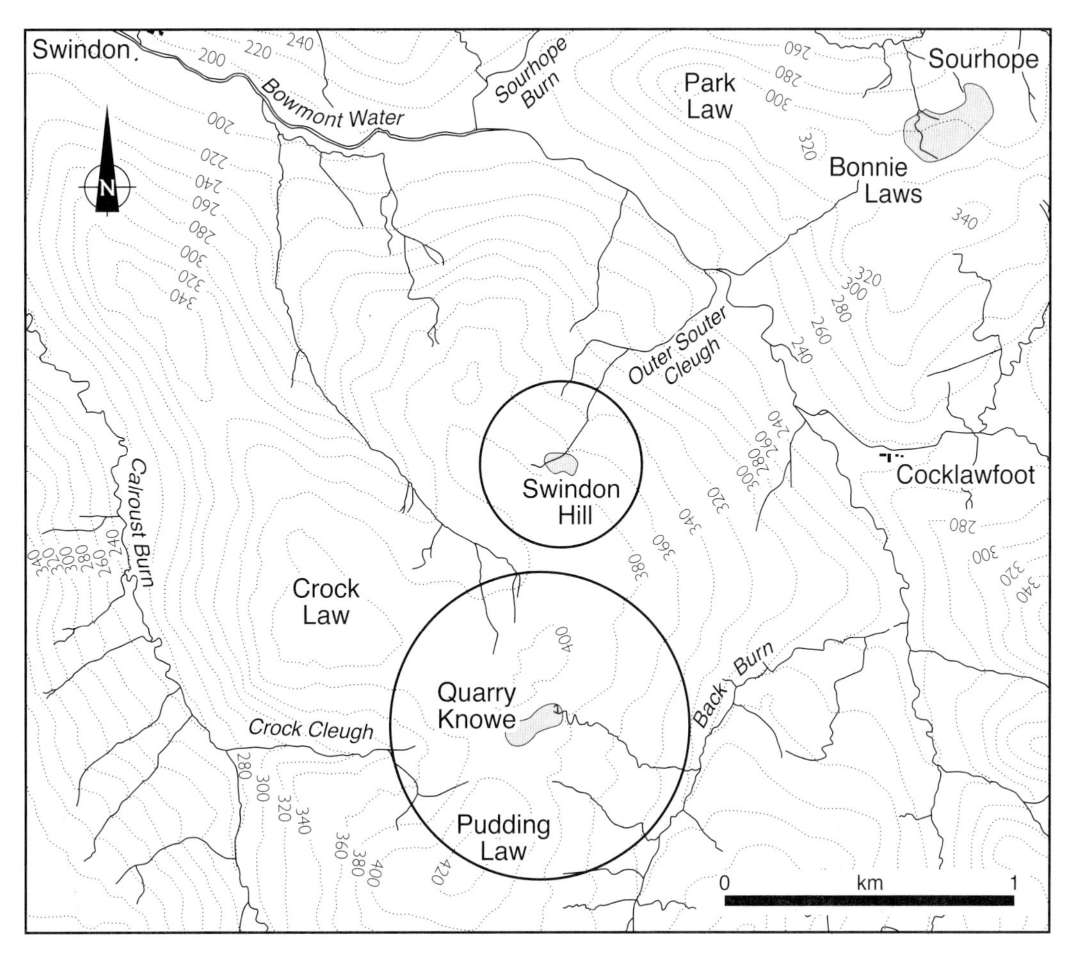

Figure 5.1

The physical and settlement geographies surrounding the Swindon Hill pollen site in the upper Bowmont Valley, showing the location of the basin peat sampled. Contour intervals are 20m. A circle of 300m diameter indicates the likely maximal pollen recruitment area around the sampling site. Also depicted are the valley mire of Sourhope (Chapter 4) in the north-east, and the basin peat at Quarry Knowe, south of Swindon Hill.

moderate and steep slopes falling to the Bowmont Water (Muir 1956; Figure 1.5), of Land Use Capability Classes 5.3 and 6.3 (Bown & Shipley 1982; Figure 1.6). The only archaeological monuments within the pollen catchment are a group of cairns and a ring ditch house north-west of the mire (Mercer in prep.).

5.3 Swindon Hill: sediment sampling, subsampling and chronology construction

The peat thicknesses and sediment stratigraphy were described from boreholes along one surveyed transect from north-west to south-east. The basin floor is uneven. The deepest and oldest sediments are gravels and gravel rich peats, often rich in wood remains, which change to grass and sedge peats occasionally interrupted by bands of *Sphagnum* (bog moss) (Figure 5.2). Table 5.1 is a typical stratigraphy from Station 2, sampled for pollen analyses and dating controls (see also Figure 5.3). This point is likely to reflect the timing and character of peat growth throughout the basin. Subsamples for ^{14}C dating were taken from cores used for pollen analysis. The five ^{14}C assays lie in a conformable sequence (Table 5.2; Figure 5.3). The modern ^{14}C age of assay GU-2493 (Table 5.2) is unsurprising given the appearance in the pollen diagram (Figure 5.4) at around 27cm depth of introduced tree taxa including *Pinus* (pine), *Juglans* (walnut), *Ulmus* (elm) and *Fagus* (beech). Five local pollen assemblage zones were defined (prefixed 'Swindon'; Table 5.3). Pollen subsamples were taken

Table 5.1

The sediment stratigraphy at the sampled site at Swindon Hill.

Unit I (0–5cm):	2.5YR 5/8 red poorly to non-humified coarse grass/sedge peat; gradual to
Unit H (5–15cm):	10 R 2.5/1 black poorly humified compressed grass/sedge peat; gradual to
Unit G (15–23cm):	10 R 3/3 dusky-red poorly humified *Sphagnum* peat; gradual to
Unit F (23–55cm):	10 R 2.5/2 very dusky-red poorly humified grass/sedge peat with *Sphagnum*; gradual to
Unit E (55–91cm):	10 R 2.5/1 reddish-black poorly humified grass/sedge peat, increasingly amorphous and well humified down-unit, particularly below 80cm, and with rare to occasional well preserved coarse wood remains and coarse fibrous *Calluna* stems/roots in basal 10cm; gradual to
Unit D (91–128cm):	10 R 2.5/1 reddish-black well humified grass/sedge peat with coarse wood remains, common and apparently fragmented between 91–97cm, abundant between 97–128cm, increasingly rare below 120cm, and with rare to occasional grass/sedge stems between 115–128cm; gradual to
Unit C (128–132cm):	black well humified amorphous peat with abundant matted monocotyledon remains and 2.5YR 5/4 reddish-brown fine-medium sand and silt scattered throughout and in occasional diffuse lenses and bands; sharp and irregular boundary to
Unit B (132–136.5cm):	black well humified amorphous peat with abundant monocotyledon remains and common to abundant 5YR 7/3 pinkish brown to 5YR 5/3 reddish-brown angular small gravels and coarse sand; sharp to
Unit A (136.5–154cm):	black dry and prismatic-structured amorphous organic clay with rare to occasional vertical fine fleshy stems/roots and abundant densely packed angular small gravels and subangular stones (*c* 2 to 3cm diameter), gravels increasing below *c* 140cm.

Table 5.2

Details of the radiocarbon assays obtained on the sediments at Swindon Hill.

Lab. No. (GU-)	*Mean Depth (cm)*	*Sediment Depth (cm)*	*No. of Cores*	*Sample Weight (gms)*	*^{14}C Age* BP ± 1σ	$\delta^{13}C$ (‰)	*Calibrated Age* BC/AD ± 1σ *and Intercept Ages*	*Mean Calibrated Age* BC/AD
2493	26.5	29–24	1 (monolith)	433.2	modern	–26.5	n.a.	
2490	77	79–75	3 (1,2,3a)	263	510 ± 50	–26	AD 1398 (1418) 1437	AD 1418
2491	95	92–88	3 (2,3a,4)	248.1	1470 ± 50	–27	AD 531 (571) 613	AD 572
2492	129.5	132–127	2 (7,8)	223.2	3100 ± 50	–28.6	1442 (1389) 1321 BC	1382 BC
2494	151.5	154–149	2 (7,8)	308.9	4720 ± 110	–28.5	3640 (3497) 3380 BC	3510 BC

Table 5.3

Local pollen assemblage zones at Swindon Hill, their characteristic pollen taxa and ^{14}C and calibrated age ranges.

Lpaz	*Depths (cm)*	*Characteristic taxa*	*Duration (cal BC/AD)*	*(cal BP)*	*(^{14}C BP)*
Swindon E	14–0	Gramineae <8µm anl-D (wild grasses) – *Calluna* (ling)	AD 1850–1985	100–0	n.a.
Swindon Dc	34–14	*Calluna* (ling) – Gramineae <8µm anl-D (wild grasses) – Cyperaceae (sedges)	AD 1700–1850	250–100	n.a.
Swindon Db	64–34	*Calluna* (ling) – Gramineae <8µm anl-D (wild grasses)	AD 1510–1700	440–250	400–250
Swindon Da	80.75–64	*Calluna* (ling) – Gramineae <8µm anl-D (wild grasses) – Cyperaceae (sedges) – *Sphagnum* (bog moss)	AD 1400–1510	550–440	550–400
Swindon C	94–80.5	*Calluna* (ling) – *Betula* (birch) – Gramineae <8µm anl-D (wild grasses) – Cyperaceae (sedges) – *Corylus/Myrica* (hazel/bog myrtle)	AD 570–1400	1380–550	1470–550
Swindon B	120–94	*Betula* (birch) – *Alnus* (alder) – *Corylus/Myrica* (hazel/bog myrtle)	810 BC–AD 570	2760–1380	2500–1470
Swindon A	152-120	*Betula* (birch) – *Alnus* (alder) – *Quercus* (oak) – *Corylus/Myrica* (hazel/bog myrtle)	3500–810 BC	5450–2760	4720–2500

at 1cm or 2cm intervals except for a short interval in lpaz B (Table 5.4). Because peat accumulation rates were slow below 95cm depth (*c* 572 cal AD), the temporal resolution of pollen analyses throughout prehistory is low, but from the early historic period is exceptionally high. Measurements of large grass pollen grains (Gramineae >8µm anl-D) are given in Table 5.5. Larger than normal grains of Ericaceae undiff. (heathers) were also defined more closely (Table 5.6). Pollen preservation states are provided for all determinable land pollen grains in Figure 5.5, and measures of the abundance and size classes of microscopic charcoal fragments in Figure 5.6.

5.4 Landscape and environmental change on Swindon Hill

Lpaz Swindon A (152–120cm): 3500–810 cal BC

The basal sediments are highly humified peats developed on a bedrock surface containing small stones and gravels (Table 5.1). Soil is not recognised beneath the peat, and is not suggested from the modest proportions of decay resistant Polypodiaceae spores (Tipping *et al* 1994) or pollen preservation characteristics, which are comparable with overlying peats (Figure 5.5). The basal radiocarbon assay (GU-2494) does not appear to be influenced by old carbon within a soil.

The reason for peat formation is unclear: correlation with events at other sites is needed in Section 8.7e to understand what happened prior to sediment accumulation. Tree taxa dominate the pollen spectra on peat inception, particularly *Betula* (birch) and *Alnus* (alder), with *Corylus/Myrica* (hazel/bog myrtle) a relatively minor component. *Quercus* (oak) is present at values around 5% tlp and probably grew locally. *Ulmus* (elm) pollen is recorded at very low percentages and it is not clear whether it grew locally. *Pinus* (pine) is recorded at percentages too low to imply local presence, although in two counts clumps of pollen grains are recorded (unpublished data) and isolated trees may have grown on the plateau. Clumps of pollen of *Alnus* and, in particular, *Betula*, are relatively common, and these trees probably grew on wetter soils in the basin, accompanied by *Humulus* (hop; *Cannabis/Humulus* pollen) and the climbing plants *Lonicera* (honeysuckle) and *Hedera* (ivy) (Figure 5.4). *Polypodium vulgare* (polypody), most abundant in lpaz A, is an epiphyte attached to tree trunks particularly of *Quercus* (oak). The ground layer of local woods probably included *Mercurialis* (mercury) and *Pteridium* (bracken), possibly

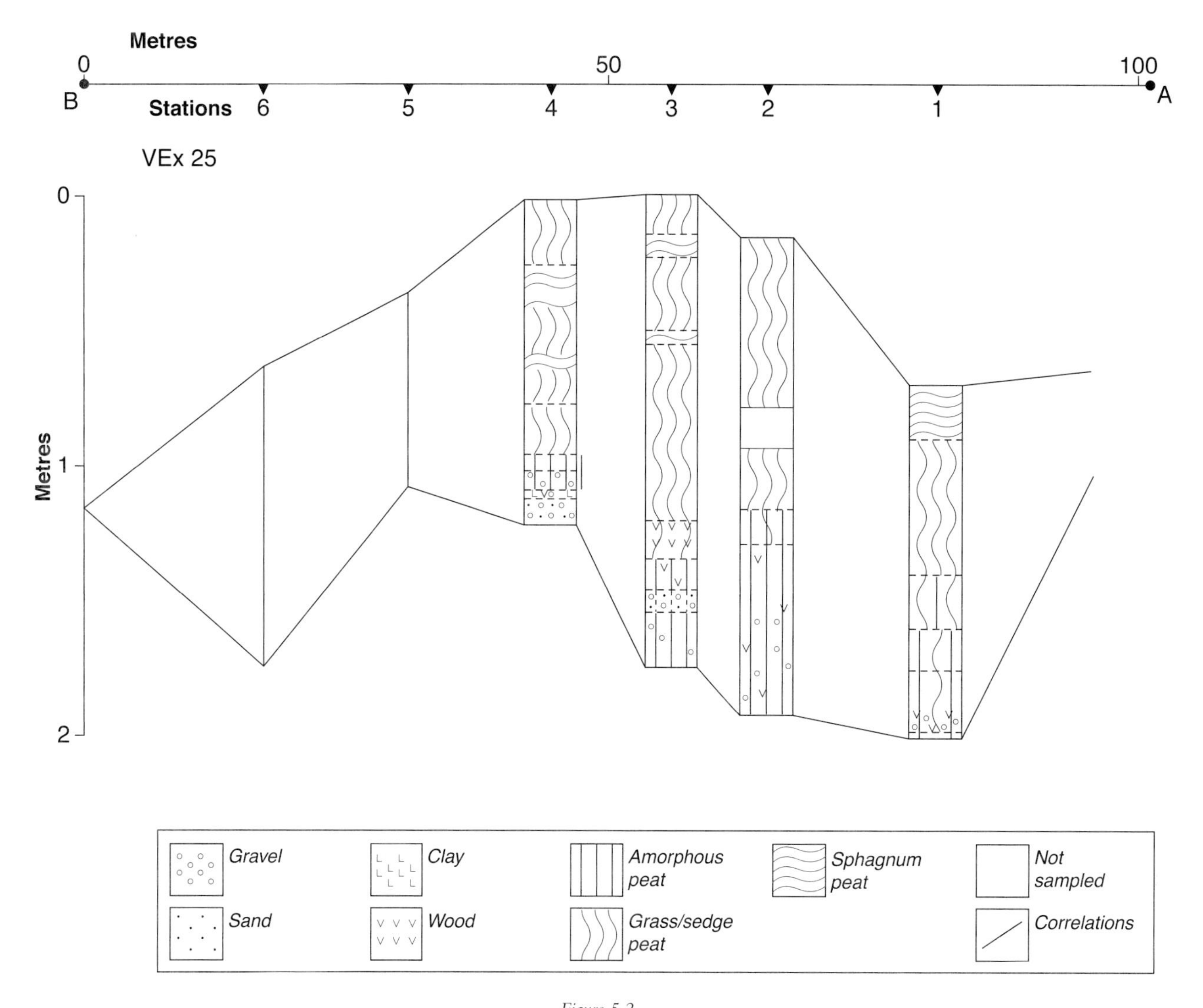

Figure 5.2
The transect and boreholes recording the sediment stratigraphy of the basin peat at Swindon Hill.

in areas of birch and oak woodland on drier slopes, with Cyperaceae (sedges), *Filipendula* (? meadowsweet), *Potentilla* (tormentil, cinquefoils), *Succisa* (devilsbit scabious) and numerous ferns (Filicales), and *Sphagnum* (bog moss) in the wetter parts.

Within the zone, *Alnus* and *Quercus* percentages decline as those of *Betula* increase, particularly marked in *Quercus* between 140 and 132cm (*c* 2350 to 1400 cal BC) (Figure 5.4) and dated by ^{14}C assay GU-2492 (Table 5.2; Figure 5.3). *Salix* (willow) appears to have briefly colonised wetter areas, able to invade gaps in the canopy cover, while the light demanding *Fraxinus* (ash) and *Crataegus* type (*Crataegus* and/or *Sorbus*; hawthorn/rowan) also grew.

Areas of grassland were present prior to this earliest recorded clearance, with herb taxa such as *Rumex* undiff. (docks) and dryland (non-batrachian) *Ranunculus* (buttercups). *Plantago lanceolata* (ribwort plantain) is not recorded until 137cm (*c* 1750 cal BC). Its absence until this time may have been due to restricted pollen dispersal through the tree cover or, because it is then consistently present as more than single grains (Figure 5.4), may signify intensified woodland clearance causal in the decline of *Quercus*. The very low microscopic charcoal percentages (Figure 5.7) suggest that clearance by fire did not occur, and grazing pressure may explain the gradual decline in dryland tree pollen percentages.

Pollen of Gramineae >8μm anl-D (cereal type; Table 5.5) is recorded from *c* 2850 cal BC until *c* 1200 cal BC (125cm). The majority of grains are well preserved, and are assigned to Andersen's (1979) Group II (*Hordeum* (barley) type). There are, however, few disturbed ground herb taxa commonly associated with cereal cultivation.

Lpaz Swindon B (120–94cm): 810 cal BC–570 cal AD

Betula (birch) continued to expand in range or pollen production, seemingly primarily at the expense of *Alnus* (alder) carr, with records of associated taxa, *Lonicera* (honeysuckle), cf. *Humulus* (hop) and *Succisa* (devilsbit scabious) infrequent. Although *Betula* probably grew on the peat surface, indicated by its wood remains and high numbers of pollen clumps (unpublished data), it may also have expanded on dry ground. *Quercus* (oak) may not have been present in the catchment after *c* 800 cal BC. Birch woodland expansion was complete by *c* 50 cal AD (100cm). This expansion was not accompanied by increases in the equally adventitious and highly competitive *Corylus/Myrica* (cf. hazel), and appears to have been selective. The purposeful growing of birch wood cannot be dismissed. There was no other intensive agricultural use of the pollen catchment. Indeed, there are markedly fewer indications of human activity, particularly of sustained grazing, with taxa like *Rumex* undiff (docks) and *Ranunculus* (buttercup) noticeably less commonly recorded. Reduced grazing pressures may have allowed

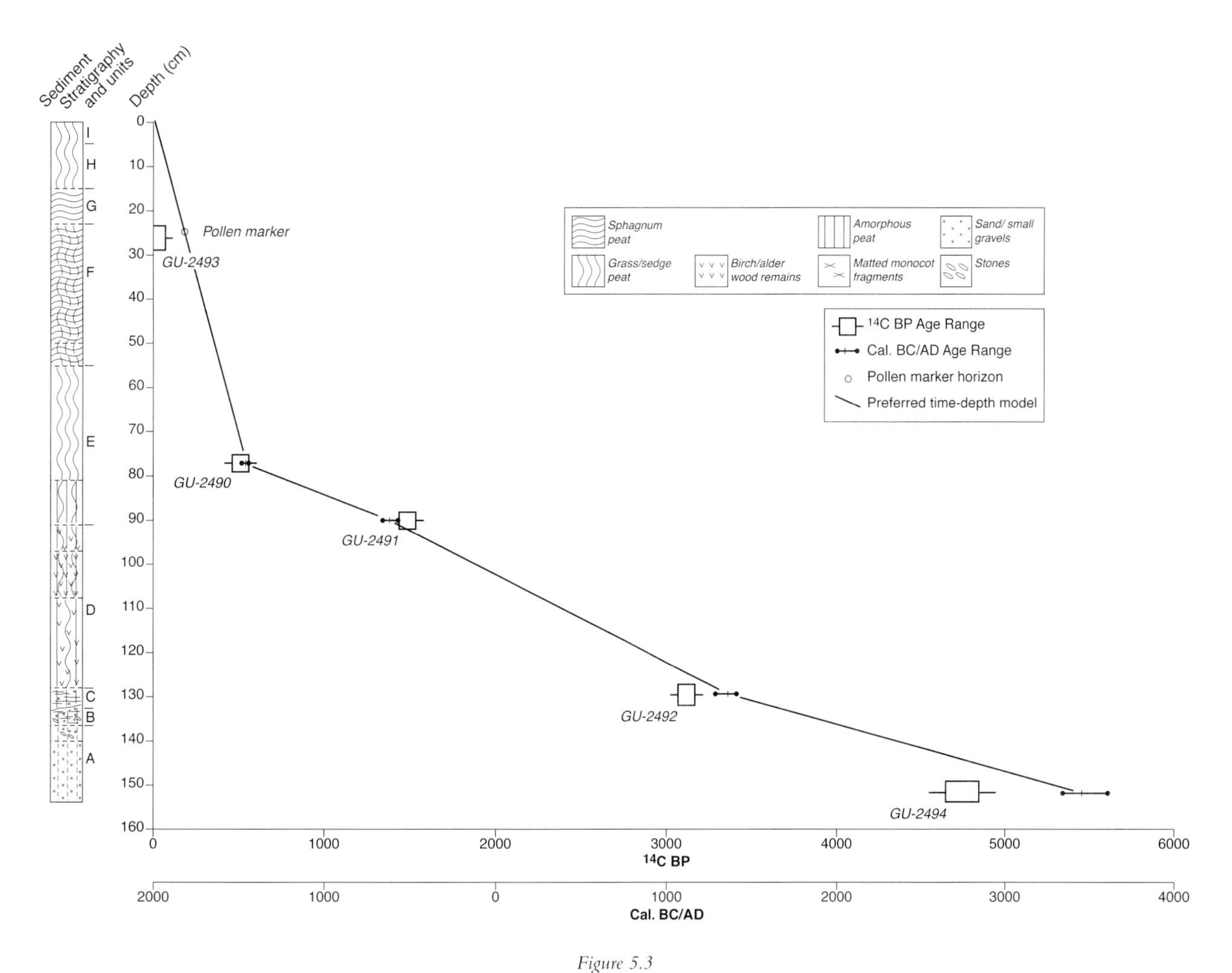

Figure 5.3
The preferred time-depth model for sediments at Swindon Hill showing ^{14}C ages BP at 1 and 2σ as cat-and-whisker plots and corresponding calibrated age ranges BC/AD at 1σ as dumb-bell plots (see Table 5.2) and the only additional control obtained from the pollen marker horizon of Agricultural Improvement tree pollen (Section 2.4c).

Table 5.4

Definitions of sediment accumulation rates between chronological controls used in the preferred time-depth model (Figure 5.3) and the sampling and temporal resolutions of pollen and microscopic charcoal analyses at Swindon Hill.

Depth between dating controls	*Cal ages* BC/AD	*Duration (cal years)*	*Accumulation rate (yrs/cm)*	*Lpaz*	*Depths (cm)*	*Pollen Analyses*		
						(a)	*(b)*	*(c)*
0–27cm	AD 1990–AD 1775	215	7.9	E, Dc		2cm	4	8
27–77cm	AD 1775–1418	357	7.1	Dc–Da	27–71	2cm	3.5	7
					71–77	1cm	3.5	3.5
77–95cm	AD 1418–AD 572	846	47	C		1cm	9	18
95–129.5cm	AD 572–1382 BC	1954	57	B	95–111	2cm	29	114
					111–121	4cm	29	228
129.5–151.5cm	1382 BC–3510 BC	2128	97	A		2cm	48	194

the expansion of *Betula* onto formerly grazed and cultivated areas, accompanied by *Pteridium* (bracken) (Rymer 1976). Cereal pollen is, with a single exception at 119cm (*c* 900 cal BC; Table 5.5) not recorded, and although pollen of disturbed ground herbs is sparingly present, including *Artemisia* (mugworts), Cruciferae (cabbage family) and Caryophyllaceae (pink family), in the absence of cereal pollen their significance is not clear.

Calluna (ling heather) communities were established after *c* 800 cal BC, although the low percentages suggest that their spatial extent was very limited (Evans & Moore 1985; Hjelle 1998; Bunting 2003).

Lpaz Swindon C (94–80.5cm): 570–1400 cal AD

Alnus (alder), *Betula* (birch) and *Corylus/Myrica* (hazel/bog myrtle) percentages decline in the lower part of the zone, prior to *c* 1000 cal AD (85cm). *Calluna* (ling heather) percentages increase substantially, although *Calluna* may have occupied only around 10 to 15% of the pollen recruitment area (Evans & Moore 1985; Hjelle 1998). It is likely that anthropogenic land management maintained heath communities free of invading tree species such as *Betula* (birch) (Hobbs & Gimingham 1984, Miles 1985, 1988). There is no evidence from microscopic charcoal counts for fire frequency or intensity to have significantly altered (Figure 5.6). Grazing pressures appear to have been increased. Gramineae <8μm anl-D (wild grasses) percentages increase to more than 20% tlp, and *Plantago lanceolata* (ribwort plantain) and *Rumex* undiff. (docks) are consistently recorded, frequently at relatively high values. Cereal type pollen, too deteriorated to be classifiable to type but with annulus diameters >8μm, are recorded between *c* 400 and *c* 750 cal AD (Table 5.5). Nevertheless, after *c* 1000 cal AD (above 85cm) wetland trees and shrubs (*Alnus* (alder), *Betula* (birch) and *Salix* (willow) may have been able to recolonise the ground around the pollen site despite the evidence for grazing.

Lpaz Swindon Da (80.75–64cm): 1400–1510 cal AD

A sediment stratigraphic change to much more poorly decayed (humified) peat occurred gradually after *c* 90cm (Table 5.1). The rate of peat accumulation defined by ^{14}C dating appears to have increased only above 77cm (Table 5.2; Figure 5.3), but this is an artifice of the methods used in age estimation (Section 2.4e). The sediment stratigraphic change is not directly dated and is poorly estimated to have occurred between *c* 900 and *c* 1300 cal AD. This change may initially have allowed slightly better

Table 5.5

Size measurements (pollen size, pollen index: Andersen 1979) of well preserved and physically damaged Gramineae (grass family) pollen grains of annulus diameters >8µm at Swindon Hill, and assessments where possible from these measurements of the probable cultivated grass (Tipping unpublished). Grains are well preserved unless indicated by (c) crumpled, (sc) slightly crumpled, or (s) split.

Depth (cm)	*anl-D*	*Size*	*Index*	*Group*	*Probable Taxon*
9	12	(c)	(c)	undiff.	
11	13	(c)	(c)	undiff.	
13	8	36.5	1.41	II	*Secale*
	8	38	1.11	II	
	9	36	1.25	II	
	9	36.5	1.21	II	
17	13	55	1.34	III	
19	11	46.5	1.45	III	? *Triticum*
	14	51	14	III	*Triticum*
	10	(s)	(s)	undiff.	
	8.5	(sc)	(sc)	undiff.	
23	13	50	1.50	III	
25	12	45.5	1.33	III	*Avena sativa*
	12	47	1.54	III	
	11	47.5	18	III	*Triticum*
	9	(c)	(c)	undiff.	
31	13	47	1.54	III	
	10	(ss)	(ss)	undiff.	
33	12	45.5	1.22	III	
	10	(s)	(s)	undiff.	
35	11	37	1.11	II/III	
37	11.5	44	1.28	III	*Avena sativa*
	10	40.5	1.18	II/III	
	12	44.5	1.28	III	
	12.5	(c)	(c)	undiff.	
43	9.5	(c)	(c)	undiff.	
47	10.5	45	1.43	II/III	*Secale/Avena*
49	9	(sc)	(sc)	undiff.	
	12	(sc)	(sc)	undiff.	
51	12	46.5	1.38	III	*Avena sativa*
	14	(sc)	(sc)	undiff.	
57	12	47.5	1.37	III	*Avena sativa*
59	9	(c)	(c)	undiff.	
61	13	48	1.40	III	? *Avena sativa*
	13	43.5	1.28	III	
	10	(c)	(c)	undiff.	
63	11.5	48	1.52	III	
65	11	(ss)	(ss)	undiff.	
67	12	44.5	1.34	III	*Avena sativa*
68	10	41	1.41	II	*Secale*
	14	45	14	III	? *Triticum*
79	12	(c)	(c)	undiff.	
80	11	38	1.33	III	*Avena sativa*
	10	37.5	1.33	II/III	*Secale/Avena*
	12	48	1.34	III	*Avena sativa*

Table 5.5 (cont.)

Depth (cm)	*anl-D*	*Size*	*Index*	*Group*	*Probable Taxon*
	12	45.5	1.22	III	*Avena* sp.
	12	(c)	(c)	undiff.	
	9	(c)	(c)	undiff.	
87	9	(sc)	(sc)	undiff.	
90	9	(c)	(c)	undiff.	
	10	(sc)	(sc)	undiff.	
92	10	(sc)	(sc)	undiff.	
	8	(c)	(c)	undiff.	
119	9	40	1.10	II	
127	9	38	1.10	II	
131	10	38.5	1.20	II	
137	10	38.5	1.13	II/III	
	9.5	38	1.23	II	
	10	36.5	1.21	II	
141	10.5	39.5	7	II/III	
	11.5	39	15	III	
	11	37	15	II/III	
	10	(c)	(c)	undiff.	
	10	(c)	(c)	undiff.	
	10	34.5	13	undiff.	
145	10	38	15	II/III	

preservation of pollen in the less compacted peat, and by 70cm (*c* 1475 cal AD) very few pollen grains were affected by corrosion in aerobic conditions, indicating a substantial and significant rise in the local water table (Figure 5.5). Above *c* 80cm (1400 cal AD) there is palynological evidence for a much wetter mire surface. Cyperaceae (sedges) values increase, and *Sphagnum* (bog moss) percentages rise steeply. Pollen grains of heathers identified as either *Andromeda* (bog rosemary) and *Arctostaphylos* (bearberry) are recorded (Table 5.6), and some may be of *Andromeda polifolia* (bog rosemary), colonising shallow pools with *Sphagnum* and aquatic species of *Ranunculus* (buttercup). *Equisetum* (horsetail) spores, and after *c* 1500 cal AD both *Potamogeton* (pondweed) and *Typha angustifolia* (lesser bulrush), probably represent the development of shallow water plant communities in standing water. Neither sediment or pollen stratigraphic change was abrupt, and because of this abrupt impacts such as the infilling by fresh peat of cut areas (Chapter 4) is an unlikely cause. A climatic change to increasing precipitation, deliberate flooding of the mire to increase sedge hay production (Vasari & Väänänen 1986; Segerstrom & Emanuelsson 2002) or increases in runoff through clearance of trees surrounding the basin are all possible explanations. The last would explain the considerable evidence for reductions in woodland, with *Alnus* (alder) percentages being reduced to values of 1% tlp over a period of a very few years, *Betula* (birch) values much reduced, and *Crataegus* type (*Crataegus* or *Sorbus*; hawthorn/rowan) pollen no longer recorded.

Calluna (ling heather) values rise to over 40% tlp, perhaps 20 to 25% of the ground within the pollen catchment (Evans & Moore 1985; Hjelle 1998). Heath communities contained several heather species (Ericaceae undiff.). Above 73cm (*c* 1450 cal AD) *Arctostaphylos* (bearberry; Table 5.4) is likely to have grown on the plateau. Bearberry is now rare in south-east Scotland, but is found in poorly grazed *Calluna* moors and grass heaths in Northumberland (Ratcliffe 1974). It is encouraged by burning (McVean & Ratcliffe 1962; Hobbs 1984; Hobbs, Mallik & Gimingham 1984), but with the exception of occasional and anomalous

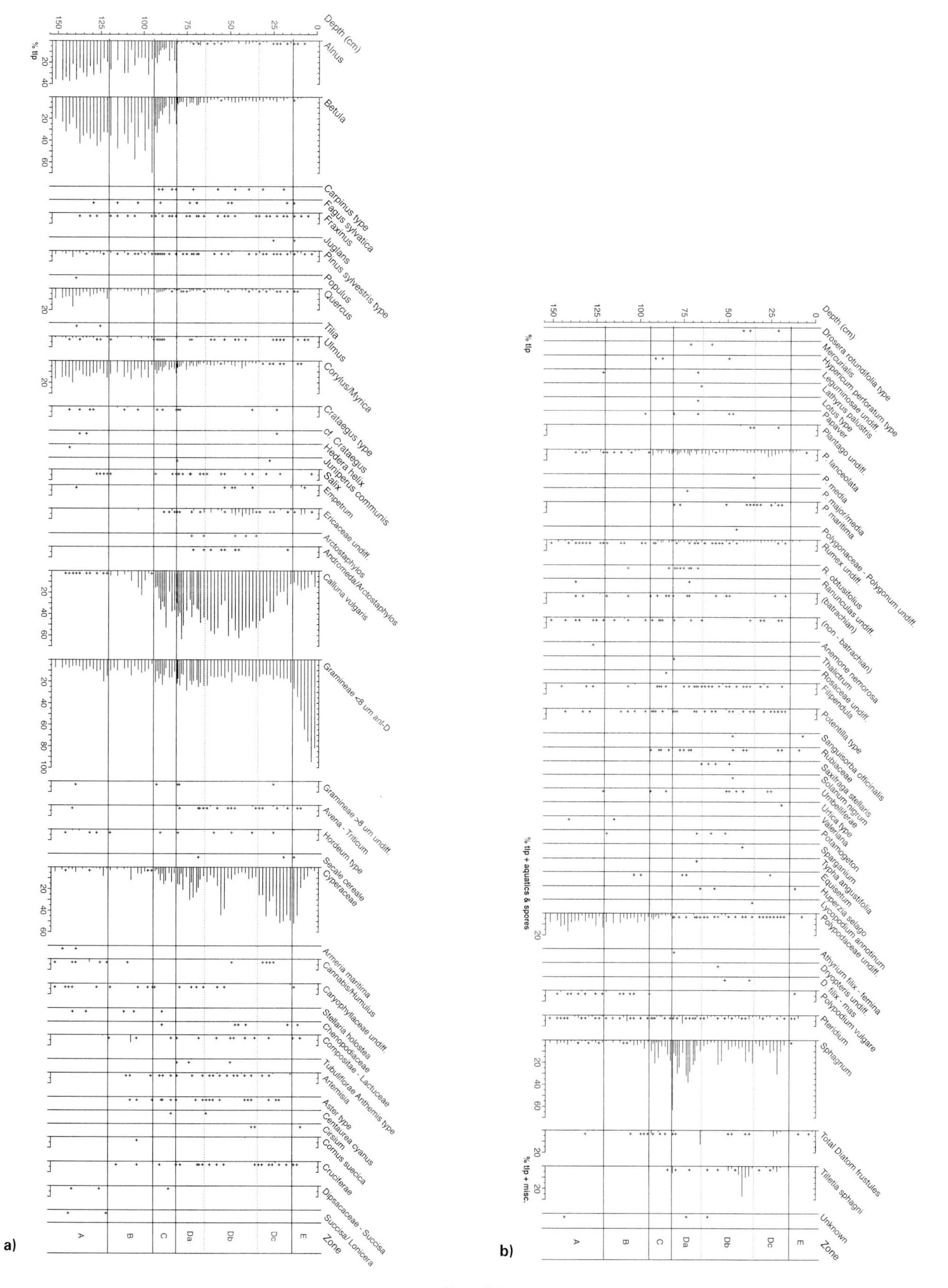

Figure 5.4

The complete pollen stratigraphy at Swindon Hill plotted against depth (cm) and calculated as percentages of total land pollen (tlp) and tlp + group (Section 2.3g). Values recorded in a subsample at <1% are marked by a cross. Local pollen assemblage zone boundaries are plotted to permit correlation. See Appendix One for a glossary of English names for Linnaean taxa.

Table 5.6

Size measurements of Ericaceae pollen grains larger than normal at Swindon Hill. For definitions of variables measured see Oldfield (1959, p. 20).

Depth (cm)	*D*	*d*	*D/d*	*p*	*2f*	*2f/p*	*morphological characteristics*	*type*
17	48	36	1.33	10	21	2.20	no endocracks visible	*Andromeda/Arctostaphylos*
35	47	30	1.56	10	20	2.00	„ „	*Arctostaphylos*
41	41	32	1.28	8	24	3.00	„ „	*Arctostaphylos*
47	45	34	1.23	12	22	1.83	endocracks visible	*Arctostaphylos*
49	42	25	1.68	15	23	1.53	no endocracks visible	*Andromeda/Arctostaphylos*
	42	26	1.61	n.d.	22	n.d.	„ „	*Andromeda/Arctostaphylos*
	38	28	1.36	8	18	2.25	„ „	*Andromeda/Arctostaphylos*
	38	27	n.d.	14	22	1.57	„ „	*Andromeda/Arctostaphylos*
57	36	28	1.30	14	16	1.14	no endocracks visible; closed and covered furrow	*Andromeda*
	43	30	1.40	8	21	2.60	no endocracks visible	*Andromeda/Arctostaphylos*
	34	27	1.26	15	n.d.	n.d.		*Erica* sp.
61	30	25	1.20	7	18	2.60		? *Vaccinium*
	40	30	1.33	7	18	2.60	no endocracks visible	*Andromeda/Arctostaphylos*
	40	27	1.48	10	29	2.90	no endocracks visible	*Andromeda/Arctostaphylos*
65	39	29	1.34	11	19	1.73	„ „	*Arctostaphylos*
	43	30	1.43	n.d.	21	n.d.	no endocracks visible	*Andromeda/Arctostaphylos*
	32	20	1.60	15	15	1.00		? *Vaccinium*
	40	30	1.33	5	24	4.80	endocracks visible	*Arctostaphylos*
71	48	30	1.60	10	n.d.	n.d.	no endocracks visible	*Andromeda/Arctostaphylos*
72	40	28	1.43	9.5	23	2.42	endocracks visible	*Arctostaphylos*

n.d. not determined

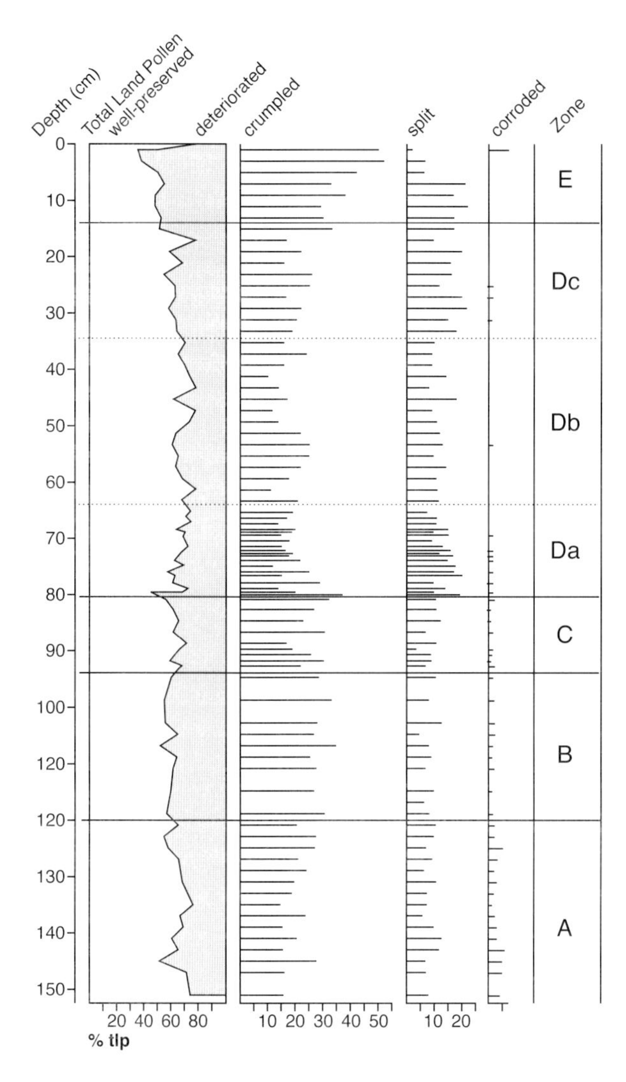

Figure 5.5
Pollen preservation states for all determinable land pollen grains at Swindon Hill plotted against depth and calculated as percentages of total land pollen (see Section 2.31): too few amorphous grains were recorded to be depicted. Local pollen assemblage zone boundaries are plotted to permit correlation.

single peaks in numbers of charcoal fragments, there is little support for an increased frequency or intensity of fires on the plateau (Figure 5.6). Other causal factors are evaluated following analysis of other sites in the valley in Section 8.10c.

Percentages of Gramineae <8μm anl-D (wild grasses) increase, particularly after *c* 1450 cal AD (73cm). Areas of grazing were significantly more important, with *Plantago lanceolata* consistently represented at high values, associated with both *P. major/media* (greater/hoary plantain) and *P. maritima* (sea plantain), *Rumex* undiff. (docks) and *R. obtusifolius* (broad-leaved dock), the last again possibly indicative of high grazing pressures (Hughes & Huntley 1988). Cereal pollen grains are infrequently recorded. Well preserved grains (Table 5.5) are predominantly of *Avena* (oat) or *Triticum* (wheat) (Gramineae Group III; Andersen 1979). *Avena sativa* (oat) is identified consistently, as also is *Secale* (rye).

Lpaz Swindon Db (64–34cm): 1510–1700 cal AD

The basin at the head of Outer Seuter Cleugh continued to be very wet. At 55cm (*c* 1575 cal AD) a *Sphagnum* (bog moss) rich peat developed at Station 2 (Table 5.1) and bands of *Sphagnum* peat are recorded at about this depth in several boreholes (Figure 5.2). *Sphagnum* spores are prominent in the pollen record in two brief phases, between *c* 1550 to 1600 cal AD and *c* 1675 to 1700 cal AD. *Tilletia sphagni* fungal spores are abundant in the upper phase (Figure 5.4). High amounts of Cyperaceae (sedge) pollen coincide with peaks in *Sphagnum* percentages. Spores of aquatic and semi-aquatic plants (*Potamogeton* (pondweed), *Sparganium* (bur-reed; Andrew 1984), *Typha angustifolia* (lesser bulrush)) indicate shallow water at the sampling site. *Drosera rotundifolia* (common sundew), recorded at *c* 40cm, would have colonised such habitats.

Trees and shrubs were probably absent from the vicinity of the site by *c* 1500 cal AD. Pastoral indicator herbs are well represented, and cereal pollen is consistently recorded, predominantly of Andersen's (1979) Group III. Grains may be exclusively of *Avena sativa* (Tipping unpublished; Table 5.5).

Calluna (ling) pollen is very abundant, occupying up to 40% of the ground (Evans & Moore 1985; Hjelle 1998). Microscopic charcoal fragments are occasionally very prominent, but average values are also consistently higher (Figure 5.6). These high frequencies are considered to represent the maintenance by burning of heather moorland. Within the Ericaceae (heathers), *Vaccinium* (bilberry) is tentatively identified (Table 5.6; Table 2.2). Its pollen cannot consistently be recognised, but two taxa frequently associated with Vaccinieta (Tansley 1939), *Cornus suecica* (dwarf cornel) and *Lycopodium annotinum* (interrupted clubmoss), are also recorded in the upper part of lpaz Db when Ericaceae undiff. are most common (Figure 5.4). *Vaccinium* heath today occurs in snow bed communities on the summit plateau of The Cheviot above *c* 800m OD (Ratcliffe 1974).

The identification of such high altitude plant communities from analyses at Swindon Hill is

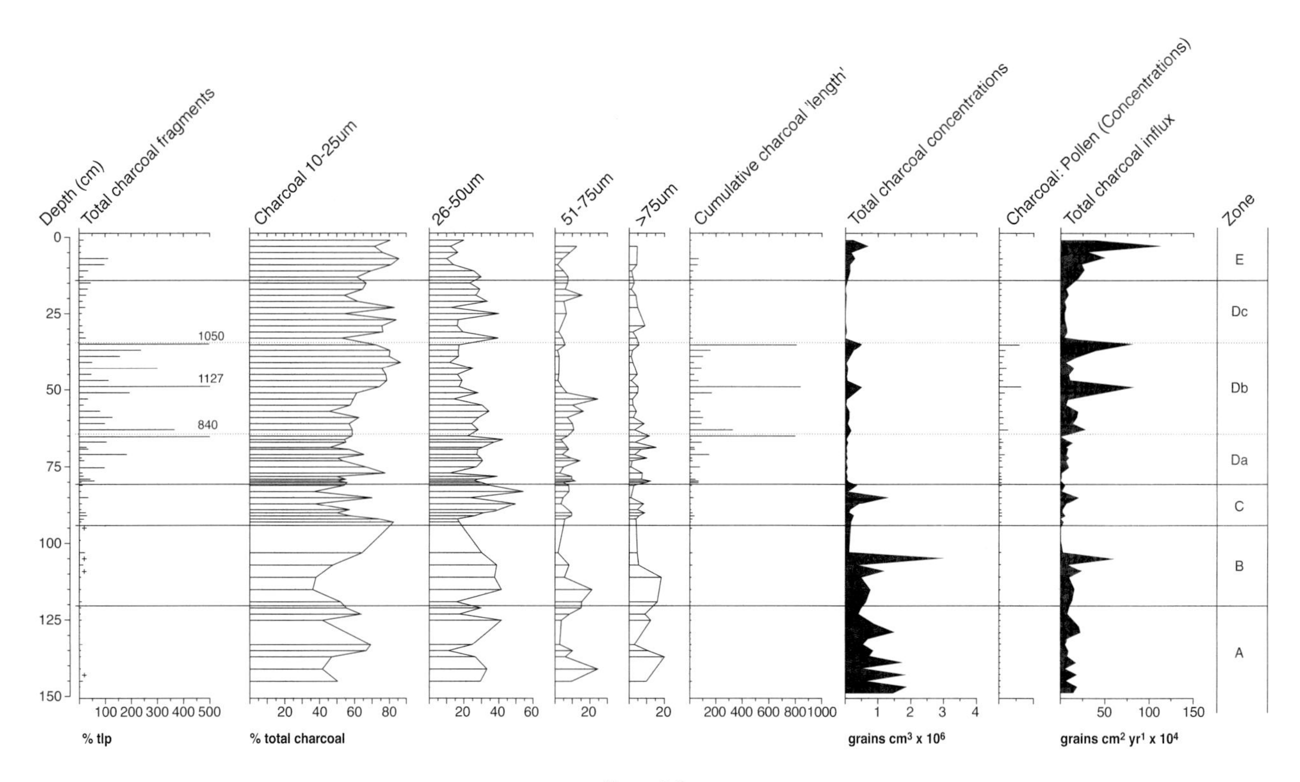

Figure 5.6
Measures of the abundance of microscopic charcoal fragments at Swindon Hill (see Section 2.3j). Local pollen assemblage zone boundaries are plotted to permit correlation.

tentative, but other heath taxa are recorded that are most common at high altitudes. *Arctostaphylos* (bearberry) is again recorded (Table 5.6), with *Empetrum* (crowberry), and both are arctic-alpine plants (Matthews 1955). *Plantago maritima* (sea plantain) is consistently recorded after *c* 1675 cal AD (40cm), a common plant on exposed mountain summits (McVean & Ratcliffe 1962). *Saxifraga stellaris* (starry saxifrage) is today found locally only on the summit of The Cheviot (Ratcliffe 1974), yet its pollen is frequent in the lower part of lpaz Db. Two grains of the arctic-alpine fir clubmoss, *Huperzia selago*, are recorded on either side of the lower zone boundary. Their appearance on Swindon Hill may be explained by altitudinal depression of plant communities during a phase of lowered temperature. Disturbed ground herb taxa such as *Artemisia* (mugworts), Chenopodiaceae (goosefoots), Caryophyllaceae (pinks) and Compositae Liguliflorae (dandelion type) may have colonised unstable, eroding soils but this is uncertain, all being also associated with patches of bare ground promoted by cereal cultivation (above).

Lpaz Swindon Dc (34–14cm): 1700–1850 cal AD

The peat surface continued to be waterlogged, promoting a poorly decayed (humified) peat (Table 5.1). One very wet phase between 25 and 15cm (*c* 1775 to 1850 cal AD) is recognised by further increases in *Sphagnum* (bog moss) and *Tilletia sphagni* spores, in very large numbers of diatom frustules (not counted systematically below 50cm), and the occurrence of *Drosera rotundifolia* (common sundew), but aquatic and semi-aquatic taxa are not represented. Cyperaceae (sedges) may have dominated the peat surface as they do the pollen counts (Figure 5.4).

A significant decline in *Calluna* (ling) is recorded above 25cm (*c* 1775 cal AD) as percentages of Gramineae <8μm anl-D (wild grasses) rise (Figure 5.4). These changes are interpreted as a more or less direct replacement of heath by dry grassland. Percentages of *Plantago lanceolata* (ribwort plantain) and other grassland herbs increase. The type of grassland cannot be identified with assurance, but King's (1962) analyses within the Bowmont Valley found that *Plantago lanceolata* is recorded only from

Table 5.7
The sediment stratigraphy at the sampled site at Quarry Knowe.

Unit D_2 (0–4cm):	5 YR 2.5/1 black well humified grass/sedge peat with occasional fresh grass roots; gradual to
Unit D_1 (4–22cm):	5 YR 2.5/2 dark reddish-brown poorly humified grass/sedge peat with common *Sphagnum* moss fragments; gradual to
Unit C (22–53cm):	5 YR 2.5/2 dark reddish-brown poorly humified grass/sedge and co-dominant *Sphagnum* rich peat; gradual to
Unit B (53–63cm):	5 YR 2.5/2 dark reddish-brown grass/sedge peat; gradual to
Unit A_2 (63–71.5cm):	5 YR 2.5/2 dark reddish-brown amorphous peat/organic rich mud with abundant grass/sedge stems and rare to occasional bleached coarse sand and rock fragments; sharp irregular boundary to
Unit A_1 (71.5–75cm):	10 YR 3/6 dark yellowish-brown structureless gritty clay with abundant bleached coarse sand and rock fragments, occasional small angular to subangular bleached stones and rare to occasional grass/sedge roots/stems penetrating from above.

neutral to base rich *Festuca* and *Agrostis* (bent and fescue) types, and not from more acid grassland.

Immediately above 34cm (*c* 1700 cal AD), prior to the decline of *Calluna*, numbers of charcoal fragments fall to relatively low and occasionally very low values (Figure 5.6). After *c* 1775 cal AD (25cm) numbers of fragments gradually increase once more, broadly coinciding with the replacement of *Calluna* by grassland. Cessation of burning may have led to reductions in the extent of *Calluna* heath (Hobbs & Gimingham 1987). The absence after *c* 1700 cal AD of other heathers (Ericaceae undiff. and cf. *Vaccinium* (bilberry), *Empetrum* (crowberry) and *Arctostaphylos* (bearberry)) is unrelated to the later decline in *Calluna*, but is presumed, together with the apparent absence of arctic-alpine taxa (except *Plantago maritima*), to represent forcing from the lower slopes and plateaux to the high altitude surfaces of The Cheviot as climate changed (see Section 8.11b).

Cereal pollen continues to be represented, the majority keyed to Andersen's (1979) Group III (Table 5.5). At 19cm (*c* 1710 cal AD) two large grass pollen grains with very large sizes and annulus diameters are identified as of *Triticum* (wheat). Between 31 and 25cm (*c* 1750 to 1775 cal AD) pollen of *Cannabis/Humulus* type is recorded, the size and pore characteristics suggesting the grains to represent *Cannabis sativa* (hemp) (French & Moore 1986, Whittington & Gordon 1987), but grains were too few in number to test this suggestion. The few grains recorded need not represent hemp cultivation on Swindon Hill itself.

Lpaz Swindon E (14–0cm): 1850–1985 cal AD

The more compact, black and more humified peat of sediment unit H (Table 5.1) is probably a product of recent drainage of the mire (Section 5.2); *Sphagnum* (bog moss) plant remains and spores are not recorded within the last *c* 120 years (above 15cm). Gramineae <8μm anl-D (wild grasses) percentages exceed those of Cyperaceae (sedges) (Figure 5.4), and to an extent this change probably represents the colonisation of the peat surface by *Molinia* (purple moor grass) communities as water levels in the peat fell. Modifications to dryland grass communities are also likely. Pollen grains of herbs growing within what was inferred to have been a neutral to base rich grassland (*Plantago lanceolata*, *Rumex*; King 1962) are not recorded in the top few centimetres of the peat. The grassland appears to have become increasingly impoverished of associated herb taxa, unlikely to have

Plate 5.2
The surface of the valley mire at Quarry Knowe, showing that *Calluna* (ling heather) plants currently dominate only drier areas of the mire, in the foreground, and are separated by wetter areas supporting sedges from the tussocky grassland landscape of the drier mineral soils rising south to the summit ridge at Windy Gyle.

occurred through grazing pressures since these herbs benefit from the maintenance of a close grazed turf. Instead, it is tentatively thought that the loss of species was due to the increasing importance of a grassland dominated by *Nardus stricta* (mat grass). Cereals appear not to have been grown after *c* 100 cal BP.

5.5 Summary of environmental change on Swindon Hill

Peat accumulation in a basin at the head of a steep valley began at around 3500 cal BC. An alder and birch carr woodland grew on wet soils adjacent to and within the basin, an oak and hazel woodland, but not necessarily elm, grew, but may have been secondary, altered by grazing pressures prior to peat inception. Cereals, probably barley, grew near the pollen site from at least 2850 cal BC. Oak trees suffered further reductions between 2350 cal BC and 1400 cal BC, probably through grazing pressures and not by the use of fire. Anthropogenic pressures on the plateau seem to have lessened after *c* 800 cal BC. Relaxation of grazing pressures may have allowed birch to colonise areas of formerly grazed dry grassland and scrub, or birch trees may have been encouraged to grow on the mire surface.

Between *c* 570 and 1000 cal AD areas of grazed grassland increased. Cereals were cultivated between *c* 400 and 750 cal AD. By around 1000 cal AD, however, damp woodland surviving around the basin was re-established, without apparent reductions in grazing pressures. At *c* 1450 cal AD this limited area of woodland was comprehensively cleared. Grassland and heath were established over the plateau. Ling heather was accompanied in a grass rich heath by bearberry, possibly representing the initial phases of climatic deterioration which led to very pronounced increases in peat accumulation on an increasingly wet peat surface at around 1500 cal AD, followed by further, short lived phases of pool development. The period between *c* 1500 and 1700 cal AD was considerably wetter and probably colder than the present day, leading to the altitudinal depression of plant communities found today about 450m higher than Swindon Hill on the summit of The Cheviot.

Nevertheless cereals, probably oats and rye rather than barley, appear to have been cultivated on the plateau from *c* 1500 cal AD until around 1850 cal AD.

Table 5.8
Details of the radiocarbon assays obtained on the sediments at Quarry Knowe.

Lab. No. (GU-)	*Mean Depth (cm)*	*Sediment Depth (cm)*	*No. of Cores*	*Sample Weight (gms)*	*^{14}C Age BP ± 1σ*	*$\delta^{13}C$ (‰)*	*Calibrated Age BC/AD ± 1σ and Intercept Ages*	*Mean Calibrated Age BC/AD*
2512	61.5	63–60	1 (monolith)	231.5	170 ± 50	–27.3	AD 1660 (1676,1747,1799,1942,1955) 1955	n.a.
2511	73.5	75–72	1 (monolith)	227.5	1220 ± 50	–27.7	AD 715 (785) 883	AD 800

Management by burning of heathers continued until about 1700 to 1730 cal AD, when burning temporarily ceased. Ling heather was, soon after, replaced initially by species rich grazed grassland, but by around 1900 to 1950 cal AD, few grassland herbs were present due to their replacement by acid grasses.

5.6 Quarry Knowe: site location, description and pollen recruitment

Quarry Knowe is a small valley mire on the same plateau as the site of Swindon Hill (Figure 5.1), 1km south of Swindon Hill. Quarry Knowe is around 2km east of the pollen sites Mow Law A and B and 4km north-west of the pollen site at Cocklawhead (Figure 1.3; Chapter 6). The mire fills a shallow elongate bedrock basin in a col between Crock Cleugh and a tributary of Back Burn at 390m asl (NT 8405 1685) (Plate 5.2). The peat is a 75cm deep veneer more than 150m long but around 20m wide, slightly domed through mirroring the underlying bedrock (Figure 5.7). The mire is little wider than that at Swindon Hill, and the likely maximal pollen recruitment area is estimated at less than the 1km diameter circle drawn on Figure 5.1, with most pollen originating in plant communities on the plateau. The soils and current land use capability classes are shared with Swindon Hill (Section 5.2), supporting a mosaic of mixed grass heath, *Calluna* (ling) and *Nardus* (mat grass) communities (King 1962). Differences in grazing density determine the proportions of heath to grass, more heavily grazed areas supporting *Nardus* (Hunter 1962). There are very few archaeological monuments known from this plateau (Mercer in prep., Mercer & Tipping; Figures 8.9 to 8.14).

5.7 Quarry Knowe: sediment sampling, subsampling and chronology construction

The consistent peat stratigraphy draped over the very uneven bedrock floor (Figure 5.7) was sampled at Station 1, the deepest point, by hand to remove peat monoliths. All analyses and dating controls come from the same sediments. Sediment unit A (75–63cm; Table 5.7) has a high minerogenic content, recognised on interpretation of dating controls to have been an organic soil. Peat with no mineral grains formed at 63cm (unit B).

Two radiocarbon assays were obtained (Table 5.8). The lower (GU-2511) is probably from within a soil (below) and is affected by carbon residing in the soil

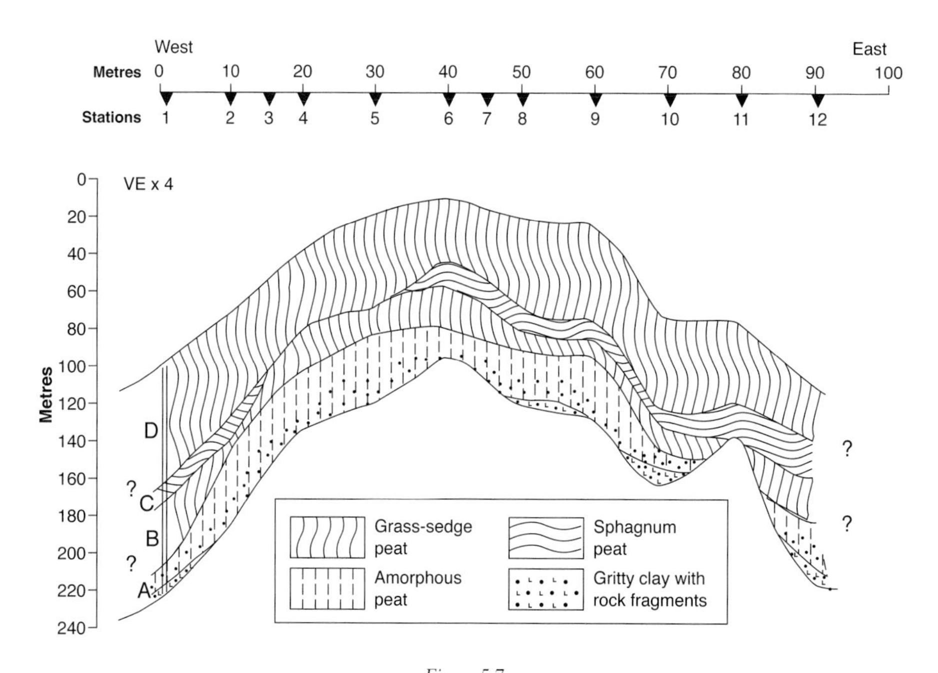

Figure 5.7
The transect and boreholes recording the sediment stratigraphy of the valley mire at Quarry Knowe.

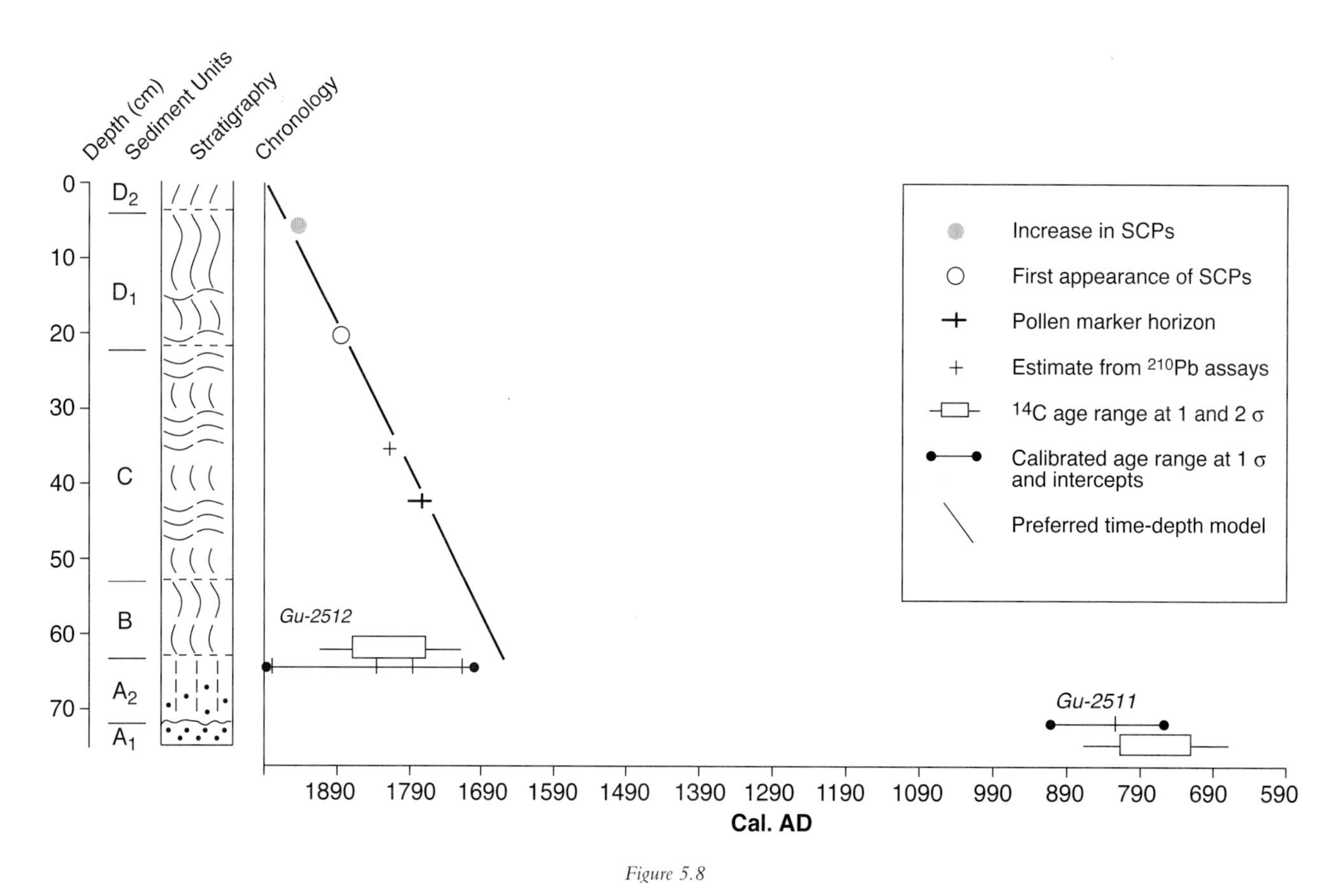

Figure 5.8
The preferred time-depth model for sediments at Quarry Knowe showing ^{14}C ages BP at 1 and 2σ as cat-and-whisker plots and corresponding calibrated age ranges BC/AD at 1σ as dumb-bell plots (see Table 5.8), and additional dating controls obtained from SCPs (Section 2.4d), the pollen marker horizon of Agricultural Improvement tree pollen (Section 2.4c) and ^{210}Pb assays (Section 2.4b).

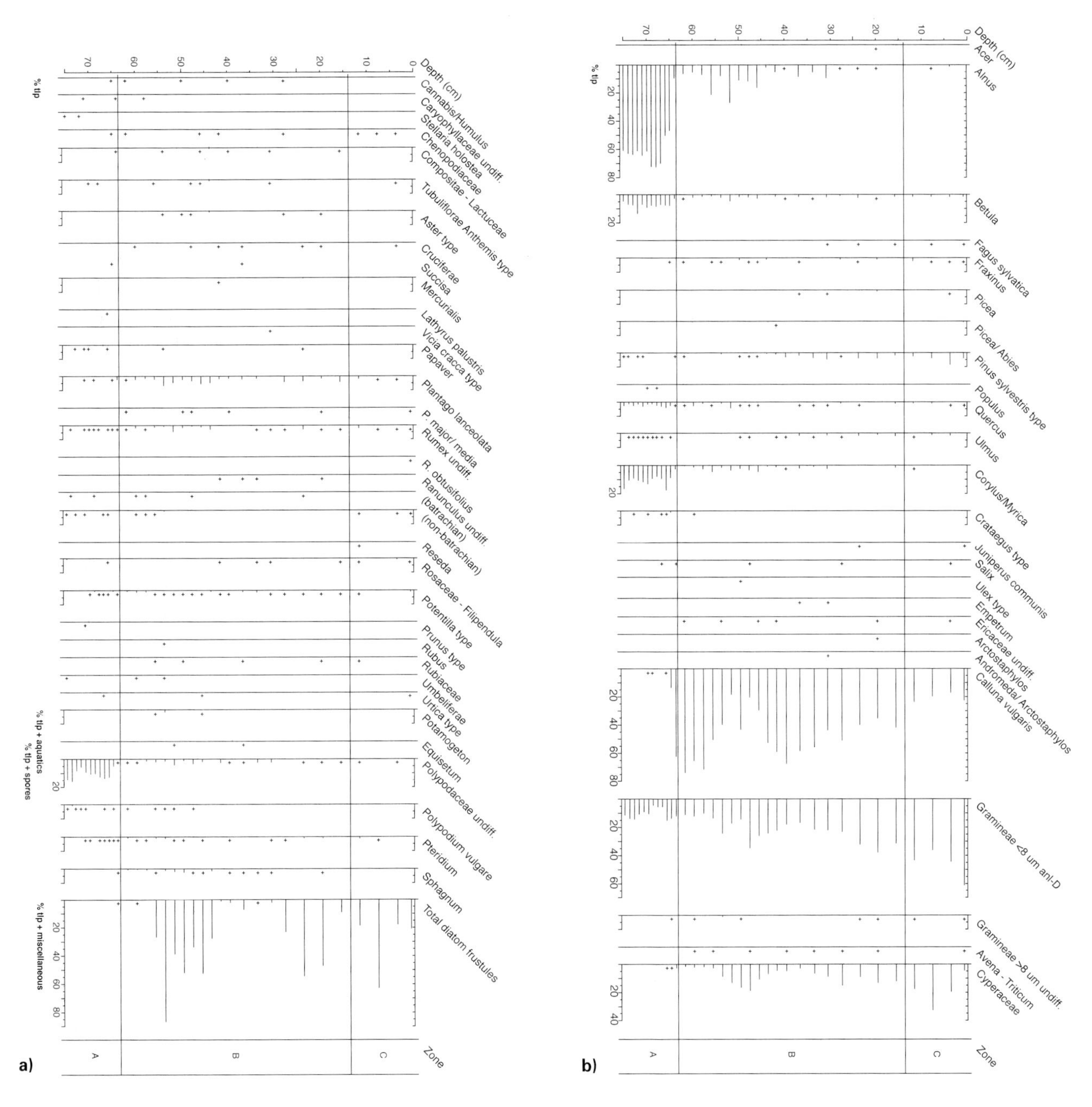

Figure 5.9

The complete pollen stratigraphy at Quarry Knowe plotted against depth (cm) and calculated as percentages of total land pollen (tlp) and tlp + group (Section 2.3g). Values recorded in a subsample at <1% are marked by a cross. Local pollen assemblage zone boundaries are plotted to permit correlation. See Appendix One for a glossary of English names for Linnaean taxa.

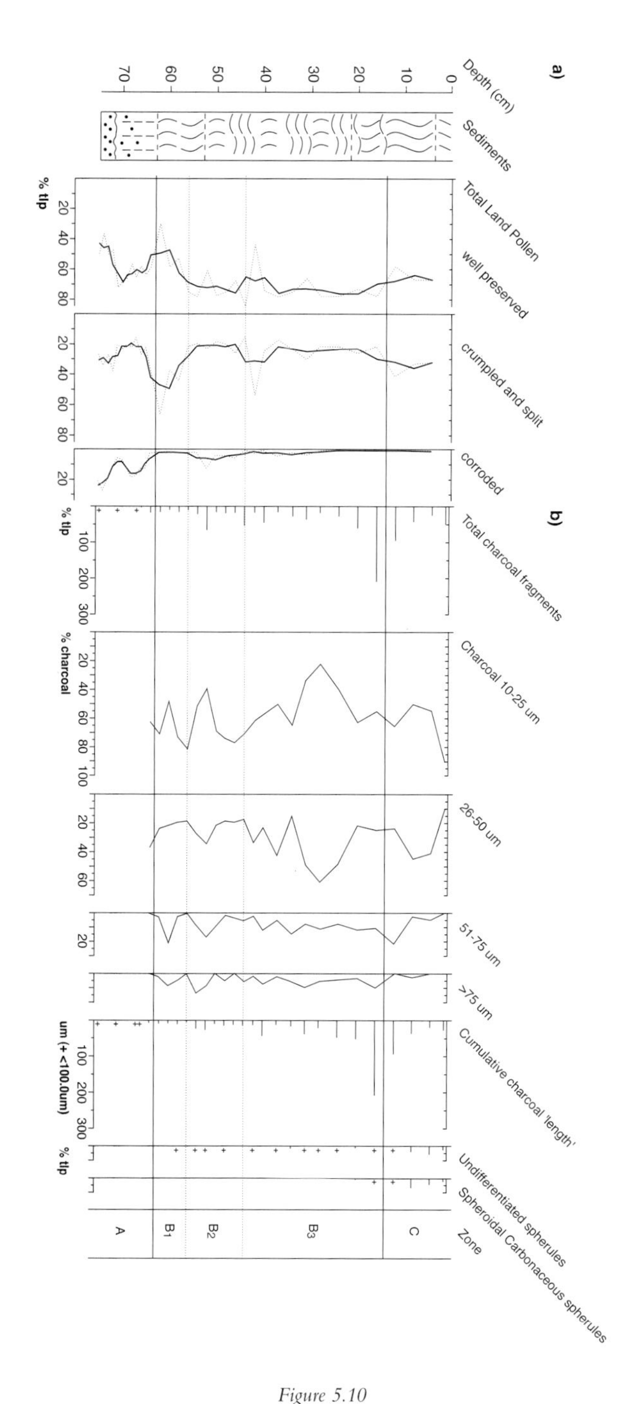

Figure 5.10

(a) Pollen preservation states for all determinable land pollen grains at Quarry Knowe plotted against depth and calculated as percentages of total land pollen (see Section 2.3l): too few amorphous grains were recorded to be depicted. Solid outlines of curves represent smoothed values; individual counts are marked by dashed curves; (b) measures of the abundance of microscopic charcoal fragments at Quarry Knowe (see Section 2.3j). Cumulative charcoal 'lengths' <100μm are marked by crosses; spherules recorded at <1% tlp are also marked by crosses. Local pollen assemblage zone boundaries are plotted to permit correlation.

for a prolonged period (Figure 5.8). The upper assay (GU-2512) has a very recent radiocarbon age, and when calibrated has a very large age range and five intercept ages, of little value in refining a chronology. The appearance of exotic tree taxa (*Acer* (sycamore), *Pinus* (pine), *Ulmus* (elm), *Fagus* (beech), *Fraxinus* (ash) and *Picea/Abies* (spruce or fir) (Figure 5.9) provide an age of 1775 ± 25 cal AD for peats at around 50cm depth (see Section 2.4c). The first appearance of spheroidal carbonaceous spherules at 20cm (Figure 5.9b) may have an age of *c* 1900 cal AD (Section 2.4d); the marked increase above 8cm is assigned an age of *c* 1940 cal AD (Wik & Natkanski 1990; Rose *et al* 1995) (Figure 5.8). Lead 210 assays (Section 2.4b) were obtained on 2cm sediment slices from the peat surface to 38cm depth; the rate of peat accumulation was linear at *c* 0.23cm/yr (A Mackenzie pers. comm.). These four independent points fall on a straight line from the present peat surface with a linear peat accumulation rate of 4.4 yrs/cm (0.23cm/yr) (Figure 5.8). Peat at 63cm above an organic soil began to form at around 1660 cal AD. Three local pollen assemblage zones prefixed 'Quarry' are defined (Table 5.9). Analyses within the peat are at 2cm intervals from 64 to 40cm with a temporal resolution of *c* nine years. Above 40cm the sampling interval is on average 4cm with a temporal resolution of *c* eighteen years.

5.8 Landscape and environmental change on Quarry Knowe

Lpaz Quarry A (75–6cm): prior to 1660 cal AD

The basal sediments are highly minerogenic (Table 5.7) and are probably organic soil horizons developed *in situ* from weathered andesite bedrock. The ^{14}C assay GU-2511 is considerably older than anticipated from other dating controls (Figure 5.8). As such the pollen assemblage of lpaz A is also of mixed age and not readily interpretable. However, in sediment unit A_2 pollen is exceptionally well preserved (Figure 5.10a), and the comparatively low values of corroded pollen do not imply prolonged burial or intensely aerobic conditions. There is little evidence from these characteristics that the pollen assemblage has any great antiquity, and the pollen assemblages in sediment unit A_2 may not have accumulated much earlier than peat inception at *c* 1660 cal AD.

Tree pollen comprises over 80% tlp and of this *Alnus* (alder) is overwhelmingly dominant. Alder woodland almost certainly grew at the sampling site, accompanied by *Corylus/Myrica* (hazel/bog myrtle)

Table 5.9
Local pollen assemblage zones at Quarry Knowe, their characteristic pollen taxa and ^{14}C and calibrated age ranges.

Lpaz	*Depths (cm)*	*Characteristic taxa*	*Duration (cal BC/AD)*	*(cal BP)*	*(^{14}C BP)*
Quarry C	14–0cm	Gramineae <8μm anl-D (wild grasses) – Cyperaceae (sedges)	AD 1920–1990	70 cal BP–present	
Quarry B	63.5–14cm	*Calluna* (ling) – Gramineae <8μm anl-D (wild grasses) – Cyperaceae (sedges)	AD 1660–1920	330–70 BP	n.a.
Quarry A	75–63.5cm	*Alnus* (alder) – *Corylus/Myrica* (hazel/bog myrtle)	prior to AD 1660	prior to 330 BP	n.a.

and *Betula* (birch), but very few other wetland plants, although *Lathyrus palustris* (marsh pea) and *Succisa* (devilsbit scabious) are recorded. *Salix* (willow) is poorly represented, and typical wet grassland herbs (King 1955) like *Galium* (bedstraws) and *Filipendula* (cf. meadowsweet), and bog taxa like *Sphagnum* (bog moss) are absent, possibly shaded out by the density of the carr woodland. Soil conditions may not have been universally damp; *Prunus spinosa* (blackthorn; *Prunus* type pollen) is common in drier Scottish alderwoods (McVean 1964), possibly with *Populus* (poplar) and *Sorbus* and/or *Crataegus* (hawthorn/rowan; *Crataegus* type).

Quercus (oak) and *Ulmus* (elm) are consistently represented, though at low values. The representation of *Ulmus* pollen only within the soil suggests these grains to be reworked, and neither oak or elm were necessarily growing locally immediately prior to peat inception. *Calluna* (ling) and other heathers (Ericaceae undiff.) were not part of the ground flora at any time prior to peat inception. Grasses (Gramineae <8μm anl-D) can comprise much of the ground flora beneath alder woods, but the consistent records of *Papaver* (poppy) and *Rumex* (docks) suggest some dry grassland away from the site, though the low representation of *Plantago lanceolata* (ribwort plantain) makes it unclear whether this was at all intensively grazed. There is no evidence for cereal cultivation at any time prior to peat inception, although open ground herbs were probably locally present. Microscopic charcoal is not at all recorded in some subsamples, a very unusual feature, and throughout this zone charcoal fragments are very poorly represented: there is no evidence of burning of the vegetation prior to peat inception (Figure 5.10b).

Lpaz Quarry B (63.5–14cm): 1660–1920 cal AD

The growth of a poorly decayed (humified) grass/sedge peat (sediment unit B; Table 5.7) occurs with the abrupt loss of *Alnus* (alder) (Figure 5.9). Local woodland was apparently removed in its entirety in less than a decade, quite possibly within a year, and was replaced by a *Calluna* (ling) heath over most of the pollen catchment. Close subsampling of the pollen record shows that values of *Calluna* and Gramineae <8μm anl-D (wild grasses) rise across the sediment boundary between soil and peat (Figure 5.9) and an hiatus in pollen deposition is not thought likely. Purposeful anthropogenic clearance of the woodland, very likely by axe and saw rather than by grazing pressures, and not by fire (Figure 5.10b), was causal in woodland loss.

Table 5.10

(a) Size measurements (pollen size, pollen index: Andersen 1979) of well preserved Gramineae (grass family) pollen grains of annulus diameters >8μm at Quarry Knowe; (b) Size measurements of Ericaceae pollen grains larger than normal at Quarry Knowe: for definitions of variables measured see Oldfield (1959, p. 20).

(a)	*Depth (cm)*	*anl-D*	*Size*	*Index*	*Group*
	20	12	49.5	16	III
	28	12	42.5	1.12	III
	34	14	46	10	III
	40	16	61	13	III
	48	12.5	51	1.12	III
	54	9	41	1.21	II/III
	56	11	43	19	III
	60	13	41.5	12	III

(b)	*Depth (cm)*	*D*	*d*	*D/d*	*p*	*2f*	*type*
	20	39	29	1.34	n.d.	n.d.	*Arctostaphylos*
	31	45	31	1.45	n.d.	14	*Andromeda/Arctostaphylos*

n.d. not determined

Peat inception may have been promoted by woodland removal and the resultant decrease in evapotranspiration. Colonisation by *Calluna* (ling) appears to have been unaided by burning. The increased representation of Gramineae <8μm anl-D may be related to the ease of pollen transfer to the now open bog surface, as might that of grassland herbs such as *Plantago lanceolata* (ribwort plantain), *Potentilla* type (tormentil, conquefoils), *Rumex* undiff. (docks) and *Pteridium* (bracken), so that it cannot be demonstrated that grazed areas away from the mire grew substantially. Some dry soils near the mire were cultivated: *Avena/Triticum* (oat/wheat) pollen demonstrates the presence of crops (Table 5.10a). *Cannabis/Humulus* pollen is recorded, and from size measurements (Whittington & Gordon 1987) the grains are likely to represent *Cannabis* (hemp), though whether this crop grew on the plateau or on the valley floor is uncertain.

After *c* 1750 cal AD extensive flooding of the bog surface occurred, recorded by the plant remains of *Sphagnum* across the mire (Figure 5.7; Table 5.7) and very large increases in the numbers of diatom frustules above 56cm, together with the occurrence of shallow water plants like *Potamogeton* (pondweed) and *Equisetum* (horsetails). Open water persisted until *c* 1800 cal AD. *Calluna* (ling) percentages decline in response to rising values of Gramineae <8μm anl-D (wild grasses), Cyperaceae (sedges) and *Alnus* (alder), possibly in the face of increasing waterlogging that also encouraged the temporary revival of *Alnus*.

For around 60 cal years after *c* 1800 cal AD (48–30cm) diatom valves are poorly represented, and *Calluna* was able to regenerate (Figure 5.9), once more with no indication that fire promoted heathland expansion (Figure 5.10b). Throughout lpa subzone B_3, Gramineae <8μm anl-D (wild grasses) percentages expand, seemingly at the expense of *Calluna*, and the invasion of heathland by grasses is considered likely. After *c* 1830 cal AD (34cm) the presence of cereal pollen cannot conclusively be demonstrated.

Lpaz Quarry C (14–0cm): 1920–1990 cal AD

The last *c* seventy years have seen the increased importance of grassland around the site (Plate 5.2). *Calluna* (ling) has not disappeared from around the site but is subsidiary to grassland communities. Values of pastoral indicator herbs have declined over this time, possibly as species poor *Nardus* (mat grass) and *Molinia* (purple moor grass) communities expanded (King 1962).

5.9 Summary of environmental change on Quarry Knowe

Prior to *c* 1660 cal AD the col straddling the Swindon Hill plateau was a damp soil supporting a dense alder carr woodland. In the later seventeenth century cal AD the wood was cut down very rapidly, making the valley wet enough to allow the accumulation of peat, and ling heather quickly colonised, without promotion by fire. A phase of severe waterlogging after *c* 1740 cal AD favoured partial regeneration of alder and a temporary decline in ling, but *c* 60 cal years later ling was re-established. Despite increasing waterlogging, drier soils on the plateau supported the cultivation of oats from *c* 1660 until *c* 1830 cal AD. The grassy heath was grazed, and over the last *c* 180 years this has given way gradually to a species poor grassland.

Chapter 6

THE SUMMIT RIDGE AND HIGH LEVEL PLATEAUX – COCKLAWHEAD AND MOW LAW

with ASTRID SCHWEIZER

6.1 Introduction

The highest parts of the northern Cheviot Hills are characterised by two types of landscape. On the broad rounded summit ridges an extensive blanket peat supports *Calluna* moor. Other high level surfaces have no peat cover and support freely drained mineral soils under grassland (Sections 1.4, 1.5; Figures 1.4 to 1.6). This chapter explores how these landscapes, high above any archaeological evidence of human land use (RCAHMS 1956; Mercer & Tipping 1994), have evolved. Figure 6.1 shows in detail the topography of tributary valleys, plateaux and summit ridges of the upper Bowmont Valley, and shows the locations of the sediment and pollen sequences analysed in Chapters 4 and 5 in relation to those discussed here. At Cocklawhead, arguably the head of the Bowmont on the summit ridge between

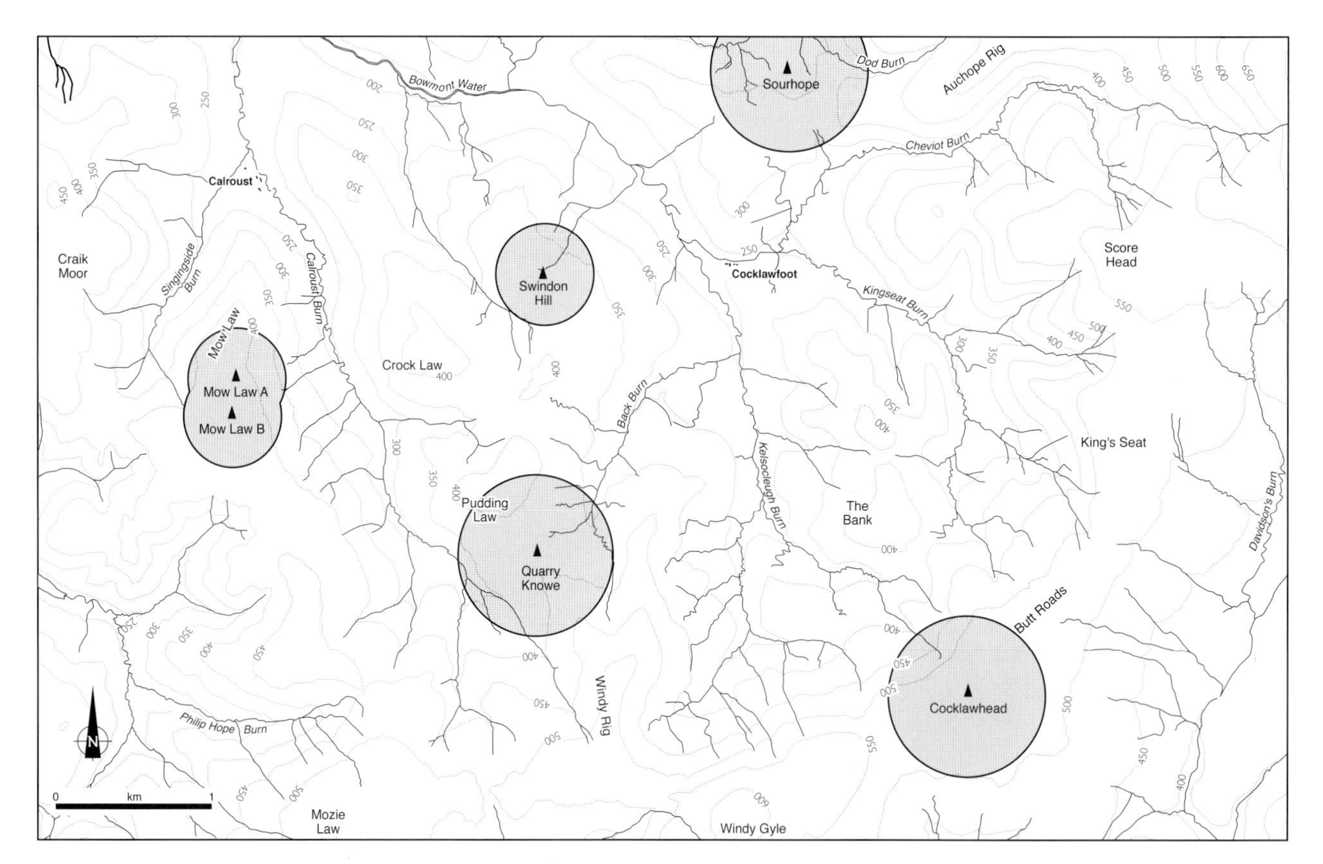

Figure 6.1

The physical and settlement geographies of the upper Bowmont Valley in relation to the peat and pollen stratigraphies and their likely pollen recruitment areas (shaded areas). This deep into the valley, only the farms of Cocklawfoot and Calroust indicate a modern human presence. The floors of upland tributary valleys flowing to the Bowmont Water are typified by the sediment sequence at Sourhope (Chapter 4), at the top of the map. Plateau surfaces easily accessed from the valleys are described from analyses at Swindon Hill and, for the later historic period, Quarry Knowe (Chapter 5). Above these, the higher and much more remote plateaux of Craik Moor, Mow Law, Crock Law and The Bank are described in this chapter from Mow Law. Above 500m asl the history of the summit ridge is described from analyses at Cocklawhead.

Plate 6.1

From the slopes of Swindon Hill, the summit ridge at Cocklawhead dominates the skyline. Above the conifer plantations on Swindon Hill and, to the left, those that hide Cocklawfoot Farm, the deep valleys of Kingseat Burn (far left), Kelsocleugh Burn (centre) and Back Burn (entering from the right) cut into a broad col above 500m asl. The spine of the drove road to Cocklawhead rises between Kingseat and Kelsocleugh Burns, past several hillforts, through the snowbeds and onto the plateau and the blanket peat above.

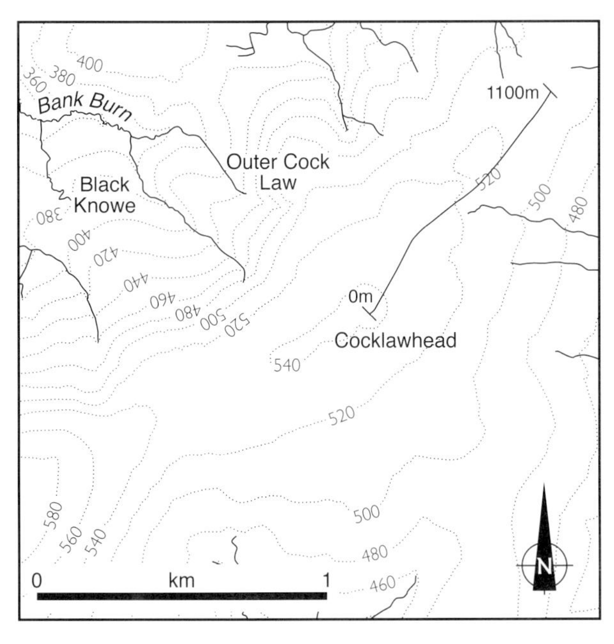

Figure 6.2

Topography of the summit ridge at Cocklawhead showing the location of the sediment transect depicted in Figure 6.3.

Windy Gyle and King's Seat, at 520m asl (Plate 6.1), the morass of sprawling blanket peat that so wearied Wainwright and almost all walkers along the Pennine Way (Section 1.1) was investigated from multiple peat and pollen stratigraphies by Astrid Schweizer (1997) to understand how long this intractable surface has existed, how and when the peat spread, how the landscape has changed and whether human beings have made any impact on these highest surfaces and slopes. Moving west over Windy Gyle and then north down the long flanks of Mozie Law (Plate 6.2), one of the most extensive plateau surfaces, on Mow Law, almost entirely level (Figure 1.4; Plates 1.1, 1.3) yet very exposed and high at 420m asl, was analysed by Richard Tipping from two neighbouring peat basins.

6.2 Cocklawhead: site location, description and pollen recruitment

A broad and furrowed drove road rises to the border from Cocklawfoot Farm, rising from the valley floor

Table 6.1
The sediment stratigraphy at Station 7 on Cocklawhead.

Unit G (0–79cm):	poorly humified fibrous grass and sedge peat, *Sphagnum* rich between 15 and 24cm, with *Calluna* stems between 54 and 79cm; gradual to
Unit F (79–137cm):	highly humified grass and sedge peat with high amorphous content; gradual to
Unit E (137–230cm):	poorly humified very fibrous grass and sedge peat, increasingly fibrous below 162cm and with *Calluna* roots between 168 and 182cm; gradual to
Unit D (230–268cm):	highly humified amorphous peat with grass and sedge remains; gradual to
Unit C (268–276cm):	poorly humified grass and sedge peat; gradual to
Unit B (276–350cm):	highly humified amorphous peat with rare coarse fibrous grass and sedge remains and *Calluna* roots at 294cm; sharp to
Unit A (350cm +):	organic rich mineral soil with angular grit.

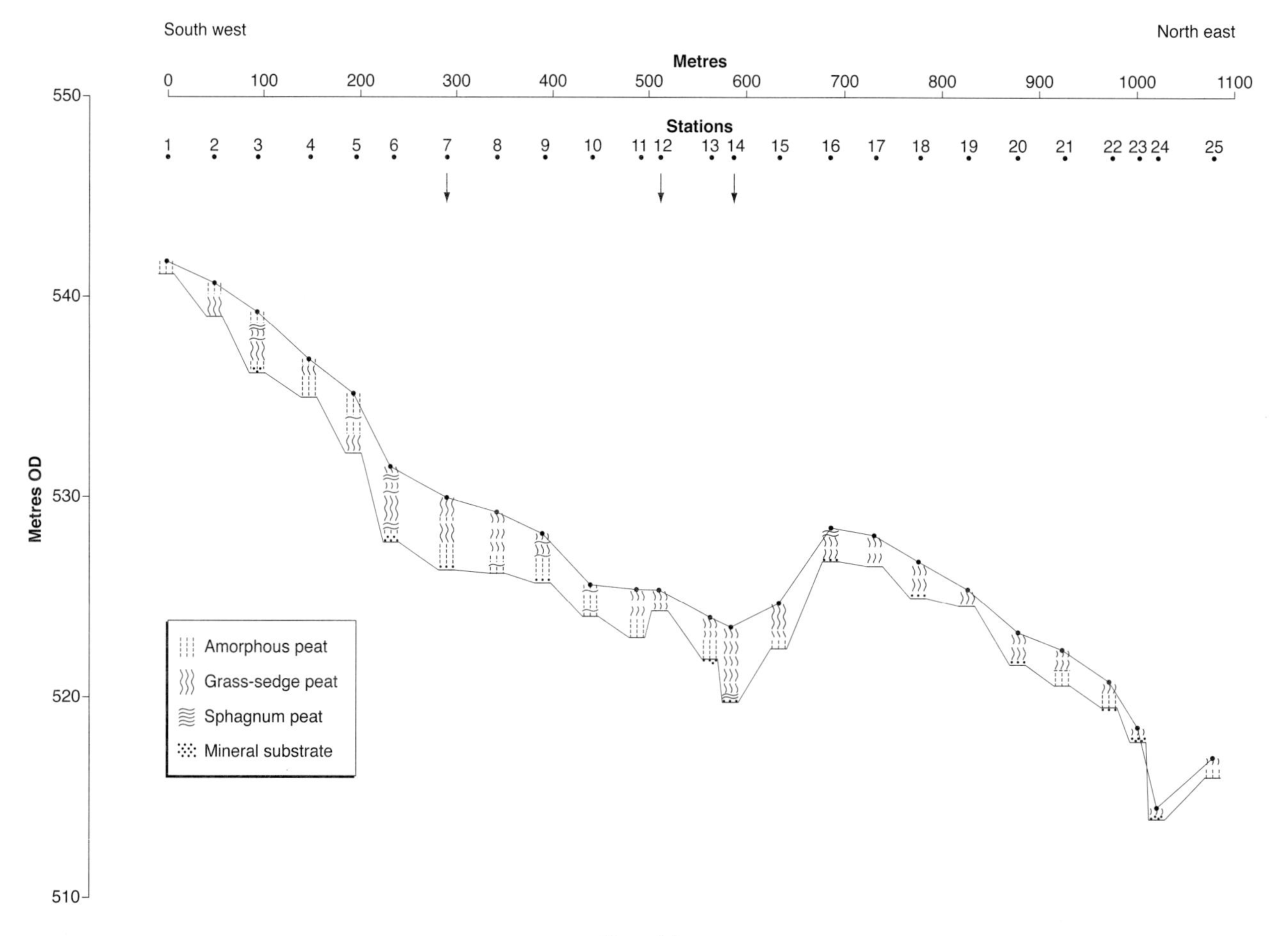

Figure 6.3
The peat stratigraphy of the Cocklawhead ridge constructed from twenty-five stations of Eijelkamp boreholes along the 1100m transect, surveyed by theodolite.

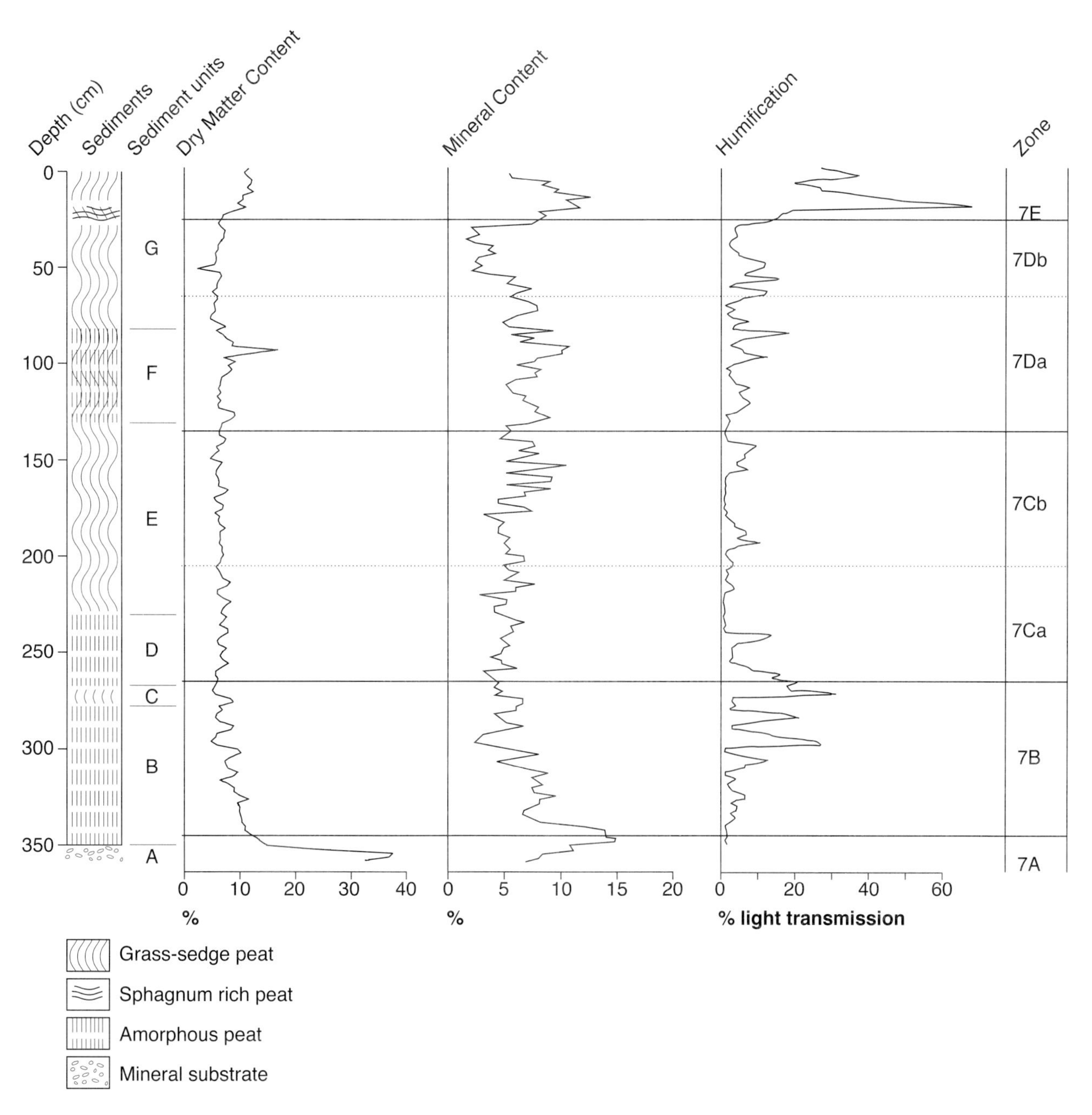

Figure 6.4

(a) The sediment stratigraphy at Station 7 on Cocklawhead (see Table 6.1); (b) percentages of dry matter in the sediments plotted against depth; (c) percentages of mineral content in the sediments plotted against depth; (d) percentages of light transmitted through peat extracts to measure humification. See Section 2.3b for details of the techniques. Local pollen assemblage zones are plotted to allow correlations to be made between the sediment and pollen stratigraphies.

at 250m asl to 540m asl at Cocklawhead, before descending to Davidson's Linn and eventually to Newcastle. The 1km-broad summit ridge (Figure 6.2) characterised by very gentle slopes (Figure 1.4) is covered with blanket peat (Figure 1.5), now frayed and gullied above the steep bedrock slopes (Wishart & Warburton 2001) and churned by sheep grazing and the feet of Pennine Way walkers. The grassy heath and bog has the lowest current land use capability (Figure 1.6). Two unenclosed platform settlements

Table 6.2
Details of the radiocarbon assays obtained on the sediments at Station 7 on Cocklawhead.

Lab. No. (GU-)	*Mean Depth (cm)*	*Sediment Depth (cm)*	*No. of Cores*	*^{14}C Age* BP ± 1σ	$\delta^{13}C$ *(‰)*	*Calibrated Age* BC/AD *± 1σ and Intercept Ages*	*Mean Calibrated Age* BC/AD
4779	29	28–30	1 (monolith)	750 ± 50	–28.1	AD 1250 (1282) 1293	AD 1270
4778	59	58–60	1 (monolith)	1120 ± 50	–27.3	AD 885 (898,906,961) 990	AD 937
4777	179	178–180	1 (monolith)	2880 ± 50	–27.7	1121 (1022) 942 BC	1031 BC
4775	236	232–240	2 (cores)	3530 ± 80	–28.1	1944 (1878, 1833, 1825, 1791, 1790) 1742 BC	1843 BC
4776	267	264–270	2 (cores)	3790 ± 70	–27.3	2317 (2197) 2048 BC	2182 BC
4774	305	300–310	2 (cores)	4240 ± 80	–27.7	2913 (2881) 2696 BC	2804 BC
4773	332	330-334	2 (cores)	4640 ± 70	-27.3	3506 (3370) 3346 BC	3426 BC

lie on Black Knowe at 360m asl, 1km north-west of Cocklawhead (Mercer & Tipping 1994; Mercer in prep.; Figure 8.5). Welfare (2002) records cord rig at the head of Coquetdale south-west of Cocklawhead. On the English side above Davidson's Burn a series of rectangular structures suggest a Medieval presence high on the ridge. The drove road crosses the border, and Cocklawhead was a key meeting place on truce days in the Border Wars between the Scots and English Middle Marches (Mack 1924; Tough 1928). Mack (1924) gives a contemporary description of the ridge in 1522 cal AD as 'a great waste ground of four miles broad and more for the most part', '... the side thereof towards Scotland is so wet a moss or marshy ground that it will neither bear corn nor serve for the pasture of any cattle'. The description is telling.

Pollen recruitment is more difficult to estimate for this exposed summit than for sites lower in the valley because increased wind strength and the reduced pollen productivity of climatically stressed local plants implies a larger component of pollen arriving to the site from the region (Markgraf 1980; Price & Moore 1984). However, peat surfaces are no different to soil surfaces in receiving the largest proportion of their contained pollen from immediately around the site (Bunting 2002). It is likely that most pollen arriving at the site is

Table 6.3
Definitions of sediment accumulation rates between chronological controls used in the preferred time-depth model (Figure 6.5) and the sampling and temporal resolutions of pollen and microscopic charcoal analyses at Station 7 on Cocklawhead.

Depth between dating controls	*Cal ages* BC/AD	*Duration (cal years)*	*Accumulation rate (yrs/cm)*	*Lpaz*	*Pollen Analyses (a)*	*(b)*	*(c)*
0–29cm	AD 1990–AD 1270	720	24.8	7E	10cm	12.4	248
29–59cm	AD 1270–AD 937	333	11.1	7Db	10cm	5.6	111
59–305cm	AD 937–2804 BC	3741	15.2	7Da, C, B	10cm	7.6	76
305–350cm	2804 BC–3800 BC	996	22.1	Db, A	10cm	11	221

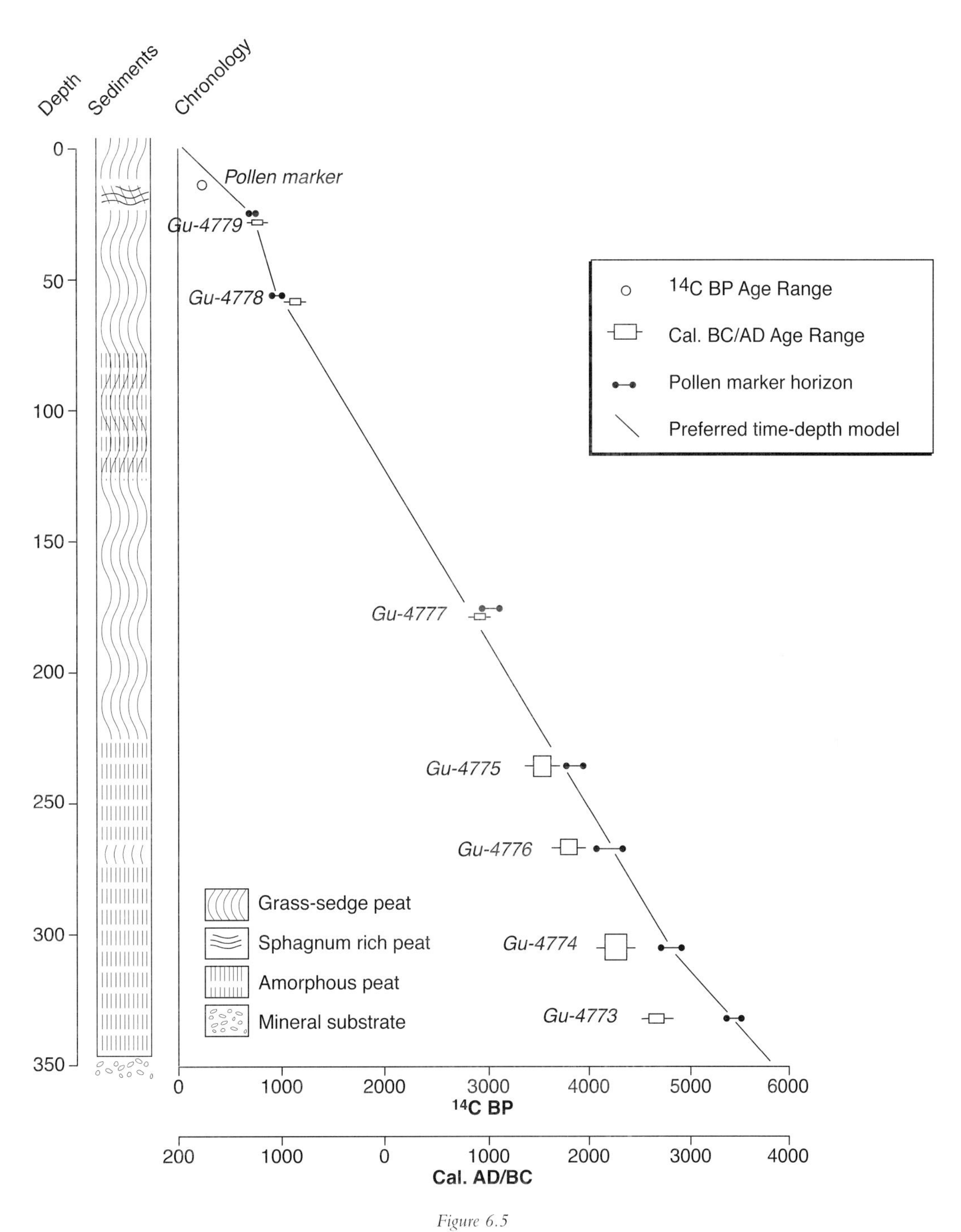

Figure 6.5

The preferred time-depth model for sediments at Station 7 at Cocklawhead showing ^{14}C ages BP at 1 and 2σ as cat-and-whisker plots and corresponding calibrated age ranges BC/AD at 1σ as dumb-bell plots (see Table 6.2) and the only additional control obtained from the pollen marker horizon of Agricultural Improvement tree pollen (Section 2.4c).

transported from around 1km of Cocklawhead (Figure 6.1), and typifies the vegetation cover and land uses of the summit ridge.

6.3 Cocklawhead: sediment sampling, subsampling and chronology construction

In parallel to the fence line that marks the border, a theodolite surveyed sediment transect 1100m long of twenty-five Eijelkamp boreholes (Schweizer 1997) characterised the peat stratigraphy in the shallow cols and ridges below Butt Roads (Figures 6.1, 6.2, 6.3). Peat depth thickens from almost nothing at Station 1 to 3.60m at Station 7, where a slight reduction in the slope to the west allowed thick peat accumulation. The summit slopes away in all other directions. Station 14a is the deepest peat (3.90m) in a water receiving trough (Figure 6.3). The oldest peat at each station is usually highly decayed and amorphous, and this generally gives way to grass and sedge peats with occasional *Sphagnum* rich bands. Wood was not recorded in any borehole (Figure 6.3).

The peat and pollen stratigraphy at Station 7 was sampled because of its substantial thickness on a water shedding slope. The basal peats at Station 14a and the adjacent Station 12 (Figure 6.3) were sampled for pollen analyses to define their ages by pollen stratigraphic correlation with the ^{14}C dated Station 7, because of their contrasting depths (Schweizer 1997). The peats were described qualitatively (Table 6.1; Figure 6.4), and those at Station 7 were defined quantitatively on 2cm contiguous slices for dry matter content, mineral content (the residue of mineral grains not combusted) and humification (Section 2.3b) (Figure 6.4).

Seven ^{14}C assays were obtained on the cores used for pollen analysis at Station 7 (Table 6.2). Basal samples from Russian cores are thick and the precision of these is low, but assays GU-4775 to -4779 are from thinner sediment slices and are more precise. The assays lie in an internally consistent sequence (Table 6.2; Figure 6.5). At around 15cm depth at Site 7, exotic tree taxa (*Fagus* (beech), *Pinus* (Scots pine), *Ulmus* (elm)) define an age of *c* 1775 cal AD. Because of low pollen sampling resolutions the precise depth of the pollen marker horizon cannot be defined.

Peat formation is not directly dated but is extrapolated to have commenced at *c* 3800 cal BC (Figure 6.5). Peat accumulation rates varied little between peat inception and *c* 937 cal AD (GU-4779), but has been slower in the last *c* 1000 cal years (Table 6.3). Pollen subsamples are consistently at 10cm intervals, and the temporal resolution of vegetation change is low (Table 6.3). The pollen record is divided into five local pollen assemblage zones, prefixed 'Cocklawhead 7' (Table 6.4; Figure 6.6). The annual pollen influx values of major taxa and for total land pollen are presented in Figure 6.7 because these aid an understanding of the local presence of trees in a context where pollen can potentially be far travelled (see Sections 2.2, 2.3h). Microscopic charcoal fragments were not recorded. Pollen preservation was generally good, but preservation states were not measured.

6.4 Landscape and environmental change on Cocklawhead

Lpaz Cocklawhead 7A (350–345cm): 3800–3700 cal BC

Peat inception at Station 7 is correlated in time using pollen analysis with the base of the peat at Station 14 (Schweizer 1997), 300m to the north-west on the floor of a low col (Figure 6.3). These two surfaces appear to have accumulated organic matter at broadly the same time. Not all of the slope between these two points was peat covered then. Pollen stratigraphic correlation between Station 7 and the basal sediments at Station 12 suggest that the peat at the latter point formed much later, within lpaz Cocklawhead 7D at some time between *c* 175 cal BC and 1370 cal AD (Schweizer 1997). Peat gradually spread to adjacent slopes, and coalescence and conversion of the plateau to blanket mire appears to have been far from rapid. The cause of peat inception at *c* 3800 cal BC is uncertain because triggering events occurred prior to peat growth. There are no indications that the surface became waterlogged. The peat was, for instance, highly humified (e.g. low % light transmission values: Table 6.1; Figure 6.4). Palynological indicators do not suggest significant surface wetness, the local vegetation cover on peat inception at Station 7 having abundant wild grass communities (Gramineae >8μm anl-D), with *Pteridium* (bracken), *Potentilla* (*Potentilla* type) and *Succisa* (devilsbit scabious) rather than Cyperaceae (sedges) or significant amounts of *Sphagnum* (bogmoss) (Figure 6.6). *Calluna* (ling) grew within a grassy heath, but probably not abundantly. Peat may have formed as a rather dry surface because soil changes such as increasing acidity inhibited microbial breakdown of organic matter.

An open and species rich woodland was present. Percentage and pollen influx estimates (Figures 6.6,

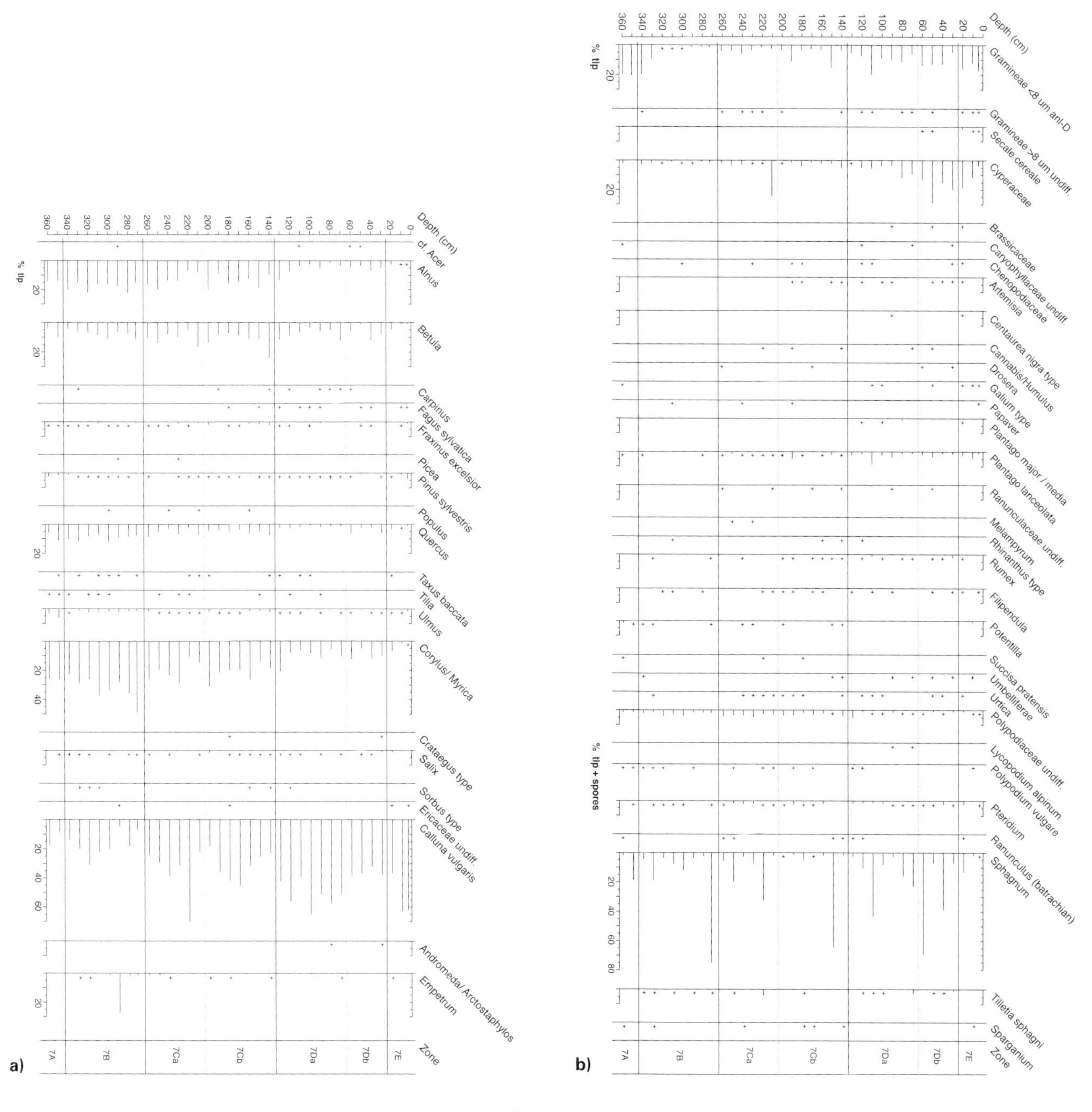

Figure 6.6

The complete pollen stratigraphy for Station 7 at Cocklawhead plotted against depth (cm) and calculated as percentages of total land pollen (tlp) and tlp + group (Section 2.3g). Values recorded in a subsample at <1% are marked by a cross. Local pollen assemblage zone boundaries are plotted to permit correlation. See Appendix One for a glossary of English names for Linnaean taxa.

6.7) suggest that *Corylus* (*Corylus/Myrica* pollen, considered to be hazel because of its high percentages and influx; Godwin 1975), *Quercus* (oak), *Ulmus* (elm), *Alnus* (alder), *Betula* (birch), *Fraxinus* (ash) and *Salix* (willow) all grew on the plateau (cf. Huntley & Birks 1983). Differences in the proportions of tree taxa between Stations 7 and 14a (Schweizer 1997) probably indicate that pollen recruitment was from local sources, reflecting small scale variation in woodland composition on the plateau (Turner 1984).

a component of natural high altitude grasslands but which probably benefited after *c* 2100 cal BC from grasses being grazed (Figure 6.6). The frequent records of *Urtica* (nettle) pollen, probably of *U. dioica* (stinging nettle) are intriguing given its avoidance by cattle and its requirement for nitrogen, often derived from manure (Greig-Smith 1948).

Within lpa subzone 7Ca (*c* 2100 to *c* 1250 cal BC) there are consistent counts of single grains of cereal type grasses (Gramineae >8µm anl-D). These are all of *Hordeum* (barley) type (Andersen Group II) (Schweizer 1997). It is not certain that these grains represent a crop because this pollen type includes a number of wild grasses. However, in the overlying lpa subzone 7Cb there were further small increases in the proportions of wild grasses (Gramineae <8µm anl-D) and associated pastoral herbs and yet the representation of cereal type pollen (Gramineae >8µm anl-D) ceases. It is difficult to identify the loss in lpaz subzone 7Cb of a natural habitat that included wild grasses of cereal type, and it is thus more likely that the cereal type grains in lpa subzone 7Ca are from cultivated barley. Grazing pressures may have altered after *c* 1250 cal BC in ways not readily interpretable, because *Rumex* became more common whilst readily grazed tall herbs like *Filipendula* (? meadowsweet) also flourished, or other environmental stresses impacted on the high altitude vegetation cover.

Despite the absence of cereal type pollen, bare and disturbed ground taxa like *Artemisia* (mugworts) were more common above 190cm (1000 cal BC). These may have grown more abundantly or closer to Station 7 because the vegetation cover became more fragmented. Above 180cm (*c* 850 cal BC using the preferred time-depth model in Figure 6.5 but directly ^{14}C dated by assay GU-4777 to *c* 1030 cal BC (Table 6.2)) the influx of mineral grains to the peat was higher in an apparent series of sediment pulses (Figure 6.4b), and mineral soils on the steeper slope above Station 7 (Figure 6.3) are thought to have been eroded. Small decreases in peat humification (increasing % light transmission; Figure 6.4c), particularly that between 159 and 145cm (*c* 585 to *c* 370 cal BC) may reflect the increased flow of water across and into the peat from the slope above, either because water flowed over bare soils more readily or through increased precipitation (Section 8.8f). The proportions of trees do not change despite this stress. Although reduced in abundance most tree species recorded at peat inception appear to have continued to grow on and near the plateau.

Lpaz Cocklawhead 7D (135–25cm): 175 cal BC–1370 cal AD

A short phase of soil stability (reduced mineral content) and a dry peat surface (much higher humification and lower % light transmission) at Station 7 (145 to 127cm; Figures 6.4b and c) developed between *c* 370 and *c* 100 cal BC, across the boundary between lpa zones 7C and 7D. The beginning of lpaz 7D coincides with the growth of a decayed grass and sedge peat (unit F; Table 6.1), suggesting either that both peat and pollen records reflect changing environments or that peat growth influenced pollen recruitment; the former is most likely because plant communities forming the peat surface do not appear to have changed significantly (below). The peat surface was generally wetter more commonly, despite the peat appearing more decayed. There were more frequent reductions in the rate of peat humification (increases in light transmission; Figure 6.4c), particularly between 100 and 80cm (*c* 300 to *c* 650 cal AD). The peat received an increased and more sustained influx of mineral matter after *c* 100 cal BC (Figure 6.4b): one pulse of inwashed sediment stands out as distorting the dry matter content of the sediment (Figure 6.4a). Mineral sediment inwashing declined only above *c* 80cm (after *c* 650 cal AD). The source of mineral matter may have been from soils eroded by water on steeper slopes, as before *c* 370 cal BC, but the pollen stratigraphic work of Schweizer (1997) discussed in lpaz 7A suggested that more gentle slopes between Station 7 and 12 (Figure 6.3) were covered by blanket peat by this time. There is no evidence for peat spread across the summit ridge to have been more rapid at this time.

The tree cover was substantially reduced (Figures 6.6, 6.7). There is no reason to think that populations of trees and shrubs except *Betula* (birch) and *Salix* (willow) grew on the plateau between *c* 100 cal BC and the lpa subzone boundary at 65cm (*c* 850 cal AD). After *c* 850 cal AD in lpa subzone 7Db the percentage representation of *Quercus* (oak) pollen is strikingly increased (Figure 6.6) but influx values show further reductions, and oak trees are not thought to have recolonised the summit ridge. With these reductions the pollen of trees away from the plateau, within the Cheviot Hills and further afield, may have become more prominent at Cocklawhead, so that the local absence of trees is hard to demonstrate. Far-travelled types include *Carpinus* (hornbeam) and probably *Fagus* (beech) and *Tilia* (lime).

Calluna (ling) heath was by the last century cal BC dominant on the peat surface across the ridge. There are infrequent records of *Andromeda/Arctostaphylos* pollen (bog rosemary or bearberry), not defined further. *Sphagnum* (bogmoss) communities were also common, and some differentiation of hummocks and pools was likely. Cyperaceae (sedges) increasingly became a major peat forming plant after *c* 500 cal AD (90cm). Grassland communities were increasingly common and were perhaps more persistently grazed. It is likely that sustained grazing pressures, though not necessarily intensive, led to woodland reductions. The pollen of Gramineae >8µm anl-D (cereal type pollen but not defined further; Schweizer 1997) is consistently recorded as single grains. Again, this is not assuredly evidence for crop growing, but given the constancy throughout the pollen record of herb and heath communities in which wild grasses of Andersen Group II occur, the reoccurrence of this type is taken to represent cereal cultivation on the summit ridge after *c* 200 cal BC. Bare ground taxa such as Caryophyllaceae (pinks), Chenopodiaceae (fat hen), *Artemisia* (mugworts), *Plantago major/media* (greater or hoary plantain) and Umbelliferae (carrot family) would at lower altitudes be assumed to have grown as weeds in arable fields, but the sedimentological evidence for soil erosion at Station 7 (Figure 6.4) makes this less certain.

Lpaz Cocklawhead 7E (25–0cm): 1370 cal AD–1990 cal AD

Within 30cm of the surface of Station 7 light transmission values are very high, and peat humification very low, in what might be interpreted as a shift to an exceptionally wet landscape (Figure 6.4c). This interpretation is not straightforward, however, because the change in humification values might be inherited from structural changes within the blanket peat. There are two components to a growing peat. The actively growing surface sediment is the acrotelm; underlying material that has partially decayed is the catotelm (Ingram 1978; Clymo 1991). Peat in the acrotelm should be less humified. However, changes in peat forming plants themselves indicate contemporaneous hydrological changes, and at Station 7 *Sphagnum* (bogmoss) plant remains become abundant at 24cm (Table 6.1), and a very pronounced shift to wetter conditions in the later fourteenth century AD is thought to be demonstrated. Peat humification rates remain low to the present day, but surfaces after *c* 1500 cal AD (*c* 20cm) were probably drier. Peat accumulation rates, however, have been markedly slower in the last *c* 750 cal years (Table 6.3; Figure 6.5), so that wetter peat did not promote faster peat growth. This is problematic unless growth rates were lowered by factors such as temperature reduction (Barber *et al* 1999; Mauquoy *et al* 2004), or because peat erosion and gullying were to have accelerated drainage. It is thought that water flooded the peat surface much more frequently but was transferred as quickly to developing gullies. These flooded surfaces received considerable amounts of inwashed mineral sediment from upstream gullies and the soils of steep slopes from *c* 1300 cal AD to the present (% mineral content; Figure 6.4b) (Wishart & Warburton 1991).

Palynological support for these interpretations is not strong, however. In this context *Empetrum* (crowberry) should preferentially have colonised better drained surfaces (see lpaz 7B; Tallis 1997) but it appears not to have (Figure 6.6). *Calluna* continued to dominate the peat surface with Cyperaceae (sedges) and Gramineae <8µm anl-D (wild grasses). Evidence for grazing is less abundant, but there were no significant changes in the ground flora of the summit ridge. All remaining trees and shrubs have nevertheless been lost from the ridge in the last 600 cal years (Figures 6.6, 6.7). Gramineae >8µm anl-D (cereal type pollen) grains are recorded consistently to within *c* fifty years of the present day, and among these, *Secale cereale* (rye) pollen is identified (Figure 6.6). This evidence for continued crop growing above 500m asl is controversial and difficult to interpret because most cereal type grains are of Andersen Group II (*Hordeum* (barley) type) and so ambiguous in meaning, and herbs that might have colonised ploughed fields will have anyway colonised eroding mineral soils. This issue is discussed further in Sections 8.10b and 8.11c, but the comment in 1522 cal AD (Section 6.2; Mack 1924) that the summit ridge will not 'bear corn' might be read as implying that drier ground at that altitude could be expected to.

6.5 Summary of environmental change at Cocklawhead

Peat began to form in bedrock depressions and on gentle to moderate slopes on the summit ridge at around 4000 to 3800 cal BC. There is no evidence for waterlogging to have initiated peat growth. Grassland communities and *Calluna* heath were present from peat inception and the vegetation history of the summit ridge has largely been one of the shifting balance between these. A species rich deciduous woodland grew of hazel, oak, elm, alder, birch, ash and willow, together with yew. Losses of elm occurred from *c* 3700 cal BC.

Plate 6.2

Standing on the slightly elevated and closely grazed summit of Mow Law, the acid grasslands of the Mow Law plateau stretch south to the summit ridge of the Cheviots between Beefstand Hill and Windy Gyle. The drove road of 'The Street' climbs this ridge but is not clear from this distance. The col of Cocklawhead is to the left. On the Mow Law Plateau the only relief from the monotony of the grasslands are the small patches of darker peat and sedge communities that mark the shallow peat basins of Mow Law A and B: Mow Law A is the closer to the right, and Mow Law B is on the left.

A series of abrupt but short lived increases in peat surface wetness occurred between *c* 2800 and *c* 1900 cal BC, and severe peat erosion by gullying is thought to have encouraged crowberry to have colonised drier areas of peat. Very dry conditions resumed, and increased human interest in the uplands may have led to some woodland reductions on both wet and dry soils as animals were grazed. From *c* 2100 to 1250 cal BC it is possible that the summit ridge was used to grow crops. Cereal type pollen is absent after *c* 1250 cal BC. Grazing continued although the management of this grazing appears to have changed because the structure of grassland communities altered. In addition there may have been climatic stresses which fragmented the vegetation cover and generated soil erosion from mineral soils across the peat. Soil stability returned after *c* 370 cal BC, and the peat was very dry until *c* 100 cal BC.

Increased peat surface wetness seems to have led to further inwashing of eroded sediment for a few hundred years between *c* 300 and 650 cal AD, and perhaps during this period peat growth developed across all gentler slopes of the summit ridge. The tree cover was substantially reduced after *c* 100 cal BC, and in the last 2000 years only birch and willow grew around the site. The blanket peat and remaining mineral soils were dominated by a mosaic of *Calluna* heath, sedges and grasses, and bogmoss in the wettest hollows, much as they are today. However, after *c* 200 cal BC it is thought that some mineral soils were used on occasions to support cereal crops, and this may have continued to the nineteenth century cal AD. Nevertheless, the ground became exceptionally wet in the late fourteenth century cal AD, and mineral soils were eroded, but accelerated peat erosion also meant that peat surfaces were more quickly drained.

6.6 Mow Law: site locations, descriptions and pollen recruitment

The extensive plateau of Mow Law is 100m lower than the summit ridge (Figure 6.1). The level andesite bedrock surface of the plateau is uniformly covered by peaty podsols of the Cowie Series (Figure 1.5) and

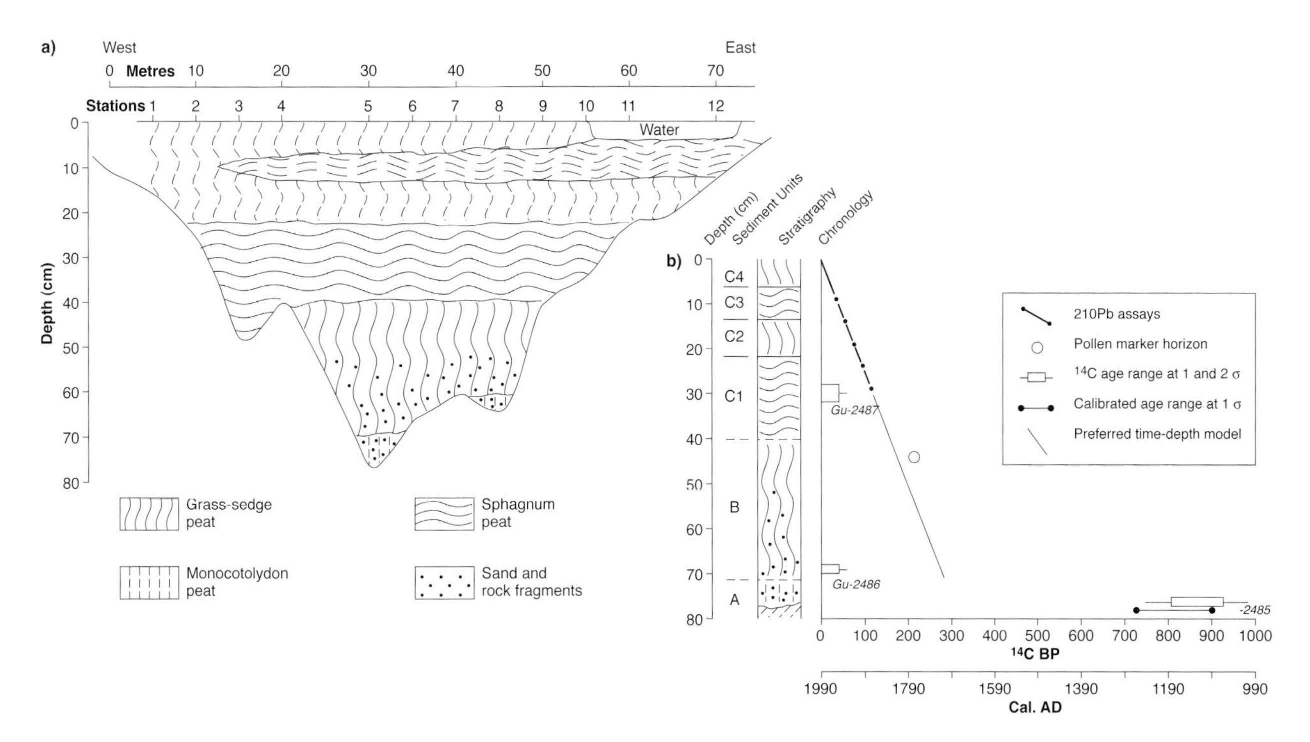

Figure 6.8

(a) The peat stratigraphy of the peat basin at Mow Law A and the sampled sequence at Station 5; (b) the preferred time-depth model for sediments at Station 5 at Mow Law A showing ^{14}C ages BP at 1 and 2σ as cat-and-whisker plots and corresponding calibrated age ranges BC/AD at 1σ as dumb-bell plots (see Table 6.6), the trend of ^{210}Pb assays (Section 2.4b), the pollen marker horizon of Agricultural Improvement tree pollen (Section 2.4c) and the first appearance of SCPs (Section 2.4d).

small patches of Sourhope Series brown forest soils (Muir 1956). Below the plateau, the steep slopes of the Calroust and Singingside Burns carry eroded and truncated skeletal soils. The plateau is used only for rough grazing (Land Use Capability 6.3; Figure 1.6) and today supports an unbroken cover of *Nardus* (mat grass) grassland communities (King 1962): *Calluna* (ling) is rare (Plate 1.3). On the plateau the only significant vegetation change occurs on two small patches of peat which support Cyperaceae (sedges) and *Molinia* (purple moor grass) (Plate 6.2). Both these patches of peat were examined because their occurrence on this dry well drained surface is unusual. They are called Mow Law A and Mow Law B.

Mow Law A is the more northerly, lying in a shallow col to the south of the domed summit of Mow Law at 420m asl (Figure 6.1: NT 8216 1788). The bog is around 60m long by 30m wide, with a small pond at the eastern end behind a subdued ridge. Around 120m south and at the same altitude the peat at Mow Law B (NT 8214 1765; Figure 6.1) has very similar dimensions at around 70m by 30m wide. The comparable and limited sizes of each bog indicate that each has the same pollen recruitment characteristics, likely to be predominantly from local and extralocal sources (Jacobson & Bradshaw 1981), within a few hundred metres of each sampled site. The likely pollen recruitment areas are depicted on Figure 6.1. The two sites share the same pollen recruitment area, typifying the plateau and the highest slopes of the adjacent valley sides. There are no archaeological monuments recorded on the plateau except 'The Street', the evocatively named drove road to Windy Rig.

6.7 Mow Law A: sediment sampling, subsampling and chronology construction

From a simple sediment stratigraphy described at twelve stations (Figure 6.8a), samples from the deepest but typical and complete sequence (Table 6.5a) were sampled from an excavated pit. All analyses and dating controls are from these samples. Three ^{14}C assays were obtained (Table 6.6; Figure 6.8b) but these are not thought to assist in chronology

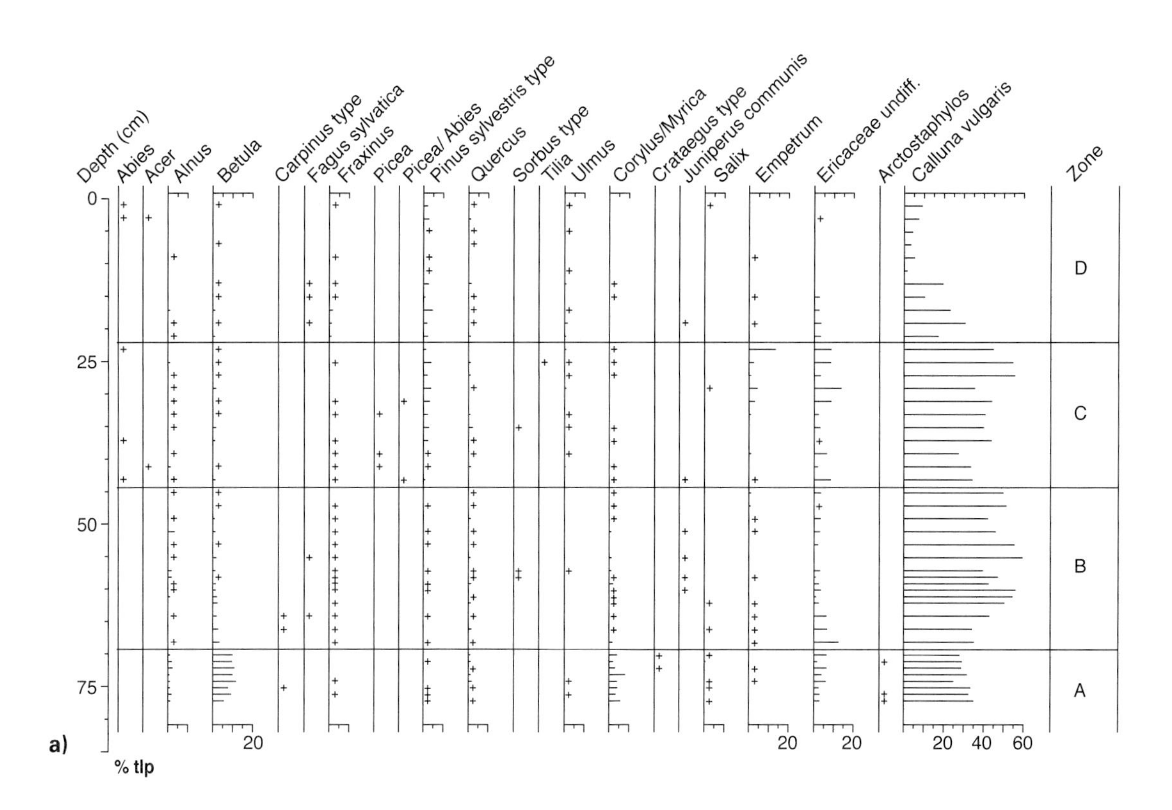

Figure 6.9

The complete pollen stratigraphy for Mow Law A plotted against depth (cm) and calculated as percentages of total land pollen (tlp) and tlp + group (Section 2.3g). Values recorded in a subsample at <1% are marked by a cross. Local pollen assemblage zone boundaries are plotted to permit correlation. See Appendix One for a glossary of English names for Linnaean taxa.

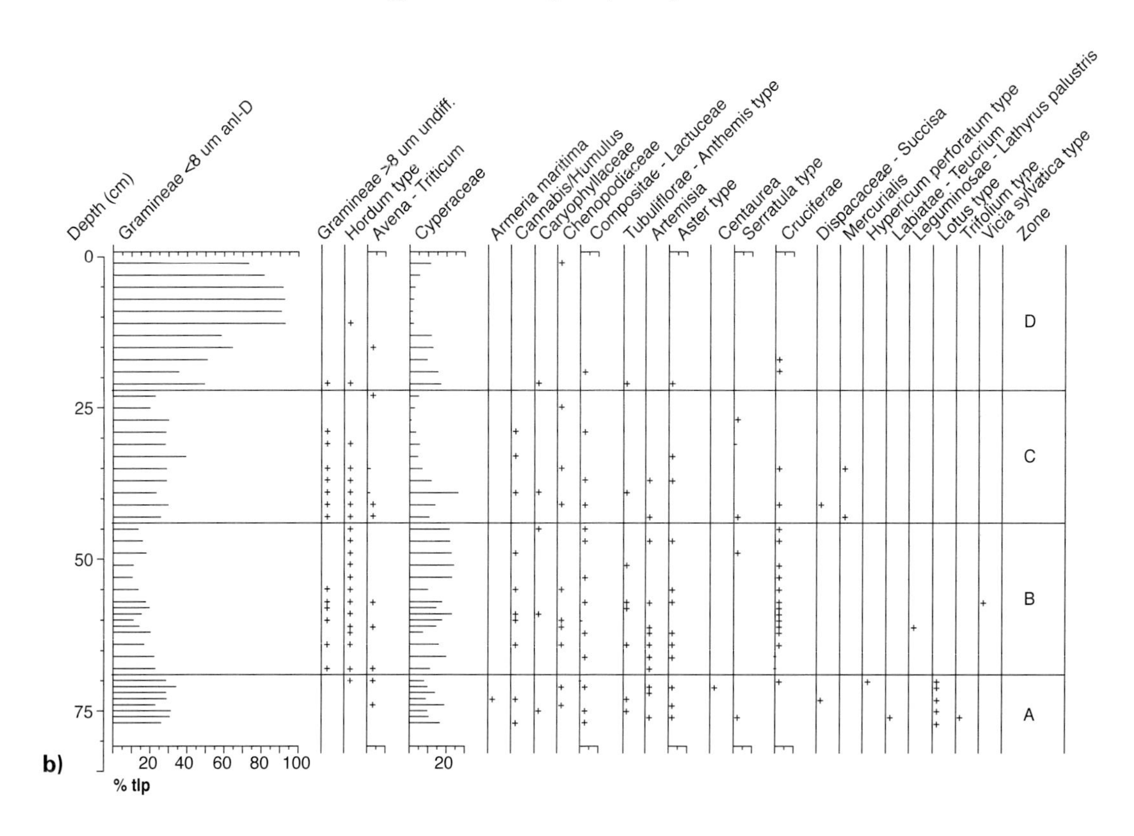

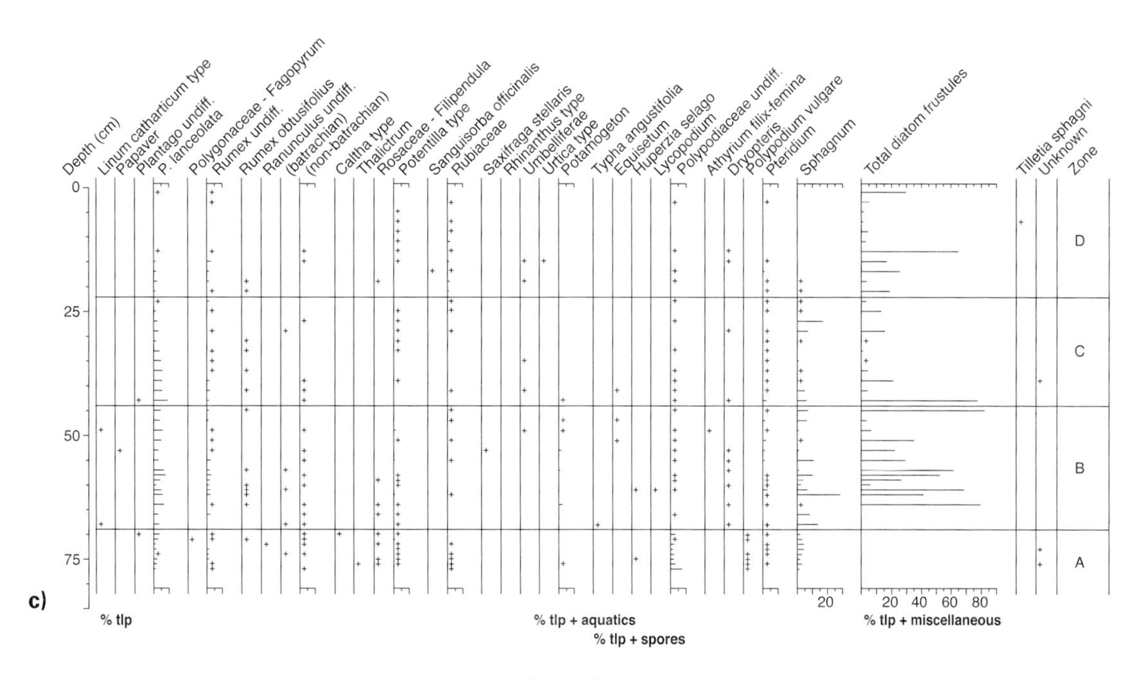

Figure 6.9 (cont.)

The complete pollen stratigraphy for Mow Law A plotted against depth (cm) and calculated as percentages of total land pollen (tlp) and tlp + group (Section 2.3g). Values recorded in a subsample at <1% are marked by a cross. Local pollen assemblage zone boundaries are plotted to permit correlation. See Appendix One for a glossary of English names for Linnaean taxa.

development. Assay GU-2485 has a much older age than other dating controls (below; Figure 6.8b). The sediment of unit A (Table 6.5a) probably contains old carbon from prolonged residence in an organic soil prior to peat growth in unit B (e.g. Matthews 1993). Assays GU-2486 and -2487 are modern in ^{14}C age and cannot be calibrated. Five sediment slices of 2cm thickness at 4cm intervals between 8 and 28cm were ^{210}Pb dated and demonstrate a linear peat accumulation rate for these depths (r^2 of 0.995) of 0.25cm per year (*c* 4 yrs/cm) (A Mackenzie pers. comm.). Pollen from trees planted at 1775 ± 25 cal AD (*Abies* (fir), *Fagus* (beech), *Picea* (spruce), *Pinus* (pine), *Ulmus* (elm)) is found above 43cm (Figure 6.9), slightly and insignificantly earlier than predicted from the trend line derived from ^{210}Pb assays (Figure 6.8b). SCPs were not recorded in sufficient numbers to contribute to analysis. A linear peat accumulation rate of 0.25cm/yr (4 yrs/cm) is adopted for sediments above 71cm, and peat inception occurred at *c* 1670 cal AD (Figure 6.8b).

Four local pollen assemblage zones are defined: lpaz Mow Law A–A to D (Table 6.7; Figure 6.9). Pollen analyses were undertaken at 1cm intervals in sediment unit A, before it became clear that this was a soil with mixed age pollen assemblages. Analyses in lpaz B–D are usually at 2cm intervals with sampling resolutions (Section 2.3d) of 2 cal years and temporal resolutions of 8 cal years. Pollen preservation states for all land pollen grains are given in Figure 6.10a, counts of microscopic charcoal in Figure 6.10b, measurements of Gramineae >8μm anl-D (cereal type) grains in Table 6.8a and of larger than normal Ericaceae grains in Table 6.9a.

6.8 Landscape and environmental change at Mow Law A

Lpaz Mow Law A–A (77–69cm): prior to 1670 cal AD

Unit A is described as a peat, but plant remains may be intrusive from the overlying peat (Table 6.1). The uniformity of pollen spectra (Figure 6.9) probably implies mixing by soil forming processes. Pollen is more crumpled than within the peat because of post depositional abrasion by mineral particles. Corrosion and degradation are surprisingly low and this may indicate that many pollen grains are not significantly

Table 6.5
Sediment stratigraphies for the sediments sampled at (a) Mow Law A and (b) Mow Law B.

Mow Law A	
Unit C_4 (0–6.5cm):	5YR 3/2 dark reddish-brown grass and sedge peat with common *Sphagnum* remains and occasional fresh grass root; sharp to
Unit C_3 (6.5–13cm):	10YR 3/2 very dark greyish-brown *Sphagnum* rich peat with occasional grass and sedge fragments and fresh grass roots; sharp to
Unit C_2 (13–22cm):	5YR 3/2 dark reddish-brown poorly humified grass and sedge peat with common to abundant *Sphagnum* remains; gradual to
Unit C_1 (22–39.5cm):	5YR 3/2 dark reddish-brown poorly humified *Sphagnum* rich peat; very gradual to
Unit B (39.5–71cm):	7.5YR 3/4 dark brown poorly humified sedge peat with rare to occasional bleached coarse sand and rock fragments below *c* 50cm; gradual to
Unit A (71–77cm):	5YR 2.5/1 black monocotyledon peat with abundant grass and sedge remains and amorphous organic matter; many coarse bleached sand and rock fragments and rare small angular bleached stones increasingly common down-unit.
Mow Law B	
Unit D (0–17cm):	5YR 2.5/1 black poorly humified grass and sedge peat with occasional fresh grass roots; sharp to
Unit C (17–25cm):	10YR 3/3 dark brown densely compacted *Sphagnum* rich peat; sharp to
Unit B (25–50.5cm):	5YR 2.5/2 dark reddish-brown poorly humified grass and sedge peat; sharp to
Unit A_2 (50.5–54cm):	5YR 2.5/2 dark reddish-brown amorphous peat with common horizontally matted fine fleshy plant remains and rare to occasional coarse-medium bleached sand and rock fragments; sharp to
Unit A_1 (54–61cm):	7.5YR 3/2 dark brown organic mud and amorphous peat with common horizontally matted fine fleshy plant remains and common coarse to medium bleached sand and rock fragments and rare small angular stones.

Table 6.6

Details of the radiocarbon assays obtained on the sediments at Mow Law A and Mow Law B.

Lab. No. (GU-)	*Mean Depth (cm)*	*Sediment Depth (cm)*	*No. of Cores (gms)*	*Sample Weight*	*^{14}C Age* BP ± 1σ	*$\delta^{13}C$ (‰)*	*Calibrated Age* AD ± 1σ *and Intercept Ages*	*Mean Calibrated Age* AD
Mow Law A								
2487	30	32–28	1 (monolith)	227.4	modern	–28.4	n.a.	
2486	69	70–68	1 (monolith)	164.9	modern	–26.9	n.a.	
2485	76	77–75	1 (monolith)	191.1	870 ± 60	–26.9	AD 1043 (1169) 1230 AD	1136
Mow Law B								
2489	53	54–52	1 (monolith)	147	920 ± 50	–27.9	AD 1027 (1047,1091,1118, 1143,1153) 1169	1098
2488	61	62–60	1 (monolith)	125.6	1480 ± 130	–28.2	AD 420 (596) 660	540

Table 6.7

Local pollen assemblage zones at Mow Law A and Mow Law B, their characteristic pollen taxa and ^{14}C and calibrated age ranges.

Lpaz	*Depths (cm)*	*Characteristic taxa*	*Duration (cal* BC/AD*)*	*(cal* BP*)*	*(^{14}C* BP*)*
Mow Law A–D	22–0cm	Gramineae <8μm anl-D (wild grasses)	AD 1860–1985	125–0	n.a.
Mow Law A–C	44–22cm	Gramineae <8μm anl-D (wild grasses) – *Calluna* (ling)	AD 1770–1860	215–125	n.a.
Mow Law A–B	69–44cm	*Calluna* (ling) – Gramineae <8μm anl-D (wild grasses)	AD 1670–1770	315–215	n.a.
Mow Law A–A	77–69cm	*Calluna* (ling) – Gramineae <8μm anl-D (wild grasses) – *Betula* (birch)	prior to AD 1670	prior to 315	n.a.
Mow Law B–B	55.5–41cm	*Calluna* (ling) – Gramineae <8μm anl-D (wild grasses) – Cyperaceae (sedges)	AD 1100–1290	890–700	1480–700
Mow Law B–A	61–55.5cm	Gramineae <8μm anl-D (wild grasses)	prior to AD 1100	prior to 890	prior to 1480

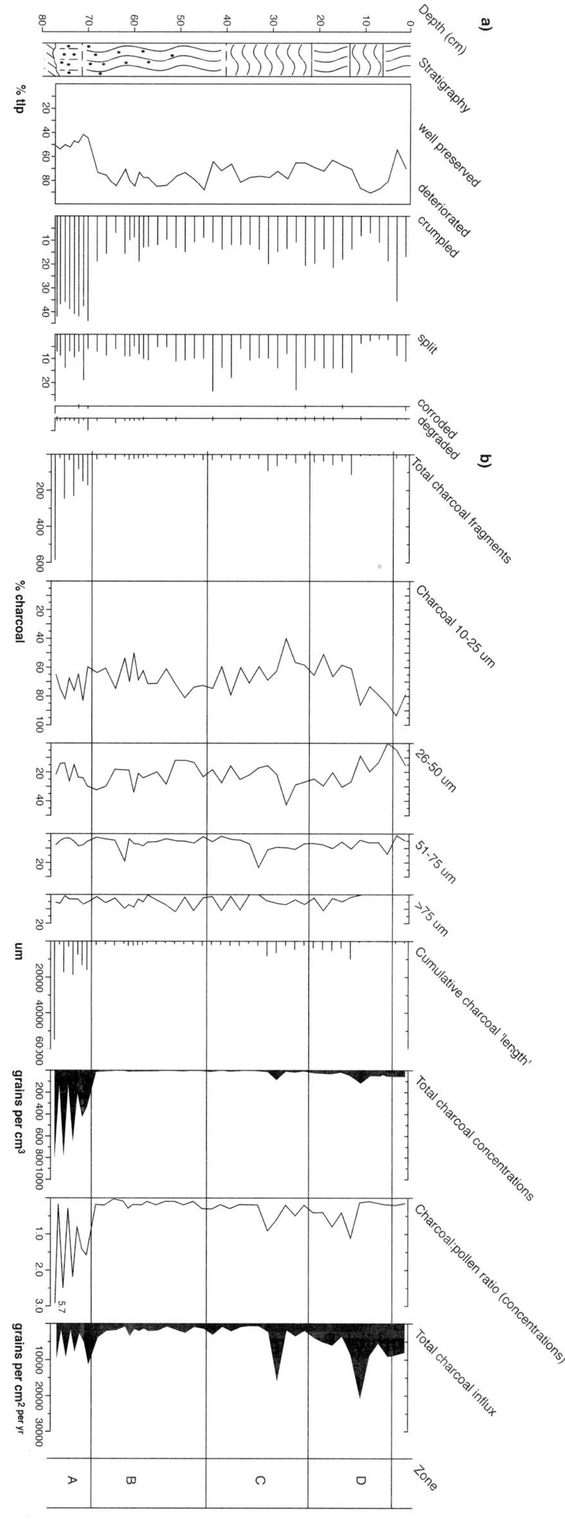

Figure 6.10

(a) Pollen preservation states for all determinable land pollen grains at Mow Law A plotted against depth and calculated as percentages of total land pollen (see Section 2.3I); (b) measures of the abundance of microscopic charcoal fragments at Mow Law A (see Section 2.3j). Local pollen assemblage zone boundaries are plotted to permit correlation.

older than in overlying peat as well as suggesting that the water table was close to the surface for as long as the soil received pollen (Figure 6.10a). Microscopic charcoal is extraordinarily abundant (Figure 6.10b), but this will have accumulated for an undefined duration in the soil without depletion. Because of this, it cannot be argued that charcoal deposition was causal in subsequent peat inception (cf. Mallik, Gimingham & Rahman 1984).

Assuming that the majority of the pollen assemblage represents a time close to peat inception, then this wet bedrock hollow was unsurprisingly filled with Cyperaceae (sedges), probably associated in a wet grassland (Gramineae <8µm anl-D) with *Galium* type (cf. *G. palustre*; marsh bedstraw), *Lotus* type (cf. *L. uliginosus*; greater birdsfoot trefoil), *Caltha* type (cf. *C palustris*; marsh marigold) and batrachian *Ranunculus* (buttercups), *Filipendula* (cf. meadowsweet) and *Potentilla* type (cf. *P. palustris* (marsh cinquefoil). Aquatics are rare, however, and open water did not exist in the hollow (Figure 6.3). Away from the hollow, dry grassland (Gramineae <8µm anl-D) communities were probably much more abundant than those of *Calluna* (ling). *Calluna* was accompanied by a number of other heathers (Ericaceae undiff.) including *Arctostaphylos* (bearberry; Table 6.9a). Some trees and shrubs, perhaps *Betula* (birch), *Corylus or Myrica* (hazel or bog myrtle), *Salix* (willow) and *Crataegus* (*Crataegus* type) may have grown on the plateau. Grassland herbs indicative of some grazing were present but not abundant. Cereal type pollen is not conclusively represented until the upper zone boundary. Areas of bare or disturbed ground probably existed, colonised in part by arctic-alpine elements (Matthews 1955) such as *Armeria* (thrift) and *Thalictrum* (meadow rue). The consistent records of *Cannabis/Humulus* in lpa zones A–C are assumed, in this open setting, to have been derived from *Cannabis sativa* (hemp), though not necessarily grown on the plateau.

Lpaz Mow Law A–B (69–44cm): 1670–1770 cal AD

A poorly humified and very rapidly growing peat (unit B; Table 6.5a) rich in Cyperaceae (sedges) was formed, and displaced some wet grassland taxa from the basin. Waterlogging is indicated by pronounced increases in *Sphagnum* (bog moss) and by the abundance of diatom frustules (not counted below 65cm through the use of hydrofluoric acid in sample preparation). Open water was present with *Potamogeton* (pondweed), *Typha angustifolia* (lesser bulrush) and *Equisetum* (horsetails). Cause in peat inception is

Table 6.8

Size measurements (pollen size, pollen index: Andersen 1979) of well preserved and physically damaged Gramineae (grass family) pollen grains of annulus diameters >8 μm at (a) Mow Law A and (b) Mow Law B. Grains are well preserved unless indicated by (c) crumpled, (sc) slightly crumpled, or (s) split.

Depth (cm)	*anl-D*	*Size*	*Index*	*Group*
Mow Law A				
11	10.5	41.5	1.02	III
15	8.5	36.6	1.43	II
21	16.5	58.0	1.36	III
23	9.0	40.5	1.25	II
29	10.0	49.5	1.47	II/III
31	9.0	39.5	1.46(c)	II/III
	11.5	35.0	1.33	III
	12.0	47.0	1.14	III
35	10.0	43.5	1.26(c)	II
	13.5	54.0	1.03	III
	8.0	39.5	1.46(c)	II
	12.5	43.5	1.23	III
	8.0	47.0	1.29	II
	13.0	50.0	1.70(c)	III
	8.5	40.5	1.25	II
	10.5	42.0	1.70(c)	III
37	8.0	36.5	1.21	Ic/II
	11.0	(c)		III
	10.0	39.5	1.36	II/III
39	12.0	49.5	1.25	III
	9.0	38.5	1.33	II
	8.5	36.0	1.25	II
	8.0	34.0	1.42(c)	Ic/II
	11.0	41.5	1.44	III
	9.0	43.5	1.02(s)	II
	9.5	36.0	1.48(c)	II
41	11.0	42.0	1.40	II/III
	9.0	46.0	1.09	II
43	12.0	55.5	1.22	III
	13.5	44.0	1.20	III
	9.5	38.0	1.11	II
45	13.0	51.0	1.12	III
	13.0	48.5	1.15	III
47	9.5	48.5	1.62(c)	III
49	12.0	49.5	1.15	III
51	11.0	50.0	1.22	III
53	13.0	54.5	1.42	III
	13.0	41.0	1.48	III
55	9.5	42.0	1.27	III
	11.0	37.5	1.42(c)	undiff.
	12.0	45.5	1.21	III
57	9.5	38.5	1.13(c)	II
	11.5	53.0	1.35(s)	III
	9.0	40.5	1.25(c)	undiff.
58	10.0	39.0	1.36(c)	undiff.
59	12.0	45.0	1.57	III
61	9.0	37.5	1.27	II
	17.0	54.5	1.22	III
	11.5	45.5	1.22	III
62	14.0	43.0	1.26	III
	12.0	48.0	1.59	III
64	12.0	46.5	1.32	III
	12.0	50.0	1.22	III
68	12.0	44.5	1.25	III
	10.0	40.5	1.25	undiff.
	9.0	43.0	1.04(c)	II
70	9.0	40.0	1.28(c)	II
	11.0	42.5	1.42	III
	12.0	46.5	1.66	III
74	9.0	38.0	1.45(c)	II
Mow Law B				
60	9.5	42.0	1.10	II
51	9.0	34.5	1.37	II

again hard to define because key changes happened prior to the event but the pollen assemblages in lpaz A–A provide clues. Woodland taxa were not present during the time the soil recruited pollen (above) and woodland clearance cannot be implicated in peat inception. The accumulation of charcoal over a long time in the soil may have eventually led to reduced drainage from charcoal blocking soil pores (Mallik *et al* 1984). If this is correct, then the timing of peat inception has no significance because the effect is cumulative; this is tested by correlation between sites in Section 8.11b. Because almost no charcoal was collected in the overlying peat (Figure 6.10b), peat inception from contemporaneous fires in the mid-seventeenth century cal AD cannot have occurred. Climatic change to increased precipitation is possible

(Section 8.11b). So is the deliberate damming of a free-draining flush or spring by farmers creating a source of open water on the plateau: sections in the low ridge ponding water at present (Section 6.6) were not seen from which to determine its origin.

There is considerable evidence for increased agricultural activity concurrent with peat inception. Of principal significance is the appearance of cereal pollen grains (Table 6.8a; Figure 6.9) including *Avena/Triticum* (oat or wheat) in contiguous subsamples and frequently represented by more than single grains. These were accompanied by disturbed ground or weed taxa such as Caryophyllaceae (pink family), Chenopodiaceae (fat hen), several species of Compositae (daisy family) and Cruciferae (cabbage family). The grassland seems certainly to have been grazed, with increases in *Plantago lanceolata* (ribwort plantain) and *Rumex* undiff. (docks), and the appearance of *R. obtusifolius* (broad-leaved dock), taken to indicate high grazing intensity (Hughes & Huntley 1988). Some tall herb communities vulnerable to grazing containing, for example, *Filipendula* (? meadowsweet) and *Ranunculus* (buttercup) were diminished. *Pteridium* (bracken) grew from before peat inception. *Calluna* (ling) may nevertheless have occupied 60 to 70% of the ground cover (Evans & Moore 1985; Hjelle 1998), with other heathers (Ericaceae undiff.) and *Empetrum* (crowberry) on drier ground, though *Arctostaphylos* (bearberry) is not recorded (Figure 6.9).

Lpaz Mow Law A–C (44–22cm): 1770–1860 cal AD

Calluna (ling) heath continued to be very significant (Figure 6.9), despite the very limited evidence for burning (Figure 6.10b), usually considered to be necessary for its maintenance, and in the face of sustained grazing, seen in the continued strong representation of *Plantago lanceolata* (ribwort plantain), *Rumex* undiff. (docks) and *R. obtusifolius* (broad-leaved dock) until *c* 1830 cal AD (30cm) when values of these pastoral indicator taxa decline. Grazing pressures may not have been high, however, with low numbers of stock or a management regime that allowed stock movement. Equally, heathers may have grown more profusely on the mire in response to a dryer surface, suggested by fewer numbers of diatom

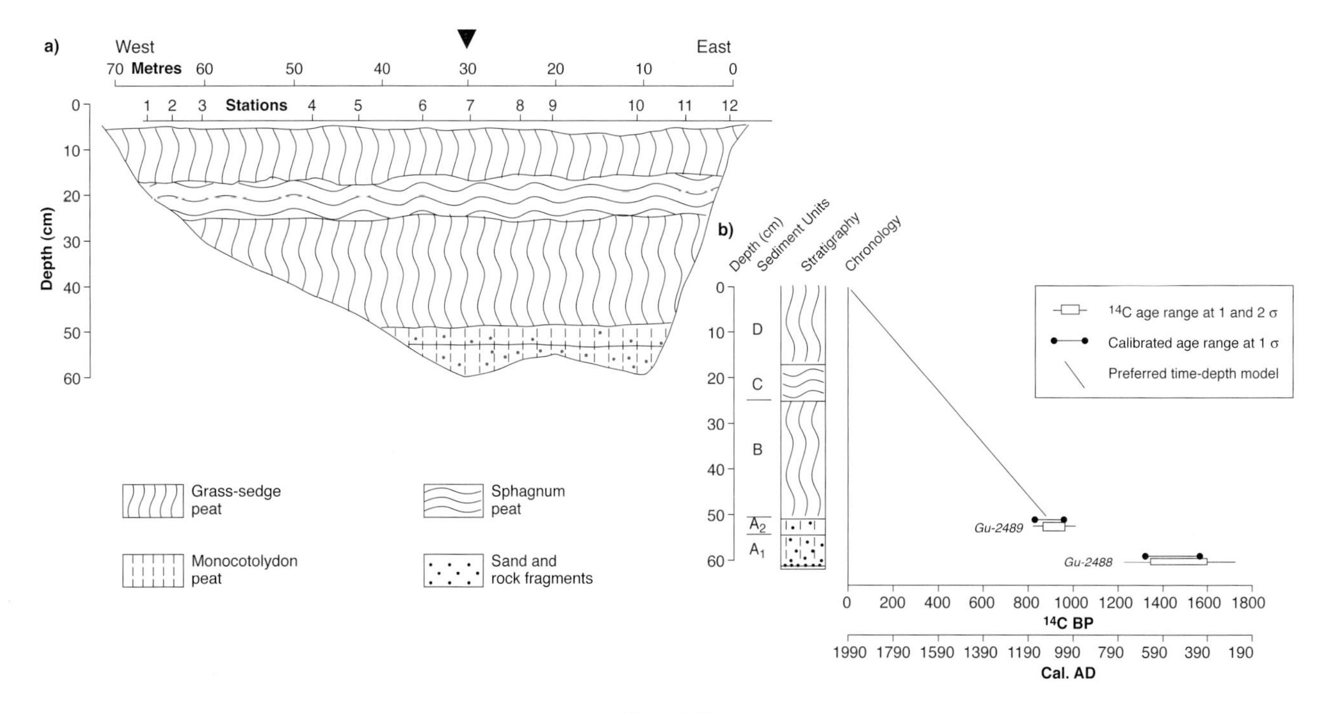

Figure 6.11

(a) The peat stratigraphy of the peat basin at Mow Law B and the sampled sequence at Station 7; (b) the preferred time-depth model for sediments at Station 7 at Mow Law B showing ^{14}C ages BP at 1 and 2σ as cat-and-whisker plots and corresponding calibrated age ranges BC/AD at 1σ as dumb-bell plots (see Table 6.6).

frustules, low proportions of *Sphagnum* (bogmoss) spores, declining values of Cyperaceae (sedges), the absence of *Potamogeton* (pondweed) and an increase in *Empetrum* (crowberry) values after *c* 32cm (*c* 1820 cal AD). The increase in Gramineae <8μm anl-D (wild grasses) values may partly have been through *Molinia* (purple moor grass) colonising a drying peat surface (Figure 6.9). However, the absence of corroded pollen (Figure 6.10a) shows that no substantial or more than seasonal lowering of the water table occurred. Arable activity was sustained until *c* 1830 cal AD (30cm) after which the numbers of cereal (Gramineae >8μm anl-D) and associated disturbed ground pollen grains were sharply reduced (Table 6.8a), taken to represent the end of cereal cultivation on the plateau.

Lpaz Mow Law A–D (22–0cm): 1860–1985 cal AD

The dramatic expansion in proportions of Gramineae <8μm anl-D (wild grasses) is thought to result from the replacement of mire surface sedge (Cyperaceae) and heath (*Calluna*, *Empetrum*, Ericaceae undiff.) communities by purple moor grass (*Molinia*); clumps of grass pollen probably signify their prolific on site growth. In addition, species poor (*Nardus*) (mat grass) grass communities probably replaced herb rich grassland across the plateau, indicated by sharp reductions in percentages of *Plantago lanceolata* (ribwort plantain) and other herbs. The pollen spectra within the last *c* 100 cal years would not, using criteria commonly employed (Behre 1981), indicate grazing of the plateau at all. It is ironic that very intensive grazing regimes are most likely to have induced this change (Section 8.11e).

6.9 Summary of environmental change at Mow Law A

Peat accumulation commenced at *c* 1670 cal AD through either climate change, impeded waterlogging through the slow accumulation of charcoal or the construction of a pond to support grazing animals. Grazing quickly removed the few trees and shrubs that grew on the plateau. Ling heath grew abundantly together with species rich grazed grassland. Cereal cultivation after *c* 1670 cal AD of oats or wheat and possibly barley continued until the mid-nineteenth century. Increasing grazing pressures may have been responsible for the transformation from species rich grassland and heaths to species poor rough pasture from the mid-nineteenth century.

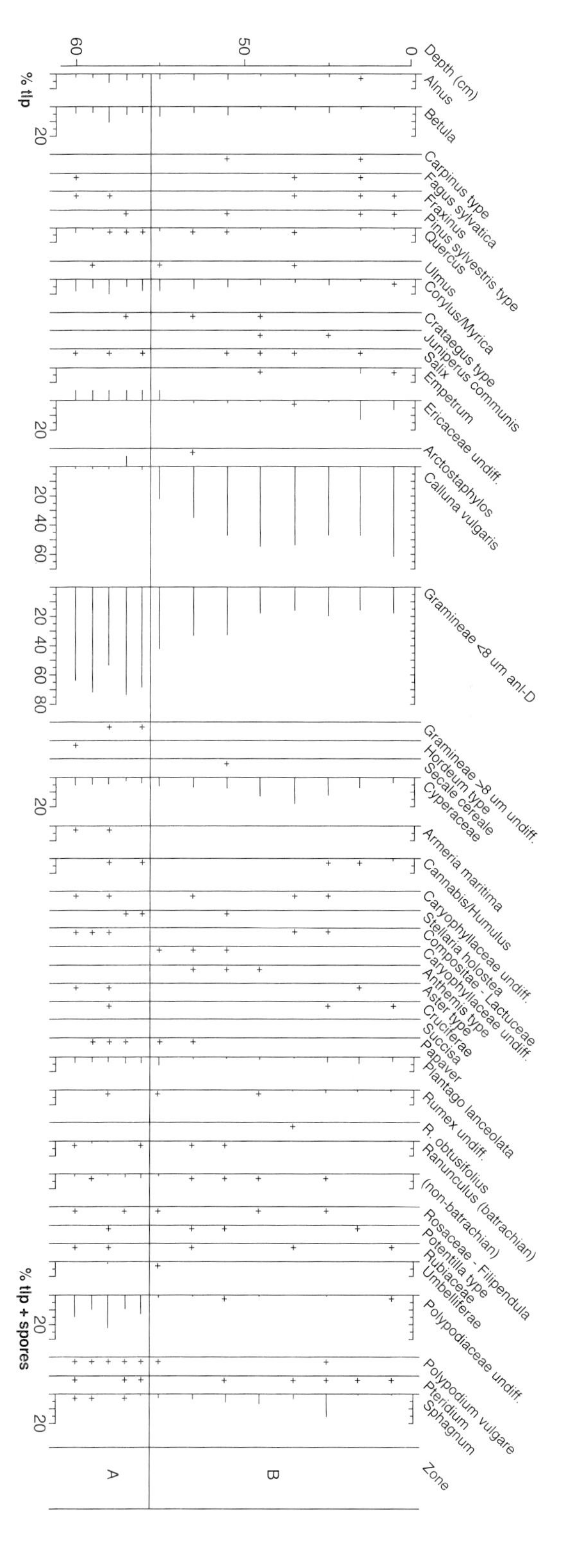

Figure 6.12

The complete pollen stratigraphy for sediments at Mow Law B between 41 and 60cm plotted against depth (cm) and calculated as percentages of total land pollen (tlp) and tlp + group (Section 2.3g). Values recorded in a subsample at <1% are marked by a cross. Local pollen assemblage zone boundaries are plotted to permit correlation. See Appendix One for a glossary of English names for Linnaean taxa.

6.10 Mow Law B: sediment sampling, subsampling and chronology construction

Excavation of a pit provided monolith tins from surface to bedrock at Station 7, the deepest part at 61cm of a simple sediment stratigraphy (Table 6.5b; Figure 6.11a). Two ^{14}C assays were obtained (GU-2488, -2489; Table 6.6b; Figure 6.10b) and are internally consistent. Both are from highly organic sediments with abundant mineral fragments (sediment units A_1 and A_2; Table 6.5b) rather than from the earliest peat in unit B, and both may be from soil horizons affected by organic matter with a prolonged residence time. This cannot be demonstrated because pollen analyses did not continue to surface sediments that should have contained planted tree taxa or SCPs. The absence of exotic tree types suggests, however, that the topmost pollen sample at 41cm (Figure 6.12) predates *c* 1775 cal AD. Lead 210 assays were not obtained. The preferred time-depth model in Figure 6.11b assumes that the organic matter in sediment unit A_2 dated by assay GU-2489 was contemporaneous and not old. Support for this is seen in the pollen record (Figure 6.12) with the virtual absence of Polypodiaceae undiff. (undifferentiated fern) spores within sediment unit A_2, suggesting that this assemblage has no residual components (Tipping *et al* 1994). Peat is thought to have commenced at *c* 1100 cal AD (Table 6.6b; Figure 6.11b), much earlier than at Mow Law A (Section 6.7).

Pollen analyses were made at 2cm intervals in sediments below 41cm (*c* 1290 cal AD) to understand landscape changes coincident with peat formation. The two local pollen assemblage zones are prefixed Mow Law B: analyses within lpaz Mow Law B–B have temporal resolutions of *c* twenty-seven years. Pollen preservation states for all land pollen grains are given in Figure 6.13a, counts of microscopic charcoal in Figure 6.13b, measurements of Gramineae >8µm anl-D (cereal type) grains in Table 6.8b and of the single larger than normal Ericaceae grain in Table 6.9b.

6.11 Landscape and environmental change in the basal sediments at Mow Law B

Lpaz Mow Law B–A (61–55.5cm): prior to 1100 cal AD

Sediments lower in unit A_1 predate *c* 1100 cal AD. They are probably derived from an organic rich soil, but this soil does not contain organic matter of a mean ^{14}C age significantly older than overlying peat (Figure 6.11b). It is likely that much pollen in lpaz B–A is from plants growing immediately prior to peat inception. The assemblage must still be distorted, however, because

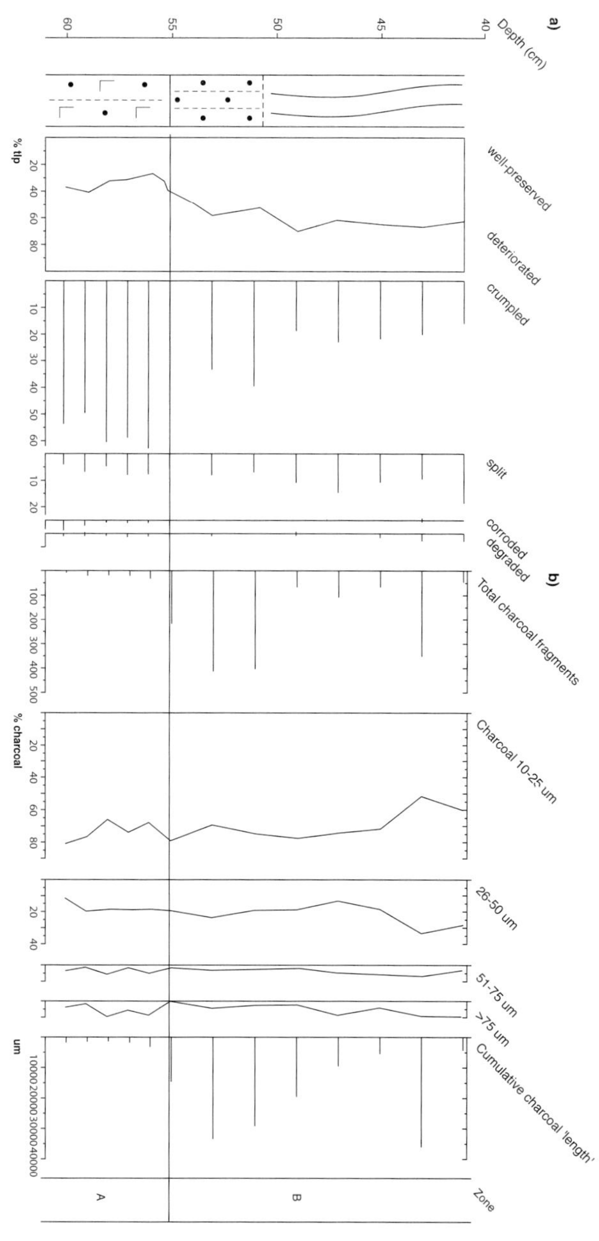

Figure 6.13
(a) Pollen preservation states for all determinable land pollen grains at Mow Law B plotted against depth and calculated as percentages of total land pollen (see Section 2.3l); (b) measures of the abundance of microscopic charcoal fragments at Mow Law B (see Section 2.3j). Local pollen assemblage zone boundaries are plotted to permit correlation.

the relatively high values of Polypodiaceae undiff. spores suggest a residual component, and it may have no stratigraphic integrity (Long *et al* 2000). Most pollen grains are either crumpled or split from post depositional abrasion, but corrosion has not resulted in a preferential loss of taxa (Figure 6.13a).

Gramineae <8μm anl-D (wild grasses) pollen is abundant, and before peat inception the hollow was dominated by damp grassland communities with Cyperaceae (sedges), *Galium* type (bedstraws), *Filipendula* (cf. meadowsweet) and *Succisa/Lonicera* (cf. *Succisa*; devilsbit scabious). Dryer grassland supported *Campanula* (bellflower), *Armeria* (thrift) and *Pteridium* (bracken). Pastoral indicator herbs are prominent, and the plateau was grazed, though not intensely. The appearance of two grains of undifferentiated Gramineae >8μm anl-D (cereal type) and one of *Hordeum* (barley) type (Andersen Group II; Table 6.8b) is not secure evidence for cereal cultivation. Open ground herbs are present, but are not necessarily indicative of anthropogenically disturbed ground. *Cannabis/Humulus* (cf. *Cannabis* (hemp)) pollen may have originated from crops on lower ground (Figure 6.12). The proportions of tree pollen types do not indicate local growth of trees or shrubs, with the possible exceptions as small stands or even single plants of *Corylus/Myrica* (hazel or bog myrtle), *Betula* (birch), *Crataegus* type (hawthorn and/or rowan) and *Salix* (willow).

Lpaz Mow Law B–B (55.5–41cm): 1100–1290 cal AD

Within the poorly humified minerogenic peat of sediment unit A_2 (Table 6.5b) pollen is better preserved (Figure 6.13a), and taxa characteristic of soils, e.g. Polypodiaceae undiff. (ferns), are only infrequently recorded, whereas peat forming taxa such as Cyperaceae (sedges) and *Sphagnum* (bog moss) are better represented (Figure 6.12). With peat inception, a dramatic rise of *Calluna* (ling) pollen percentages probably represents a heath with other Ericaceae and *Empetrum* (crowberry) that displaced the grassland. Associated with this is a six-fold increase in the numbers of microscopic charcoal fragments (Figure 6.13b). Anderson (1997) argued that *Empetrum* populations suffer severely in periods of increased fire frequency because this plant is more flammable, but this is not supported here. The increase in charcoal abundance commences just below

Table 6.9

Size measurements of Ericaceae pollen grains larger than normal at (a) Mow Law A and (b) Mow Law B. For definitions of variables measured see Oldfield (1959, p. 20).

Depth (cm)	*D*	*d*	*D/d*	*p*	*2f*	*type*
Mow Law A						
71	34	24	1.42	n.d.	n.d.	*Arctostaphylos*
76	49	34	1.44	n.d.	n.d.	*Arctostaphylos*
Mow Law B						
53	32	23	1.39	8	7	? *Arctostaphylos*

n.d. not determined

the stratigraphic change to peat, and may have been instrumental in peat inception through impedance of soil drainage (Mallik *et al* 1984). There seems little doubt that heath communities were favoured by burning, and anthropogenic firing of the vegetation seems the simplest explanation. The smallest sized fragments continue to dominate, but these sized fragments may be preferentially produced by heather plants. Despite the expansion of heathland, grass communities were still abundant, and continued to be grazed, perhaps more intensively after *c* 1225 cal AD (46cm). There is no evidence for cereal cultivation.

Above the uppermost pollen analyses the sediment stratigraphy features a prominent band of *Sphagnum* peat (Unit C; Table 6.5) which probably represents a markedly wetter bog surface, estimated to have developed between *c* 1585 and 1700 cal AD.

6.12 Summary of environmental change at Mow Law B

Before *c* 1100 cal AD the plateau was covered by a grazed grassland, and supported no or very few trees or shrubs and virtually no heaths. At around 1100 cal AD a major increase in the frequency and/or intensity of anthropogenic burning of the vegetation encouraged the expansion of heath communities, and may have initiated peat accumulation in the small basin.

Chapter 7

FLUVIAL HISTORY AND GEOMORPHIC CHANGE IN THE NORTHERN CHEVIOT HILLS

7.1 Introduction

There is a close link between soil quality and land use capability at present, and there is no reason to assume that this was different in the past. Many soils in the valley are currently thin and truncated skeletal complexes (Muir 1956; Sections 1.5, 1.6). The relation between these and deeper, better developed brown forest soils and podsols suggests that soil erosion on valley sides has at times been severe, although there is little evidence that soils are currently eroding (Section 1.5). It is likely, therefore, that the capacity of some soils to support agriculture has deteriorated over time. Vegetation changes of the scale and kind described in Chapters 3 to 6, driven very much by farming endeavours, should have led to substantial changes in the ways that slopes and soils developed, and there is thus the deterministic and simplistic possibility that past agricultural activities led on occasions to the impoverishment and decline of farming itself in the valley. However, with the exception of the extraordinarily complicated changes in the lake sediments at Yetholm Loch (Chapter 3) and the phases of soil loss on the summit ridge at Cocklawhead (Chapter 6), the peat stratigraphies investigated in earlier chapters have not provided evidence for major disturbance of soils and slopes. This absence of evidence can be explained by the limited transport of sediment across rough peat surfaces and by most peat sequences typifying level to gently sloping

Plate 7.1

The upper reaches of the Bowmont Water above Swindon Cottage (the conifers opposite the farm in Plate 1.11 are in the distance). The photograph shows the river at waning flood stage during avulsion (abrupt channel change) from its then active channel (1990 cal AD) to the left into an older channel to the right, that mapping evidence suggests was the active channel last in 1947 cal AD. Streams frequently avulse into former channels because the sediments plugging the old channel are more easily erodible and at lower altitudes than surrounding gravel stream banks.

plateaux with little potential for soil loss. These are not appropriate sequences from which to understand the timing, mechanisms, scale and causes of soil erosion on valley sides. Yet if the data from Yetholm Loch and Cocklawhead are of more than local significance, geomorphic change must have been important in Holocene landscape evolution.

Because they are eroded, slopes themselves are unlikely to provide stratigraphic and dating evidence of soil erosion. The approach adopted here is the construction of a fluvial chronology for valleys in the northern Cheviot Hills (Figure 1.2). This approach has been a major area of research for more than twenty years (e.g. Shotton 1978; Gregory 1983; Needham & Macklin 1992; Macklin & Lewin 1993, 2003; Brown 1997; Macklin 1999). This aspect of the work in the northern Cheviot Hills has been published more fully than palaeoecological analyses (Tipping 1992, 1993, 1998a, 1999; Mercer & Tipping 1994) but not in detail. In montane and upland landscapes such as the Cheviots, rivers are typified by steep gradients, high discharges and an abundance of easily eroded glacial, fluvioglacial and periglacial deposits (Section 1.2d), so that even on valley floors stratigraphic sequences are exceptionally rare. Rivers are highly active, with channels sweeping across valley floors by lateral meander migration and, more commonly, abrupt channel diversion (avulsion) (Plate 7.1). These processes destroy deposits and evidence for past fluvial activity (Newson 1981; Passmore *et al* 1993; Howard & Macklin 1999; Higgitt, Warburton & Evans 2001).

Nevertheless, evidence survives of some of the major stratigraphic changes in some valleys. Terrace aggradation results in the accumulation of sediments on the valley floor resulting from the temporary storage of channel gravel and floodplain (overbank) deposits (Brown 1987a). These are cut and fill terrace sequences, higher and older terrace surfaces being separated by low cliffs from lower and younger surfaces because of a trend to progressive incision in the Holocene (Macklin & Lewin 1986; Howard & Macklin 1999). Older terrace fills and the terrace

Plate 7.2

Low but extensive terrace surfaces on the valley floor at Swindon Cottage (see Plates 1.11 and 7.1) showing their dissection by palaeochannels. In the middle distance an incised burn, with a tongue of conifers, descends from Swindon Hill and has built out an alluvial fan onto the valley floor which can be shown to have last been active in the seventeenth and eighteenth centuries cal AD (Tipping 1993). To the right and downstream of this, the highest terrace across the river carries broad rig cultivation traces and the nineteenth-century walls of the farmstead of Old Swindon.

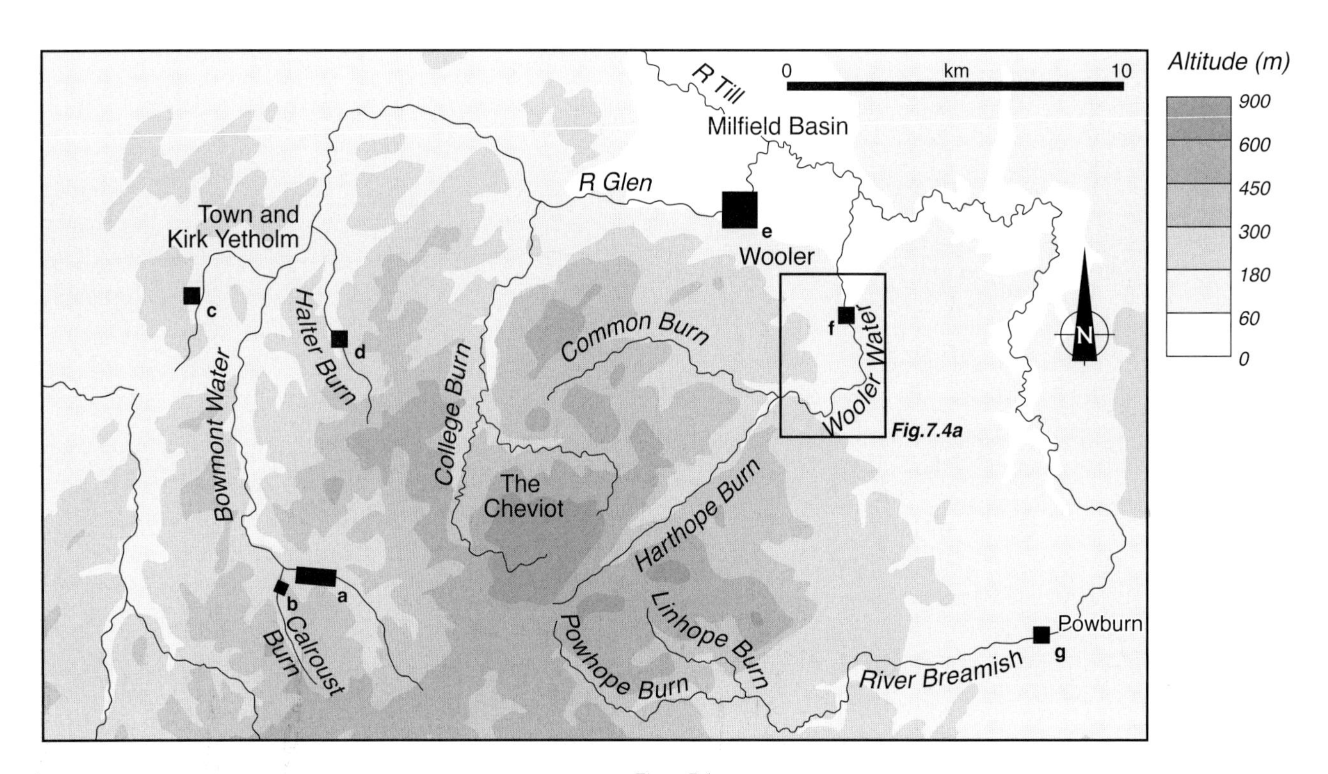

Figure 7.1
Topography and drainage pattern of the northern Cheviot Hills showing the locations of the reaches or sequences investigated to construct a fluvial chronology: (a) Swindon Cottage, (b) Calroust, (c) Yetholm Loch (Chapter 3), (d) the Halter Burn, (e) the River Glen at Akeld Steads, (f) the Wooler Water and (g) the River Breamish at Powburn.

surfaces defining them can be extensively developed (Plate 7.2): younger fills are frequently dissected by active streams. Rare stream bank exposures provide evidence for multiple phase fluvial deposition (Plate 7.3) and contemporaneous *in situ* peats deposited away from active channels. These often provide the only dating controls. The incompleteness of the chronology for upland landscapes is a major deficiency, caused by the erosion of older deposits and the variety of fluvial responses to change, not all of which leave sedimentological evidence. Aggradation and incision are both products of accelerated fluvial activity, and each can be a response to the same event in different reaches of the same catchment (Schumm 1977).

A direct link, however, between valley floors and geomorphic changes on valley side slopes cannot be assumed. Increased river activity need not affect slopes if channel density and drainage efficiency are high. Much sediment aggrading in these unstable river systems derives not from slopes but from the reworking of valley floor sediment. The construction of a fluvial chronology does not necessarily imply an understanding of landscape instability. Linkages between slope erosion and accelerated fluvial activity are not always immediate since sediment can be stored at the base of slopes and in alluvial fans and debris cones (Brown 1987a), possibly leading to lags between the timing of initial triggers and sediment supply to the river (Burrin 1985; but see Lewin 1981; Richards *et al* 1986). Because valley floors act as sediment sinks for the catchment, collecting and redistributing material from all around, riverine sediments present a generalised record of change, one that cannot often precisely define sediment sources (Macklin & Aspinall 1986), particularly in areas of uniform geology such as the Cheviot Hills (Section 1.5).

Fluvial changes are only responses to causal factors: changes can also be autogenic, with no external input. They are very valuable indicators of landscape change, but require clear correlations with other data in Chapter 8. The success of such correlations is entirely dependent on the quality of dating controls (Tipping 2000a). For many years, competing causal explanations were sought in climate change and human activity. Cause was linked to past human activities for northern Cheviot systems by

Plate 7.3

Actively forming gravel bar sediments on the Swindon Cottage reach of the Bowmont Water, which yielded OSL ages that could not define the recent age of the sediments, probably because exposure to sunlight has still been inadequate to fully bleach sand grains (Smith *et al* 1990). The low winter sunlight picks out the curving shapes of broad rig cultivation on the till and colluvial slopes of the valley side in the background.

Tipping (1992) and Mercer and Tipping (1994), but this position is re-evaluated in the light of increased data on Holocene climate change (Chapter 8). A middle ground has emerged in which human activity is seen to have destabilised slopes and loosened soils but climatic events, in particular prolonged increases in precipitation, pushed soils into rivers (Macklin & Needham 1992; Macklin 1999; Coulthard & Macklin 2001), although this compromise does not entirely resolve the debate (Tipping 2000a). The collective archaeological, palaeoecological and geomorphological data within the upper Bowmont Valley are re-examined to explore this and other issues in Chapter 8.

7.2 The catchments and analyses

Figure 7.1 depicts the major northern Cheviot valleys radiating from The Cheviot (Section 1.4). The search for stratigraphic sequences from which to develop a fluvial chronology was exhaustive within the upper Bowmont Valley, but otherwise the data are from chance observations or new analyses of previously published work. The need to extend analyses to valleys away from the Bowmont emerged with the recognition that the valley contains a truncated fluvial chronology, extending in time only a few hundred years from the present (Tipping 1993). Five reaches only within the gravel rich upland valleys were investigated (Tipping 1992, 1993), at (a) Swindon Haugh, (b) Calroust, (d) the Halter Burn, (f) the Wooler Water and (g) on the River Breamish at Powburn (Figure 7.1). These provide analyses of fluvial change that are far from continuous. Dating controls were able to be obtained on single short lived depositional phases within sequences that are demonstrably more complicated, but which could not be dated using the techniques applied (Plate 7.3). To obtain a more continuous record of fluvial sedimentation a sediment stratigraphic sequence at Akeld Steads in the Milfield Basin (Borek 1975) was re-examined and ^{14}C dated (Tipping 1998a; locality e; Figure 7.1). This sequence is a stacked fill in which the oldest sediments lie at the base of an aggrading sediment stratigraphy (Howard & Macklin 1999). The Yetholm Loch sediment record (locality c; Figure 7.1) was described in Chapter 3, where the

actively forming when the farm was built, and incision from this surface had probably occurred. The modern road into the upper valley, constructed after 1822 cal AD, runs between Belford and Swindon Cottage on gravels of Terrace II, implying some stability of the valley floor before this time, although it still floods sufficiently to claim lives (Archer 1992). The older road into the heart of the valley mapped by Stobie (1770) keeps to the high ground above Mowhaugh (Figure 1.3; Tipping 1993). Pollen analyses from the peat ^{14}C dated at Calroust showed that tree types associated with mid-eighteenth-century plantations (Section 2.4c) were not recorded. Together these constraints suggest that peat formed between *c* 1670 and 1770 cal AD, probably towards the older end of the range. Younger terrace surfaces (Swindon III and IV) are of uncertain geomorphic significance. There is no clear evidence that these terrace fills represent separate aggradations, and they may only be terrace surfaces bevelled across Terrace Swindon II sediments by periodic lateral channel migration.

The entire width of the valley floor on these reaches is probably younger than 300 cal years old. The valley floor was totally transformed by the aggradation of very coarse gravels in channels with much higher discharges than currently observed (McEwen 1985). The valley

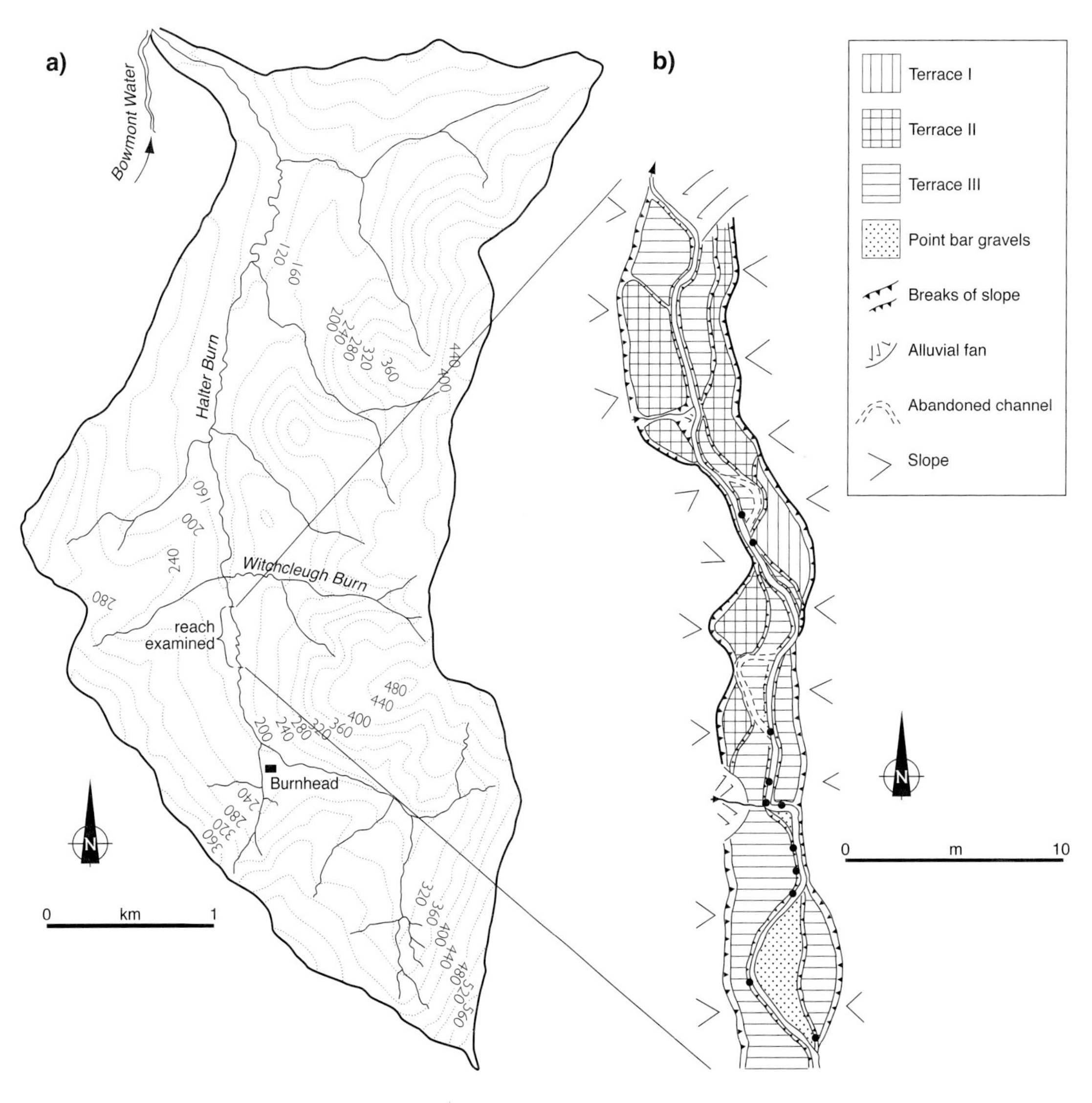

Figure 7.2
(a) The catchment of the Halter Burn; (b) the mapped reach showing the distribution of terrace surfaces and other features of the valley floor.

floor is probably still adjusting to this extreme event. McEwen (1985) studied horizontal channel changes on the upper Bowmont Water over the last *c* 250 years using cartographic data. The mid-eighteenth century cal AD Bowmont Water was seen by McEwen (1985) as stable but this interpretation relies heavily on the veracity of Roy's mapping (Tipping 1993). Geomorphological and sedimentological data suggest a different picture (cf. Rumsby & Macklin 1994).

7.4 The Halter Burn

Data on fluvial change in this upland valley east of the Bowmont (Figure 7.1) have been used by Tipping (1992) and Mercer and Tipping (1994) but not presented in detail before. The Halter Burn has a small catchment (basin area *c* 190km^2, basin length 6.2km) in andesites and superficial Quaternary deposits in which a 3rd Order (Strahler) stream 7km long falls from 490m OD on The Curr some 400m to the Bowmont Water east of Kirk Yetholm (Figure 7.2a). Incised below the till and periglacial deposits mantling the lower slopes is a narrow valley floor, widening sufficiently to contain a complex terrace sequence north of Burnhead Farm. A 400m reach up and downstream of the only ^{14}C dateable stratigraphy was mapped and surveyed to Ordnance Datum (Figure 7.2b).

Three terrace surfaces are identified. The highest, Terrace I is 2 to 2.5m above the river, composed of coarse to very coarse gravel and is undated. Terrace II is around 0.5m below this: it too is undated. Exposed in stream bank sections is Terrace III, the youngest and most extensive terrace surface (Figure 7.2b), *c* 1.4m above the river. Its complex sediment stratigraphy comprises a series of shallow gravel rich channel fills and silty overbank deposits. Figure 7.3 is a 10m long measured left bank section in the sediments of Terrace III. Prior to sediment aggradation in this terrace fill, the river had incised through the deposits of Terraces I and II and into glacial till. On this till surface a gleyed soil developed, and within the soil grew a shrub or young tree (<20 years old; the species was not identified). Roots of this shrub were ^{14}C dated to 2557 to 2407 cal BC (Table 7.1). The roots were

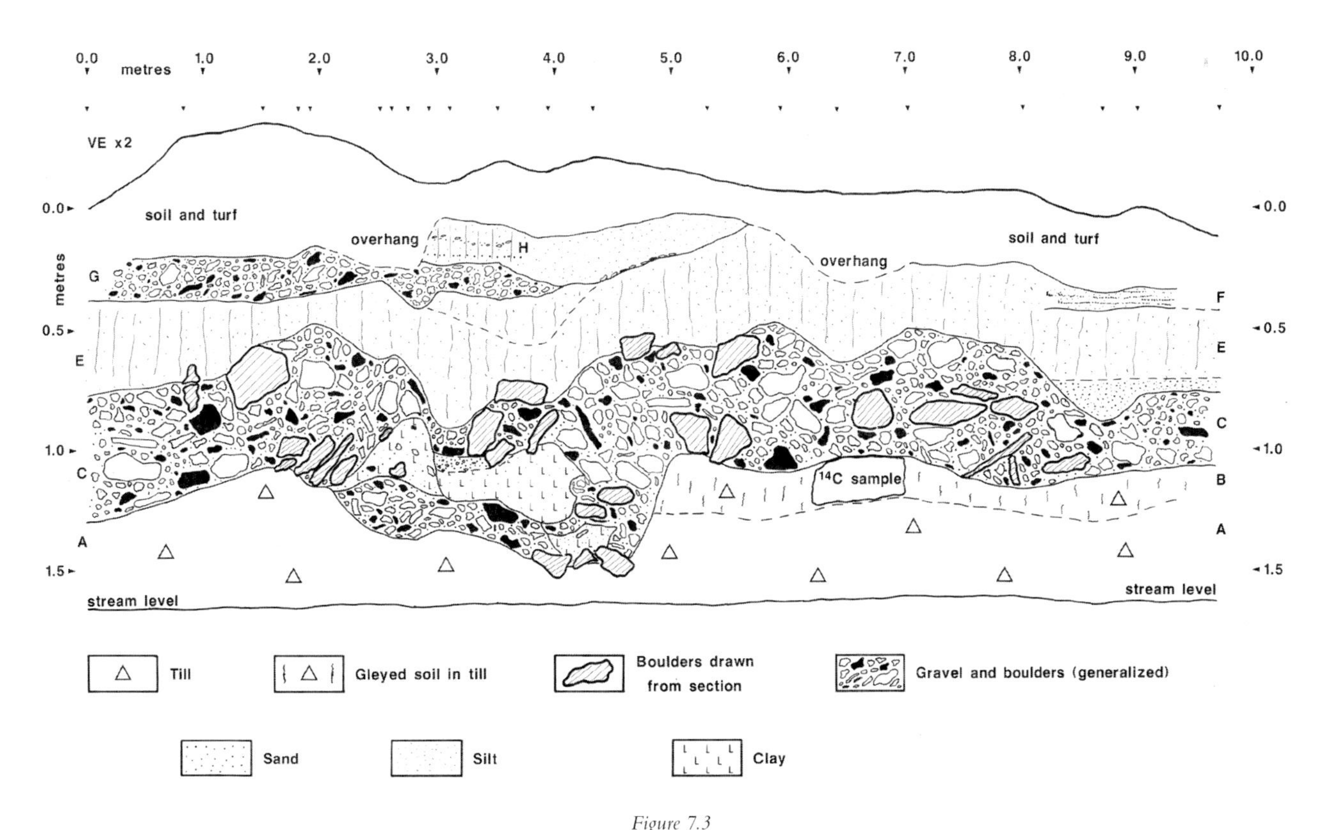

Figure 7.3
Measured section of fluvial sediments in Terrace III of the Halter Burn showing the position of the ^{14}C dated sample of wood (SRR-3664; Table 7.1) at the base of the stratigraphy.

probably preserved through rapid burial by overlying coarse gravels which eroded the upper roots. The roots are not intrusive and are thought to closely predate subsequent gravel deposition. This gravel, with boulders with long axes >1.5m, was initially highly erosive, incising into and removing the gleyed soil over all but a small area. Stream power probably greatly exceeded that of the present stream. Subsequent events in aggradation are not dated. Laterally extensive overbank silts overlie the gravels and finer gravels and silts continue to the terrace surface. Incision from this terrace surface with almost no valley widening except at point bars is the only recorded event from that time. This single dated point indicates that terrace surfaces not significantly higher above the present river than Terrace II at Swindon Haugh (Section 7.3) can be substantially different in time. This Early Bronze Age activity is also the youngest stratigraphic evidence in the catchment: there is no evidence in the Halter Burn of the late historic events seen on the upper Bowmont Water, and this absence of evidence is endorsed by Dixon's (2003, illus. 6) depiction of extensive Medieval monastic structures in the Halter Burn to the edge of the cliff above the valley floor, showing that no lateral erosion of the valley floor has occurred in the last several hundred years.

7.5 The Wooler Water at Earle Mill

The Harthope Burn and Wooler Water catchment is one of the major river systems draining The Cheviot (Figure 7.1), cutting through andesites in a fault controlled valley (Common 1953; Section 1.4), its narrow straight upper valley floor incised below a complex array of glacial and periglacial sediments. Fluvial deposits in these upper reaches are, predominantly, active gravel bars and low, undated but probably recent terraces (Milne 1982). Below the confluence with the Common Burn (Figure 7.1) the river descends a steep bedrock gorge called the Happy Valley at Skirl Naked (Figure 7.4a) in a piedmont reach spilling onto the flat valley floor west of Coldgate Mill. Geomorphological mapping and surveying to Ordnance Datum between the Happy Valley, where the Harthope Burn becomes the Wooler Water and the town of Wooler, defined five terrace surfaces (Figure 7.4a). A measured section across the valley at transect A–B is drawn in Figure 7.4c. Most terrace fills and surfaces are much more substantial features than those described in the uplands, and some have been named rather than numbered.

Fluvioglacial gravels mantle the lower and middle slopes of the hills, typical of areas surrounding the core of the Cheviot Hills, and descend to the valley floor to around 90m asl in tall cliffs 25m above the present very deeply incised river (Figure 7.4a). These surfaces are frequently studded with kettle hole depressions indicating an origin in Late Devensian deglaciation from Tweed Valley ice sheets (Figure 1.2), and are related to subglacial meltwater channels (Clapperton 1971b).

Regional deglaciation may have occurred as late as *c* 13 000 cal BC (McCabe, Knight & McCarron 1998; Teasdale & Hughes 1999). On the Wooler Water the lowest fluvioglacial gravel surfaces were abandoned as the river incised at least 25m to below the present valley floor (Figure 7.4b). The Haugh Head Terrace then aggraded, with at least 10m of poorly exposed coarse gravels to around 75m asl at Earle Mill. The Haugh Head Terrace is the 'gravel plain' mapped by Clapperton (1967) and Clapperton, Durno and Squires (1971). From just west of Coldgate Mill (Figure 7.4a) this right bank terrace surface has a gradient of around 13.7m/km, and widens considerably to more than 450m north of Haugh Head. The coarse gravels were probably eroded during incision from the fluvioglacial fills (Clapperton 1967). The Haugh Head Terrace is not directly dated but internal stratigraphic evidence and dating controls from the subsequent deposition of the Earle Mill Terrace (below) constrains its age. Rarely, exposures show the coarse gravel fill of the Haugh Head Terrace to directly overlie lacustrine laminated silts and clays formed at a late stage in deglaciation from a large lake in the Milfield Basin (Butler 1907; Clapperton 1967, 1971; Payton 1980, 1992; Tipping 1998a). Deposition of the Haugh Head Gravels is more likely to have occurred after regional deglaciation, and occurred prior to the earliest Holocene period (below). It may be of Younger Dryas age (*c* 10 500 to 9500 cal BC) but is probably slightly earlier (below; Section 7.8).

Clapperton (1967) and Clapperton *et al* (1971) did not recognise later terrace fills nested below the Haugh Head Terrace within the incised gorge of the Wooler Water, but the Wooler Water has incised through the Haugh Head Terrace and subsequently built up and incised through three lower and later terrace fills (Figure 7.4b). The most substantial of these, the Earle Mill Terrace, formed following incision of around 8m from the Haugh Head Terrace surface: sections at Earle Mill seen in 2003 show the basal sediments of the Earle Mill Terrace close to present river level. The

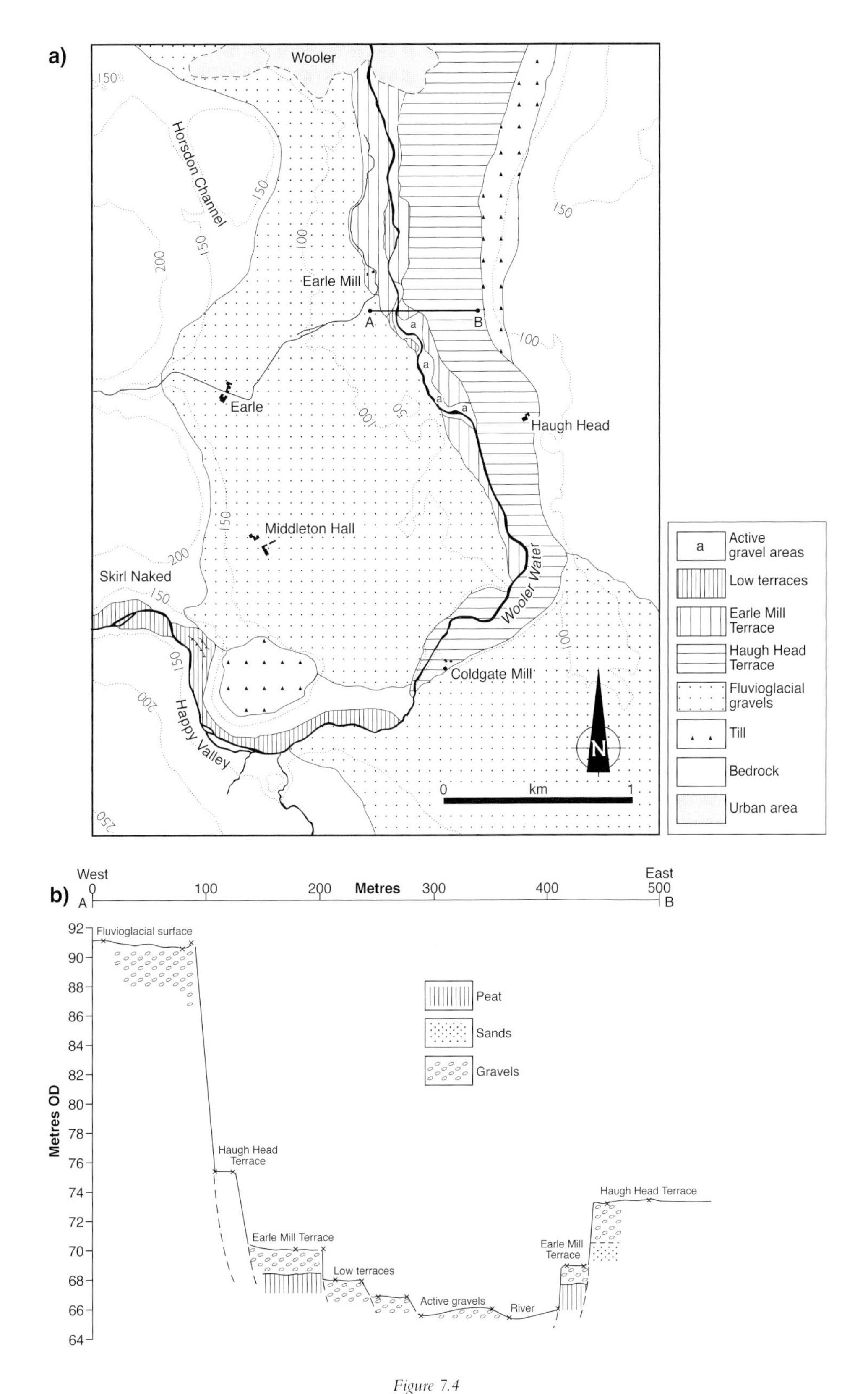

Figure 7.4

(a) The mapped reach of the Wooler Water between the Happy Valley and Wooler, showing the distribution of terrace surfaces and active gravel bars; (b) a section across the incised valley of the Wooler Water at transect A–B showing the altitudes of terrace surfaces and schematic representations of their stratigraphies.

Table 7.2
Sediment stratigraphy of the Earle Mill Terrace near Earle Mill, modified from Clapperton *et al* (1971).

0–30cm:	sand, gravel, pebbles and boulders
30–67cm:	bands of fine, medium and coarse sands and silt
67–155cm:	black grass-sedge peat with silt incorporated at the top of the unit, and lenses of wood remains and abundant macro-remains of *Carex* spp. (sedge) and *Phragmites communis* (common reed) stems and common *Equisetum* spp. (horsetails)
155–166cm:	discontinuous creamy white marl of calcified *Carex* spp. debris
166–172cm:	well preserved *Carex-Phragmites* peat
172–188cm:	silt
188cm +:	structureless matrix supported gravel

Earle Mill Terrace has a clearly defined surface some 3m below that of the Haugh Head Terrace, 3.5 to 4m above the present river, mapped over *c* 1.5km above and below Earle Mill with a gradient of around 8.5m/km. The fill of the Earle Mill Terrace is complex. Basal sediments are fine grained calcareous silts, silty clays and marls above a floor of coarse gravels. These indicate a low velocity stream or pond. The calcium is derived from solution of some gravels in the stream banks. These fine grained sediments are replaced by 2 to 3m of a highly organic fen or reedswamp peat. Clapperton *et al* (1971) thought that peat might have infilled kettle hole depressions within the 'gravel plain' but it is widespread across the incised valley floor and is interpreted here as representing the formation of peat on a valley floor when river flow was very limited. Table 7.2 is a sediment stratigraphy described by Clapperton *et al* (1971) at Earle Mill.

Clapperton *et al* (1971) tried to define the age of the peat from pollen analyses. Pollen was sparse in the calcareous peat. The date of peat initiation is not clear but is thought to have been very early in the Holocene period, predating the appearance of trees in the region (before *c* 8750 cal BC; Chapter 3). Peat accumulated until after the *Ulmus* (elm) decline at *c* 4000 cal BC. The Earle Mill Terrace aggradation seems to span most of the Holocene. Incision prior to this, from the Haugh Head Terrace, happened prior to or in the earliest Holocene, probably during the Younger Dryas Stadial. Throughout peat formation, over some 5000 cal years, there was no demonstrable fluvial transport of mineral sediments. The peat is succeeded gradually by a coarsening up sequence of fluvial sediments, commencing with silts incorporated within the uppermost layers of peat and culminating in the deposition of a very coarse gravel (Table 7.2). The sediments are well sorted, strongly trough cross bedded sands and silts, with gravel lenses and more laterally extensive gravel beds, strongly imbricated downstream, and often exhibiting point bar stratification. At their coarsest, gravels are 'principally of poorly bedded gravel and cobbles, from 20mm to 90mm in size, contained in a coarse sandy matrix ... 2 to 2.5m thick' (Clapperton *et al* 1971, 14–15). The contact between peat and overlying minerogenic fluvial sediments is conformable. The age of the uppermost peat was defined by ^{14}C dating (Tipping 1992; Mercer & Tipping 1994). To avoid the possibility of hard water error from peat-forming plants, wood that had fallen onto the peat surface was selected by sieving, and branches, twigs and trunk wood combined in the radiometric assay (Table 7.1). Sand buried the peat at some time between 2250 and 1950 cal BC.

The date of incision from the Earle Mill Terrace is not dated. Two terrace surfaces around 2m lower than the Earle Mill Terrace are mapped (Figure 7.4b) but are undated. These gravel rich terraces lie respectively *c* 2 and 1m above the coarse gravel point bar deposits of the present river. These low terraces may be very recent because Archer (1992) describes the very rapid trenching by the Wooler Water through the Earle Mill and Haugh Head Terraces at Haugh Head itself since World War II, not through natural change but through quarrying upstream of river gravels.

7.6 The River Breamish at Powburn

The River Breamish flows eastward to drain to the River Till (Figure 7.1). The upland streams of the Linhope and Rowhope Burns were not investigated and the work (Tipping 1992) described only the valley floor sediments east of Ingram (Figure 7.5), around 15km east of the upland watershed to the Harthope Burn. About 1km upstream of Ingram the only substantive terrace surface in the area mapped commences, the Powburn Terrace, widening to more than 1.5km between Brandon and Branton (Figure 7.5). Below Brandon the present river is increasingly incised to depths exceeding 4.5m. Along the centre of the valley over 6m of gravels have been proved from commercial boreholes beneath the Powburn Terrace surface (Northern Aggregates Ltd pers. comm.). Gravel quarries have worked the valley floor since the 1930s (Clapperton 1967), and continue to work the deposits westward (Welfare unpublished). Powburn Quarry was visited in 1988, when fresh faces were exposed from the flat terrace surface at around 90m asl to underlying till in the area depicted in Figure 7.5.

The basal unit was a reddish-brown glacial lodgement till, 2m below the terrace surface at the valley side but deeper than 6m in the central axis. The surface was not weathered but a soil may have been eroded during aggradation of overlying fluvial gravels. Above the till were thin (20 to 25cm) clay rich structureless gravelly sands representing the earliest fluvial activity at the base of the Powburn Terrace fill. Within this basal facies two separate minerogenic rich peat lenses were found, Localities 2 and 3, around 80m apart on the north side of the quarry. Locality 2 was around 3.6m below the ground surface; Locality 3 was shallower at 2.3m depth. These were up to 65cm thick and were laterally extensive over several metres. Both were covered by several metres of fluvial sands and gravels. These two lenses were ^{14}C dated (Tipping 1992) by assays SRR-3660 and -3661 (Table 7.1). Sample thicknesses were large because the assumption is that individual lenses accumulated very fast in this wet environment. The amounts subsampled allowed the ^{14}C dating of different organic components.

Rootlets growing in the 24cm of felted peat sampled for assay SRR-3660 were sorted by sieving into two size components, roughly separating fleshy fine roots from Gramineae (grasses) or Cyperaceae (sedges) from coarser woody roots, to find out whether one was intrusive. The two components agree in ^{14}C age at 2σ precision estimates, though not at 1σ (Table 7.1). It is not possible to determine which fraction is the more correct, but it is assumed that the younger, coarser roots are intrusive from overlying surfaces subsequently eroded. This lens was buried by aggrading coarse gravels after 803 to 769 cal BC (*c* 786 cal BC). Pollen analyses of three spectra within the peat (Tipping 1992) show that

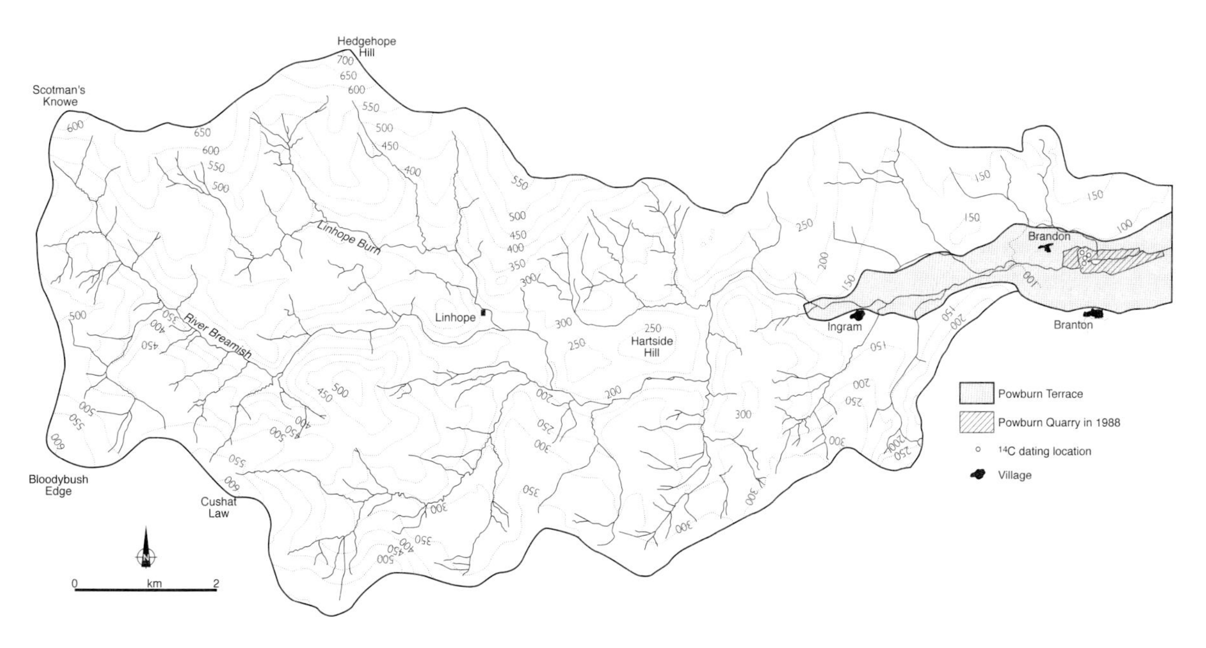

Figure 7.5
The catchment of the River Breamish west of Powburn Quarry, the extent of the Powburn Terrace filling the valley east of Ingram, and the location of the quarry at Powburn in 1989 when visited.

Plate 7.4
The surface of the very wide surface of the Powburn Terrace below Ingram in the Breamish Valley (see the car at extreme left for scale), looking south west from Heddon Hill to Fawdon Dean and showing the furlongs of broad rig cultivation that collectively suggest the river had ceased to flood by some time in the Medieval period.

tree taxa of wetland affinity, *Alnus* (alder) and *Betula* (birch) were abundant, possibly on the wet and marshy valley floor itself. Dryland trees are poorly represented, with only *Quercus* (oak) and *Corylus/Myrica* (cf. hazel) probably growing on the dry slopes. Gramineae <8μm anl-D pollen (wild grasses) was not abundant although the occurrence of *Plantago lanceolata* (ribwort plantain) suggests some pasture within the pollen catchment. However, perhaps because of the abundance of trees on the valley floor the landscape above the valley floor is not well depicted in the pollen analyses.

Coarse rootlets sieved from the 20cm of fibrous peat at Locality 3 (assay SRR-3661a; Table 7.1) were significantly younger at 2σ precision than either of two chemical fractions obtained from amorphous organic matter. Coarse rootlets may have intruded from above into this lens. The humin fraction (assay SRR-3661c; Table 7.1) is more likely than the humic acid fraction to contain decayed rootlets, and this may also be too young. Perhaps the most reliable assay is from humic acids derived from amorphous peat (assay SRR-3661b; Table 7.1), suggesting that this lens was buried, firstly by fluvial sands and then by gravels, after 395 to 267 cal BC (*c* 331 cal BC). The peat at Locality 3 was almost certainly buried by aggrading fluvial sediment after Locality 2, and this peat was around 1.5m higher than Locality 2 towards the edge of the valley floor. Five pollen spectra (Tipping 1992) describe a peat forming under very wet conditions in which *Equisetum* (horsetails) and Cyperaceae (sedges) were abundant. However, the wetland trees dominant on the valley floor earlier at Locality 2 had been lost.

At both Localities 2 and 3 the peats were conformably covered by fluvial sands, matrix supported and clast supported imbricated medium to very coarse gravels, coarsening upward over 2 to 3m in a series of shallow channels. The very coarse calibre of the gravels, the very limited occurrence of fines (except infilling abandoned channels), the high frequency of channels, and the absence of sedimentary structures within the gravels all suggest that the gravel fill was laid down by braided rivers, not a single thread stream as at present. Stream powers were far in excess of those pertaining today. The major sources of this coarse sediment were fluvioglacial deposits within the catchment (Clapperton 1967). Attempts to define the rate of fluvial

Table 7.3

Details of the radiocarbon assays obtained on fluvial sediments in the River Glen at Akeld Steads.

Lab. No. (SRR-)	*No. in Fig. 7.7*	*Station*	*Mean Depth (cm)*	*Sediment Depth (cm)*	*Organic Component Dated*	*^{14}C Age* BP ± 1σ	*δ^{13}C (‰)*	*Calibrated Age* BC/AD ± 1σ *and Intercept Ages*	*Mean Calibrated Age* BC/AD
5172	(8)	1	44	41–46	humic acid	2730 ± 45	−29.2	909 (843) 819 BC	864 BC
5173	(7)	10	85	80–90	humic acid	4070 ± 40	−28.4	2837 (2582) 2500 BC	2669 BC
5174	(6)	1	87	84–90	humic acid	3320 ± 45	−29.5	1673 (1605, 1557, 1541) 1521 BC	1597 BC
5175	(5)	1	122.5	120–125	humic acid	3710 ± 45	−29.2	2174 (2128, 2080, 2045) 1986 BC	2080
5176	(4)	10	197.5	195–205	humic acid	6575 ± 45	−28.4	5563 (5447) 5440 BC	5501
5177	(3)	1	256	251–261	humic acid	6510 ± 45	−28.4	5444 (5437) 5384 BC	5414
5178	(2)	1	417	412–422	humic acid	9940 ± 40	−29.4	9362 (9122, 9116, 9081) 9052 BC	9207 BC
5179	(1)	1	465	460–470	humic acid	10080 ± 45	−28.1	9905 (9650, 9404, 9397) 9181 BC	9543 BC

aggradation in this gravel were made by ^{14}C dating two organic rich silt and sand lenses representing shallow channels infilled with sediment following avulsion. Towards the centre of the valley at Locality 1, 2.6m below the terrace surface but relatively much higher in the sequence than either Localities 2 or 3, a poorly humified fine fibrous peat filled a 4m wide channel to a thickness of *c* 15cm. Plant remains could not be separated, but the amorphous organic matter was chemically differentiated into humic acid and humin fractions (assay SRR-3659a and b respectively; Table 7.1). The fractions are not different in age, and the average indicates a date of channel infilling between 85 and 142 cal AD (*c* 114 cal AD). Four pollen spectra (Tipping 1992) suggest that trees were absent from the valley floor and the slopes above, that Gramineae <8μm anl-D (wild grasses) dominated the landscape and that grazing pressures were probably significant. This channel was then filled with a highly organic structureless clayey sandy silt and then overlain erosively by 2m of coarse gravels. In cliffs over 4m high bordering the River Breamish, Locality 4 comprises coarse to very coarse clast supported gravels except for one shallow and eroded channel from 80 to 110cm depth filled with silty clay, organic towards the base but peat rich only in thin bands. Assay SRR-3662 (Table 7.1) was too small to be physically or chemically separated. The whole sample yielded an age of 9751 to 9094 cal BC (*c* 9422 cal BC) despite the sample being the highest in the sequence. The ^{14}C assay is thought to be in error for reasons that are unclear.

The coarse gravels do not rise to the terrace surface except in a few places. Instead, the uppermost deposit is a structureless sandy silt overbank sediment some 1 to 2.5m thick filling shallow channels in the gravel, deposited before the River Breamish began to incise through the terrace fill. This formed after *c* 114 cal AD. Some archaeological data can be used to suggest historic landscape change. The portable finds of Neolithic axes from the Powburn Terrace surface at Brandon (Jobey 1961) and Branton, and the Early Bronze Age socketed axe from Branton (Schmidt & Burgess 1981) cannot date the sediment. The village of Brandon sits squarely on the Powburn Terrace surface (Figure 7.5). It is first recorded in the early twelfth century cal AD (Hodgson 1923). This is assumed to have been built after the terrace surface had ceased to be frequently inundated by floods. Upstream at the gorge of Ingram, however, flooding and stream bank erosion remained a serious problem into the sixteenth century cal AD (Dodds 1997). Beautifully preserved patterns of broad rig ploughing across the Powburn Terrace surface (Plate 7.4), not older than the ninth century cal AD (Fowler 2002) and potentially much later (Halliday 2003), are suggested by Welfare (unpublished) to be structured into fields between contemporary stream courses. This suggests that the terrace surface carried streams when these fields were ploughed, and if a Medieval age for broad rig is accepted, that fluvial incision, now exceeding 4m between Branton and Brandon (Figure 7.5), may have occurred after the Medieval period.

7.7 The River Glen at Akeld Steads

The River Glen is the name for the Bowmont Water below its confluence with the College Burn (Figure 7.1; Plate 7.5). East of this confluence the valley changes character from the steep, narrow gravel rich and actively avulsing valley floors of the uplands to the broad extensive silt laden floodplains of the lowlands of the Milfield Basin. The basin itself is the largest in north-east England, and has been infilled since deglaciation by a complex series of fluvioglacial and glaciodeltaic gravels, proglacial lacustrine sediments and wide ribbons of fluvial silts and sands (Butler 1907; Clapperton 1970; 1971a; Payton 1980; Tipping 1998a; Waddington 1999). Borek (1975) produced an undated pollen diagram for a valley floor peat at Akeld Steads (Figure 7.6) which suggested that a complete Holocene sediment stratigraphy could be retrieved from the floodplain of the River Glen. Tipping (1998a) identified that the location of this stratigraphy could be further used to understand the temporal relation between peat growth and fluvial sedimentation across one transect (a–b; Figure 7.6) by recording the spatial and temporal distributions of sediments from these sources (Figure 7.7). This transect extends across half the width of the floodplain. It is unlikely that major events have been missed by the river lying some distance away (Tipping 1998a). This sediment stratigraphy showed that peat growth was periodically disrupted by the deposition of silts and sands pushed across the peat surface by floods: eight ^{14}C assays (Table 7.3) allowed the definition of temporal change, presented in detail by Tipping (1998a) and only summarised in this report.

Plate 7.5
The floodplain surface of the lowland River Glen just upstream of Akeld Steads, looking west towards the northern Cheviot Hills. Beneath this single surface are over 6m of sediments that have accumulated since the earliest Holocene period.

Filling the Milfield Basin following deglaciation were lake clays, to an altitude of around 45m asl (Clapperton 1971). The lake appears to have still existed to altitudes higher than 40m asl after *c* 10 150 cal BC (Payton 1992). However, patchy valley floor peats at Akeld Steads formed at the base of the steep slope at *c* 33m asl (Station 1: Figure 7.7) at around 9540 cal BC (assay SRR-5179: Table 7.3). This implies very major incision of some 6 to 7m from the former lake surface between 10 150 and 9540 cal BC, between the later part of the Lateglacial Interstadial and the early Holocene period.

From *c* 9450 cal BC the River Glen at Akeld Steads has been aggrading, not necessarily continuously, but producing a layer cake stratigraphy in contrast to upland rivers draining the Cheviot Hills (Sections 7.3 to 7.6). From *c* 9200 cal BC until *c* 5400 cal BC (assays SRR-5178 and -5177 at Station 1; Figure 7.7; Table 7.3), fluvial activity was ineffectual in preventing peat growth on the valley side. At 5400 cal BC silts and clays probably derived from increased overbank flooding pushed across the peat to Station J, synchronously at *c* 5500 cal BC (assay SRR-5176; Table 7.3). Reductions in fluvial deposition at the valley edge are then indicated by peat growing across former overbank sediments between Station J and 1 (Figure 7.7), dated by assays SRR-5176 and -5175 (Table 7.3), before *c* 2080 cal BC. To the south-west, towards the present river, there is no apparent reduction in fluvial sedimentation after 5400 cal BC (Stations 6–4; Figure 7.7). Incorrect correlations between stations may explain the inconsistency of assay SRR-5173, which is older though seemingly higher in the stratigraphy than assays SRR-5175 and -5174 (Figure 7.7; Table 7.3). Using the internally consistent series of assays at Station 1 (Figure 7.7), a phase of peat colonisation occurred between *c* 2080 cal BC (SRR-5175) and *c* 1600 cal BC (SRR-5174) but its scale is unclear. Shortly after *c* 864 cal BC (SRR-5172: Figure 7.7; Table 7.3) the replacement of peat by mineral sediments across the entire transect is thought to have been caused by later, perhaps nineteenth-century, mineralisation of drained peats. It has no fluvial significance save that the sediment stratigraphy for the last *c* 3000 years has been destroyed, and correlations with other catchments in this period cannot be made.

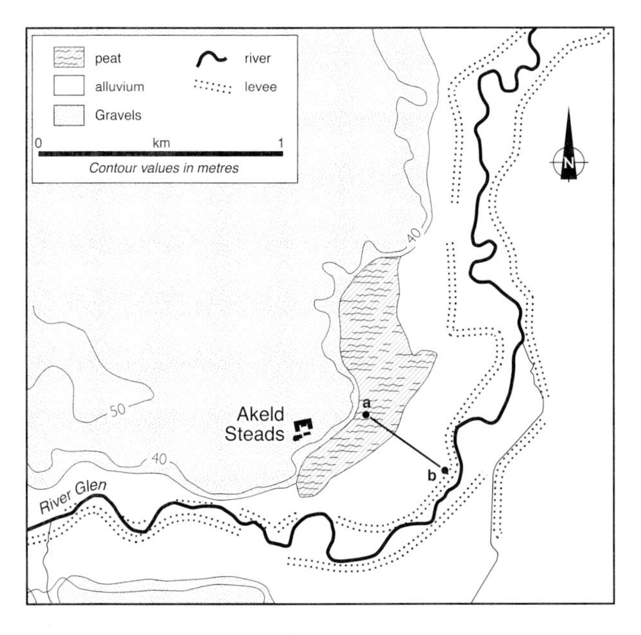

Figure 7.6
The valley floor of the River Glen at Akeld Steads (see Figure 7.1), showing the fluvioglacial gravels of a former delta on high ground above 40m asl, the erosional edge to the alluvium of the floodplain and the position and extent of peat at the edge of the alluvium.

7.8 A fluvial chronology for the northern Cheviot Hills

Figure 7.8 tries to define phases of accelerated fluvial activity from the reaches examined. The types of fluvial activity differed markedly between upland and lowland catchments. In upland catchments at Swindon Haugh and the Halter Burn the thicknesses of aggraded sediments were rarely more than a metre or so within one phase. This is probably a product of the very limited availability of coarse grained fluvioglacial sands and gravels and the abundance of thick till sheets. The gravels that filled the entire valley floor at times of accelerated activity were reworked from pre-existing fluvial deposits, concentrated over time by the winnowing of clays and silts. Rivers stripped out much of the evidence of former depositional phases. They reworked valley floor sediments and spread coarse gravels out in avulsing channel fills, with only limited deposition of fine grained overbank flood sediments. The comprehensive destruction of existing sediments in these contexts by fast flowing, highly charged rivers, much more powerful than at the present day, means that only the last phase is recorded with any clarity. In the upper Bowmont Valley this occurred only 300 cal years ago, waning after *c* 1770 cal AD. Astonishingly in the neighbouring Halter Burn, the last major depositional event was 4000 cal years ago.

in several upland catchments obliterated virtually all evidence of former conditions, but these short lived impacts make regional correlations difficult. Only lowland catchments show any evidence for alluvial deposition prior to *c* 2500 cal BC. At around this time the Halter Burn and Wooler Water catchments became highly active, not necessarily synchronously but sufficiently close in time to define the period 2500 to 2000 cal BC as one of exceptional geomorphic change. Similarly, events recorded in the first millennium cal BC were transforming and widespread. The historic period appears to have been one of relative quiescence until heightened activity, aggradational and erosional, occurred within the last 300 cal years.

In this discussion one critical element has not been considered; cause. What each of these major fluvial events signifies is a response to change but they cannot by themselves reveal what were causal factors. Resolution of this problem must remain until the next and final chapter.

Chapter 8

AN ENVIRONMENTAL HISTORY OF THE NORTHERN CHEVIOT HILLS

8.1 Introduction

Chapters 3 to 6 explored the sedimentological and palynological records of the seven pollen sites analysed within the Bowmont Valley. Chapter 7 described what is understood of the evolution of rivers and valley floors through the Holocene period in the northern and eastern Cheviot Hills. This final chapter will synthesise these different strands, and incorporate additional lines of evidence from archaeological survey and excavation and from documentary sources.

Comparisons will be drawn with sequences around the Bowmont Valley. Chapter 1 defined the extent of the northern Cheviot Hills (Figure 1.2). The area around the northern Cheviot Hills pertinent to this analysis is difficult to define rigidly because upland regions broadly similar to the Cheviot Hills and Southern Uplands extend south along the Pennine ridge to below Sheffield and north around the headwaters of the River Tweed to approach Edinburgh and Glasgow (Figure 8.1). A renewed sensitivity to regional differentiation in the explanation of landscapes is increasingly apparent in writings on the major themes addressed in this report, in patterns of past climate (Huntley 1999; Magny *et al* 2003; Langdon & Barber 2004), in the extent and continuity of 'natural' regions determined by geology and climate (Brown, Horsfield & Thompson 1993; Brown, Birks & Thompson 1993), in past vegetation patterns (Tipping 1994), in archaeological typologies and associated chronologies (RCAHMS 1997; Dark 2000; Barclay 2001), documented settlement and land use (Thirsk 2000; Williamson 2002, 2003) and in geomorphic responses to either climate change or land use pressures (Macklin 1999; Brunsden 2001; Macklin & Lewin 2003). This chapter will focus on processes and events in a region from the Forth Estuary to the Stainmore Pass, the largest gap in the Pennines and

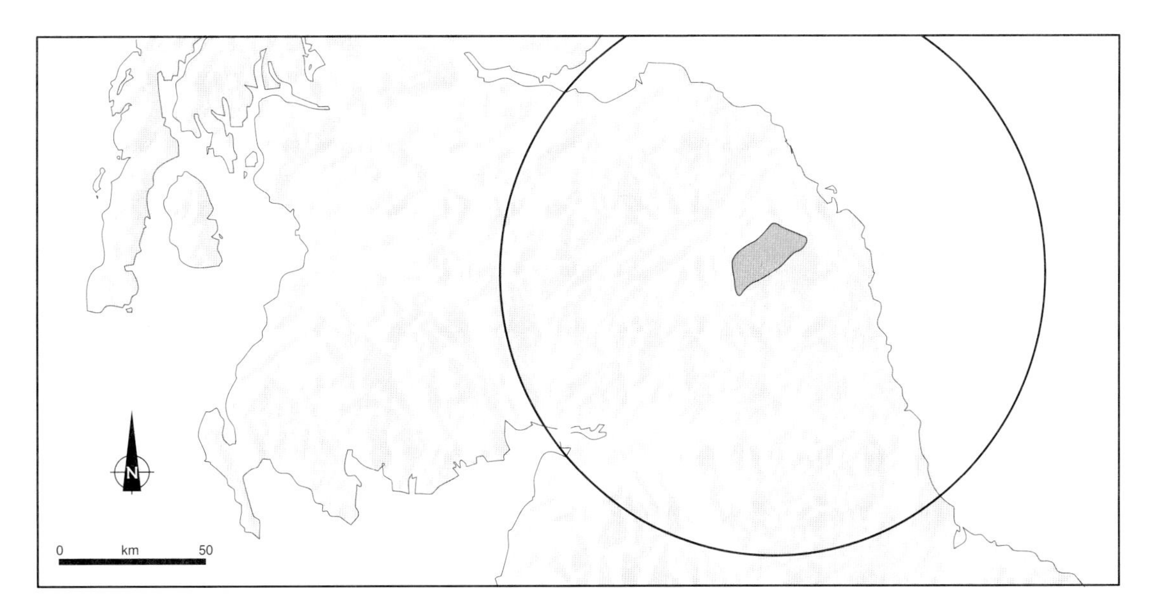

Figure 8.1

(a) The uplands of Britain and the region around the northern Cheviot Hills concentrated on in this chapter; (b) the region shown at larger scale with the locations of archaeological sites and landscapes, records of vegetation history, geomorphic sequences and palaeoclimatic analyses described in Chapter 8.

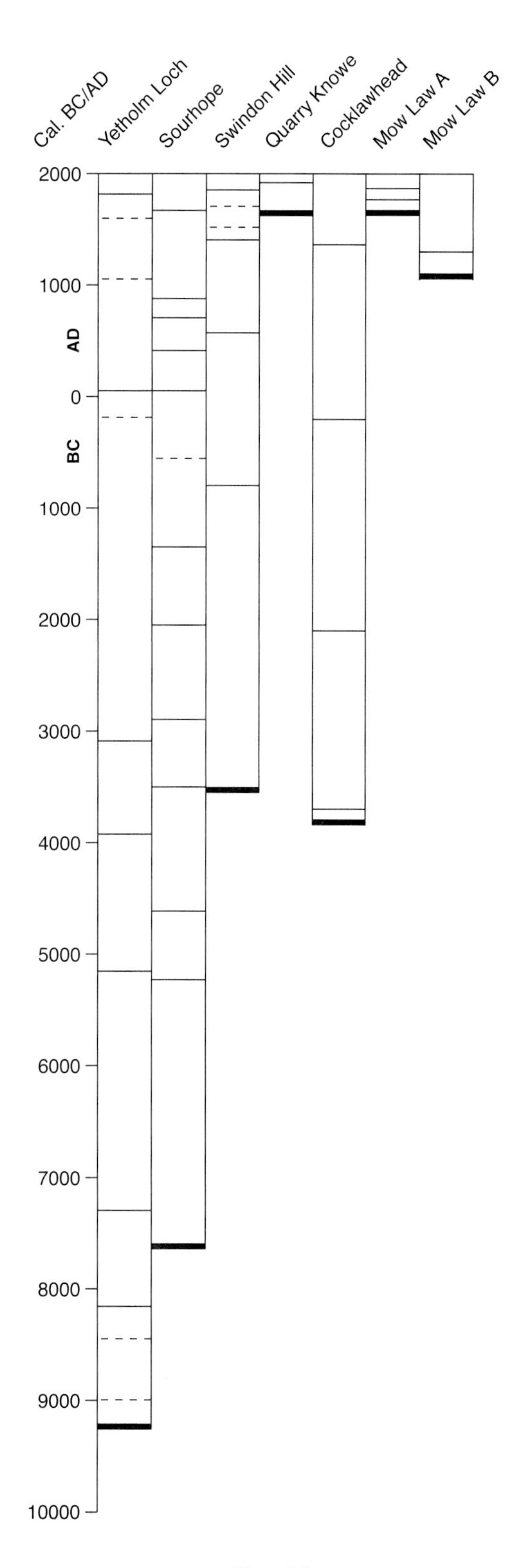

Figure 8.3
Event boundaries depicting environmental change in the northern Cheviot Hills identified by the temporal occurrence of pollen assemblage zone and subzone boundaries at the seven pollen sites in the Bowmont Valley (Tables 3.5, 4.3, 5.3, 5.9, 6.4 and 6.7) .

Table 8.2
The periods of major landscape change in the northern Cheviot Hills defined from Figure 8.3 and other data.

1400 cal AD to 2000 cal AD	(550–0 cal BP)
500 cal AD to 1400 cal AD	(1450–550 cal BP)
250 cal BC to 500 cal AD	(2200–1450 cal BP)
2500 cal BC to 250 cal BC	(4500–2200 cal BP)
3900 cal BC to 2500 cal BC	(5900–4500 cal BP)
5200 cal BC to 3900 cal BC	(7200–5900 cal BP)
7600 cal BC to 5200 cal BC	(9600–7200 cal BP)
9300 cal BC to 7600 cal BC	(11300–9600 cal BP)
prior to 9300 cal BC	(prior to 11300 cal BP)

BC comparisons can be made between the lowlands at Yetholm Loch and the interior upland valleys typified by the site of Sourhope (Chapter 4), but it is not possible from this data-set to describe landscape change in the fullest sense until *c* 4400 cal BC, after which there are pollen records from higher surfaces at Swindon Hill (Chapter 5) and Cocklawhead (Chapter 6), and much detail for the last *c* 1000 years from other sequences (Figure 8.3).

8.3 Setting the stage: events before 9300 cal BC

8.3a Devensian lateglacial interstadial geomorphic activity and climate changes

The direct evidence for landscape change prior to the formation of lake sediments at Yetholm Loch (Chapter 3) is for a series of fluvial depositional and erosional events best understood on the Wooler Water and at Akeld Steads (Sections 7.5, 7.7; Tipping 1998a). The scale of these dwarf almost all subsequent events in the fluvial records. The aggradation of the extensive, thick and exceptionally coarse braided river gravels beneath the Haugh Head Terrace, spilling out from the Harthope Burn south of Wooler, is distinct from and later than the kettled outwash formed during regional deglaciation (Clapperton 1967, 1971b). The Haugh Head Terrace formed during the Devensian Lateglacial period. This was characterised by an early very warm interstadial period between *c* 12 000 and 11 000 cal BC called the Lateglacial or Windermere Interstadial and a subsequent severe climatic deterioration called the Loch Lomond or Younger Dryas Stadial between *c* 11 000 and 9800 cal BC (Walker *et al* 1994; Walker *et al* 1999). The Haugh Head Terrace formed a deltaic spread of gravels pushing into 'Lake Ewart' in the Milfield Basin, and was contemporaneous with part of the infilling of this huge lake with fine grained laminated lake sediments (Clapperton *et al* 1971). This association, however, provides no precise temporal control because the lake appears to have existed, albeit discontinuously, over a long period from regional deglaciation until after *c* 10 150 cal BC, within the Younger Dryas Stadial (Payton 1992).

Further north the extensive fluvial and deltaic gravel surfaces forming the Milfield Plain north and west of Akeld Steads were supplied by braided rivers from the River Glen and, ultimately, from much of the northern Cheviot Hills and the Southern Uplands *via* the Kale Water and the valley now containing Yetholm Loch (Figure 7.1). Gravel terraces border both Linton Loch (Mannion 1975, 1978) and Yetholm Loch (Section 3.1). Comparable terrace surfaces are developed within the College Burn, the River Breamish and patchily in the Harthope Burn (Clapperton 1967), but within the narrower valleys draining the Cheviot such as the Bowmont Valley they have largely been removed by subsequent erosional events.

It seems likely that the deposition of the Haugh Head Terrace was a product of changing environmental conditions after regional deglaciation. Climate change is the most likely cause for fluvial events of this scale, and conventionally the most well understood candidate for such profound landscape disturbance would be the abrupt climatic deterioration of the Younger Dryas Stadial (Rose *et al* 1980; Rose & Boardman 1983; Harvey 1985; Frenzel 1995; Tipping 1995c; Moores, Passmore & Stevenson 1999). The impacts of this exceptionally severe period of lowered temperatures and reduced precipitation (Tipping 1991) are seen in sediment and biostratigraphic records close to the Bowmont Valley, though not as yet within the valley (Figure 8.4). These records have collectively shown that even within the Lateglacial Interstadial, from *c* 12 400 cal BC, climatic deterioration occurred in a series of abrupt reductions in temperature, and probably in precipitation, which destabilised and eroded soils and fragmented dryland and aquatic plant and animal communities. Pulses of landscape instability were characteristic of the interstadial climate, not only of

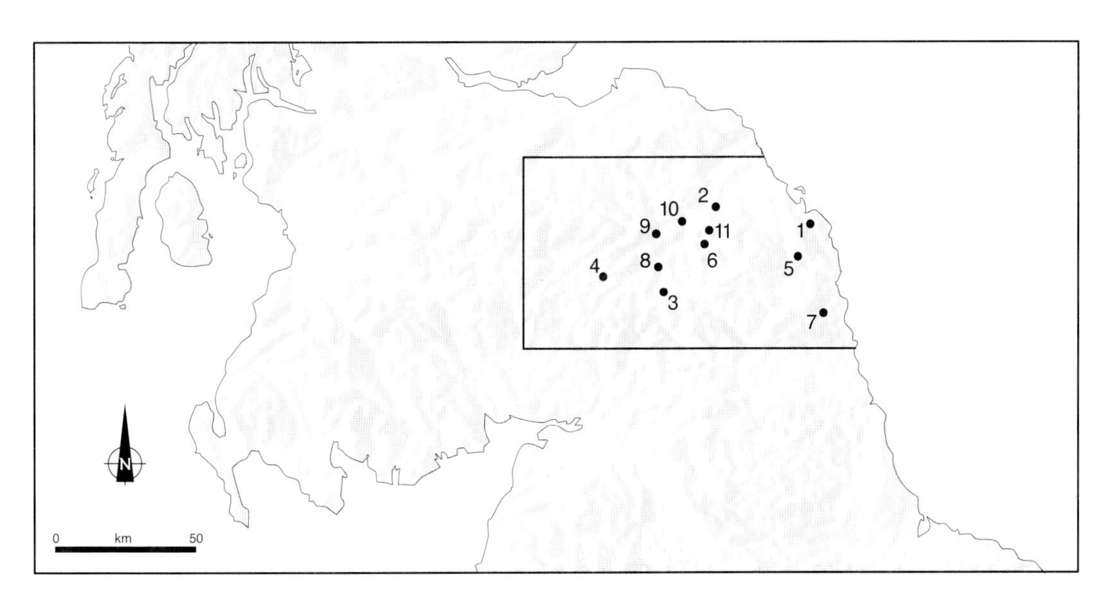

Figure 8.4

Devensian Lateglacial and earliest Holocene sediment stratigraphies close to the northern Cheviot Hills (within the box). Analyses at The Dod (Shennan & Innes 1986) are unlikely to represent Devensian Lateglacial sediments (Tipping 1997b) but it is an early Holocene vegetation sequence. Localities are numbered on Figure 8.4 and listed below in alphabetical order: (1) Bradford Kaims (Bartley 1966); (2) Din Moss (Hibbert & Switsur 1976); (3) The Dod (Innes & Shennan 1991); (4) Kingside Loch (Tight 1987); (5) Lilburn (Jones, Keen & Robinson 2000); (6) Linton Loch (Mannion 1978); (7) Longlee Moor (Bartley 1966); (8) Wester Branxholme Loch (Tight 1987); (9) Whitlaw Mosses (Webb & Moore 1982); (10) Whitrig Bog (Mitchell 1948; Brooks, Mayle & Lowe 1997; Mayle, Lowe & Sheldrick 1997; Turney, Harkness & Lowe 1997; Brooks & Birks 2000); (11) Yetholm Loch (this report).

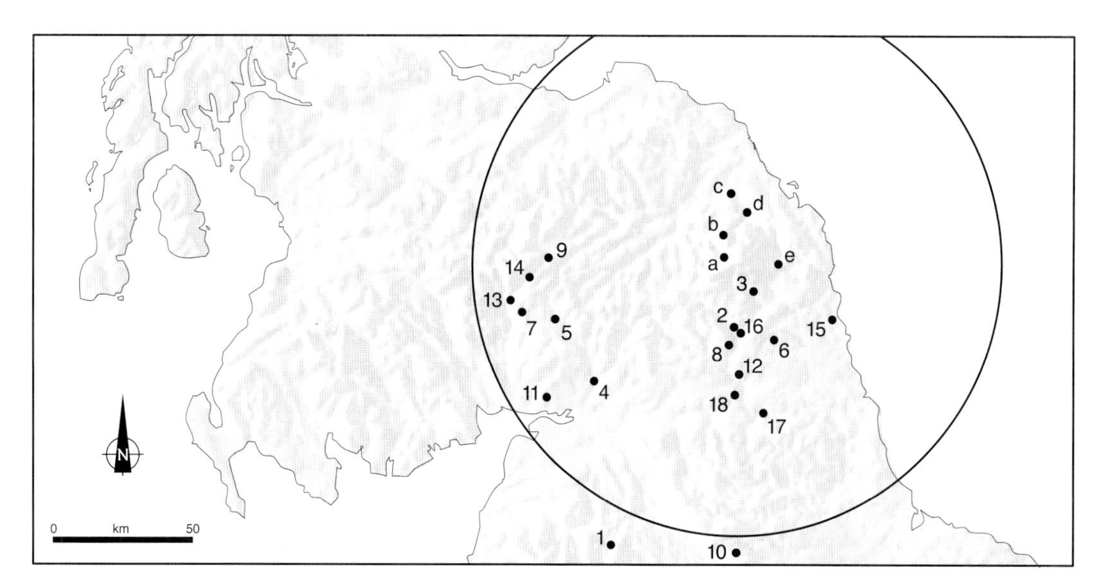

Figure 8.6

Holocene fluvial chronologies in the region used in analysis of Holocene geomorphic change (not necessarily referred to directly in discussion). Sites in this study (Chapter 7) are lettered. Localities in other studies are numbered on Figure 8.6 and listed below in alphabetical order: (a) Swindon Haugh and Calroust Burn, Bowmont Water; (b) Halter Burn, River Glen; (c) Akeld Steads, River Glen; (d) Earle Mill, Wooler Water; (e) Powburn, River Breamis. (1) Ambleside, Rydal Water (Potter 1976, 1979); (2) Brownchester, River North Tyne (Moores *et al* 1999); (3) Callaly Moor (Macklin *et al* 1991); (4) Dovecote Farm, River Irthing (Cotton *et al* 1999); (5) Eskdalemuir (Tipping unpublished); (6) Farnley, River South Tyne (Macklin *et al* 1992); (7) Frenchland Burn, River Annan (Tipping 1999b; ; Tipping *et al* 1999); (8) Habitancum, River Rede (Passmore *et al* 1991; Passmore & Macklin 1997); (9) Hopecarton Burn (Tipping & Halliday 1994); (10) Howgill Fells (Harvey *et al* 1981); (11) Kirtle Water, Solway Firth (Tipping 1995c); (12) Lambley, River South Tyne (Passmore *et al* 1993; Passmore & Macklin 2000, 2002); (13) Moffat Basin, River Annan (Tipping 1999b; Tipping *et al* 1999); (14) Moffat Water (Dunsford 1999); (15) Scotswood, River Tyne (Passmore *et al* 1992); (16) Snabdaugh, River North Tyne (Moores *et al* 1999); (17) Teesdale, River Tees (Dunsford 1999); (18) Thinhope Burn (Macklin *et al* 1992, 1994).

lpaz Yetholm B). The interpretation is of an hiatus in lake sedimentation at the sampled site induced by a sustained phase of lowered lake level, caused in turn by prolonged climatic aridity. Lake level records across western and north-west Europe have demonstrated this phase (Gaillard 1985; Digerfeldt 1989; Magny 1992, 1995; Harrison & Digerfeldt 1993; Tipping 1996b). At Yetholm Loch lake levels rose again by or at *c* 7750 cal BC. A comparable pattern of lake level rise is seen at nearby Linton Loch, though not discussed in such terms by Mannion (1978, 1982), where marl sediments at the lake edge began to accumulate after sediments in the basin centre, immediately after the establishment of *Corylus* (hazel). There are very few other palaeoclimatic records of this age in the region, and few other lake stratigraphies examined in detail. Raised moss peat sequences this old in the region (Figure 8.5), such as at Burnfoothill (Tipping 1995a), Bolton Fell (Barber *et al* 2003; Hughes & Barber 2004) and Walton Mosses (Hughes *et al* 2000), which are sensitive to climate change later in the Holocene were at this point in their development probably less so (Hughes *et al* 2000), although a distinctly dry peat surface developed at Bolton Fell Moss for a few hundred years before *c* 7800 cal BC (Hughes & Barber 2004).

At both Yetholm Loch and Linton Loch the sedimentological changes implying climate change probably included the accelerated erosion of catchment soils, and it is likely that climatic deterioration caused a partial fragmentation of plant communities. This phase of soil erosion was of unknown severity: there is no demonstrable indication that sediment supply to river systems in the northern Cheviots was accelerated (Chapter 7; Figure 7.8), or to most other river systems in the region which have stratigraphic records extending to the early Holocene, on the lower Tyne (Passmore *et al* 1992) and near Otterburn on the North Tyne (Moores *et al* 1999) (Figure 8.6). In the south-west of the region, rivers draining the Moffat Basin did begin to transport eroded sediment from before 8000 cal BC (Tipping 1999b; Tipping,

Milburn & Halliday 1999), but the scale of this impact is unclear.

This lake lowering also coincided with the immigration to the Bowmont Valley of *Corylus* (hazel). Hazel colonised the British Isles at around 8300–7800 cal BC (Hibbert & Switsur 1976; Boyd & Dickson 1986; Birks 1989). Synchroneity on this scale implies rapid colonisation with little impedance from competition with existing plant communities, edaphic constraints or topographic barriers. In detail, the rate of hazel colonisation across the British Isles has been regarded as anomalous since Deacon (1974) first evaluated the often marked differences in radiocarbon age of local establishment (see also Turner & Hodgson 1981; Boyd & Dickson 1986; Birks 1989; Huntley 1993). A link between climate change and hazel colonisation seems increasingly likely (Huntley 1993; Tallantire 2002), with Linnman (1981), Digerfeldt (1989) and Huntley (1993) suggesting that an arid climate in particular would facilitate establishment.

Another control on understanding the rate of colonisation and establishment, which also has climatic origins, is the rate of sediment accumulation. Tipping (1995b) argued that apparent contrasts in the timing of hazel establishment around the Solway Firth were largely governed by site specific differences in the rates of peat growth, determined in turn by changes in effective precipitation. Differences between sites in the radiocarbon age of the expansion of hazel may, in this model, be more apparent than real. These changes will have had two effects, in creating hiatuses in sediment accumulation at some sites such as Yetholm Loch or the basin edge sequence at Linton Loch (Mannion 1978), or the peat surface at Burnfoothill Moss (Tipping 1995b), where the first gradual rise of hazel pollen is not recorded, and distorting the precision of ^{14}C age controls at other sites. Differences in the behaviour of the early Holocene hazel pollen curve between the closely grouped sites of Din Moss (Hibbert & Switsur 1976), Linton Loch (Mannion 1978) and Yetholm Loch (Figure 8.4) suggest that sedimentological controls are important in how we should explain this feature.

The establishment of hazel in the British Isles has also long interested palaeoecologists because it occurred significantly earlier, in a relative sense, than in earlier interglacials (West 1980). This observation led to speculation that hazel may have been promoted by manipulation of the environment, notably by fire, or introduced by human communities who valued hazel as a food source (Smith 1970; Huntley 1993). Neither suggestion has been supported in recent years, although hazel has been confirmed as a valued, perhaps managed resource later in the Mesolithic period (Mithen *et al* 2001).

Stratigraphic comparisons between pollen and charcoal records tend not to show an association between the colonisation of hazel and increased fire frequency (Edwards 1990; Edwards & Ralston 1984; Simmons 1993; Tipping 1994; *contra* Huntley 1993). Fire was not absent from the northern British landscape at the beginning of the Holocene (above, Section 8.4a), although the recent emphases on the human use of fire, accidental or purposeful, at occupation sites (Day & Mellars 1994; Law 1998; Cummins 2000) tend to distort our knowledge of fire in the 'natural' world. Abundant amounts of charcoal can occur at some peat sequences during the regional appearance of hazel, as at Bolton Fell (Hughes & Barber 2004) (Figure 8.5), but these are still rare. Small increases in fire frequency or intensity at Yetholm Loch (Section 3.3: lpaz Yetholm B) occurred after the establishment of hazel. However, more or larger fires can be expected during phases of climatic aridity (Huntley 1993; Tipping 1996b; Bradshaw, Tolonen & Tolonen 1998; Tipping & Milburn 2000). Before we assume that fire in the early-mid-Holocene period must have been anthropogenic (Moore 1996; Cummins 2000), it is necessary to recognise the exceptional variability in climate that characterised this and later times. British woods do not catch fire naturally (Rackham 1980) only under the present climate and land uses.

8.5 The maturing of the landscape 7600–5200 cal BC

8.5a Valley floor peat growth at Sourhope and landscape stabilisation

From *c* 7700 cal BC it is possible to explore contrasts between the very different landscapes of the lowland around Yetholm Loch (Chapter 3) and the deeply incised interior of the Bowmont Valley at Sourhope (Chapter 4). Peat may have formed on the wide meltwater channel at Sourhope earlier than this date, but probably not significantly earlier (Section 4.3: lpaz Sourhope A). It is tempting to link peat growth to rising lake levels and increasing effective precipitation at Yetholm Loch, but this is not demonstrated: the mire at Sourhope seems to have been well drained for over a thousand cal years after inception. Another possibility is that a reduction in geomorphic activity across the valley floor at Sourhope permitted the development of peat. This cannot be demonstrated either. However, at Yetholm Loch the rate at which eroded soils were introduced during the drier climate after *c* 8100 cal BC (Section 8.4c) had declined by *c* 7700 cal BC. This may have been through the re-establishment of a complete vegetation cover in response to elevated soil water tables. The peat at Sourhope has since inception been free of major bands of inwashed soil particles. Increasing soil stability even on the very steep north-facing slopes south of the Sourhope channel (Figure 4.1) may have allowed organic matter to have accumulated without subsequent removal by rivers in particularly damp and cold hollows like Sourhope. The absence of peat of this age at more enclosed bedrock basins like Swindon Hill (Chapter 4) or from the flat summit ridge at Cocklawhead (Chapter 6) makes it clear that peat formation was not a general phenomenon at this time in the valley: the peat at Sourhope is exceptional rather than typical.

8.5b Filling the landscape with trees

Early postglacial landscapes in the northern Cheviot Hills are understood only in lowland contexts (Section 8.4), but in a regional context they appear to have been extraordinarily uniform in the types and distributions of major plant communities (Tipping 1994, 1997b, 1997d). *Betula* (birch) and *Corylus* (hazel) woods were seemingly ubiquitous, probably because of the very broad ecological tolerances of these trees and the lack of competition from existing plants during colonisation

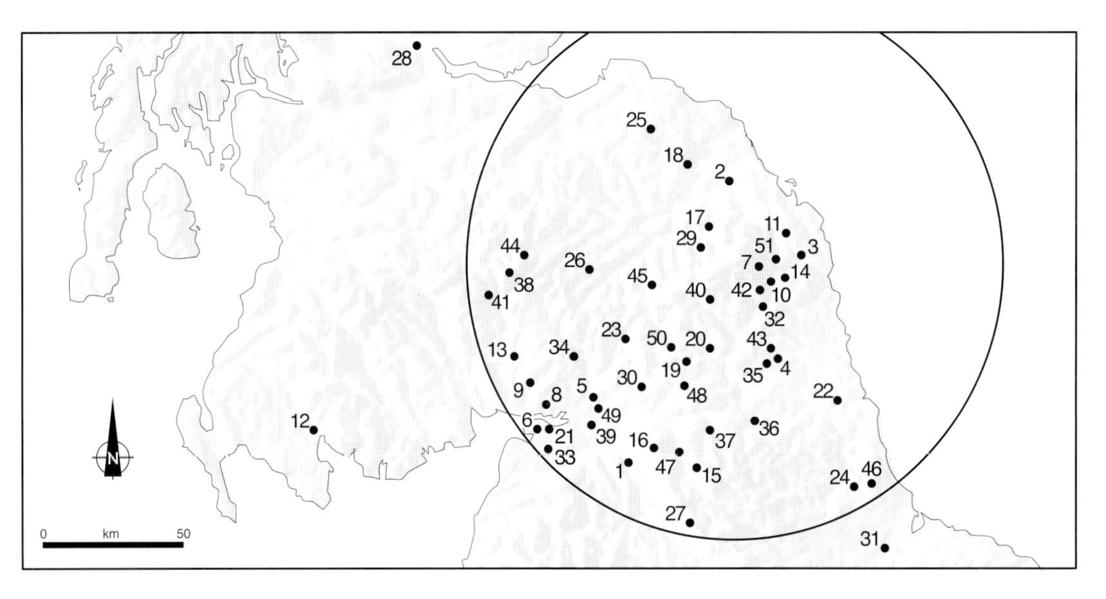

Figure 8.7

The major Holocene vegetation histories assessed in or critical to the region (not necessarily referred to directly in discussion). Localities are numbered on Figure 8.7 and listed below in alphabetical order: (1) Abbot Moss (Walker 1966); (2) Akeld Steads (Borek 1975; Tipping 1998a); (3) Black Lough (Moyle 1980); (4) Bollihope Common (Turner, Roberts & Ward 1973); (5) Bolton Fell (Barber 1981; Dumayne-Peaty & Barber 1998); (6) Bowness Common (Walker 1966); (7) Broad Moss (Davies & Turner 1979); (8) Burnfoothill (Tipping 1995b); (9) Burnswark (Squires in Jobey 1978); (10) Callaly Moor (Macklin *et al* 1991); (11) Camp Hill (Davies & Turner 1979); (12) Carsegowan (Dumayne-Peaty 1999a); (13) Catharine Hill (Tipping & Milburn 2000); (14) Cauldhope (Manning & Tipping unpublished); (15) Cow Green (Turner *et al* 1973); (16) Cross Fell (Turner 1984); (17) Din Moss (Hibbert & Switsur 1976); (18) Dogden Moss (Dumayne-Peaty 1999b); (19) Fellend Moss (Davies & Turner 1979); (20) Fozy Moss (Dumayne-Peaty 1999a); (21) Glasson (Dumayne-Peaty 1999a); (22) Hallowell (Donaldson & Turner 1977); (23) Hopecarton (Tipping & Halliday 1994); (24) Hutton Henry (Bartley *et al* 1976); (25) Johnscleugh (Hall & Tipping unpublished); (26) Kingside Loch (Tight 1987); (27) Kirkby Stephen (Skinner & Brown 1999); (28) Letham Moss (Dumayne-Peaty 1999a); (29) Linton Loch (Mannion 1978); (30) Midgeholme (Innes unpublished; Wiltshire 1997); (31) Neasham Fen (Bartley *et al* 1976); (32) Otterburn (Moores *et al* 1999); (33) Oulton Moss (Walker 1966); (34) Over Rig (Boyd unpublished; Tipping 1997c); (35) Paw Law (Sturlodottir & Turner 1985); (36) Pow Hill (Turner & Hodgson 1981); (37) Quick Moss (Rowell & Turner 1986); (38) Rotten Bottom (Tipping 1999c); (39) Scaleby Moss (Walker 1966); (40) Stanshiel (Campbell *et al* 2002); (41) Stanshiel Rig (Cayless 2000; Cayless & Tipping ; 2002); (42) Steng Moss (Davies & Turner 1979); (43) Steward Shield Meadow (Turner, Roberts & Ward ; 1973); (44) Talla (Chambers *et al* 1997); (45) The Dod (Innes & Shennan 1991); (46) Thorpe Bulmer (Bartley *et al* 1976); (47) Valley Bog (Squires 1978); (48) Vindolanda (Manning *et al* 1997); (49) Walton (Dumayne-Peaty 1999a); (50) Wester Branxholme (Tight 1987); (51) Wether Hill (A Davies pers. comm.).

and establishment readily overriding any inherent altitudinal, edaphic and climatic variability.

The temporal pattern of mid-Holocene woodland colonisation accords in nearly all respects with that previously known within the region (Hibbert & Switsur 1976; Innes & Shennan 1991) (Figure 8.7), and from the British Isles as a whole (Birks 1989). After *c* 6750 BC *Ulmus* (elm) and *Quercus* (oak) colonised the lowlands and the Tweed Valley, most commonly at the expense of *Betula* (Turner & Hodgson 1983). *Ulmus* appears to have become established some hundreds of years before *Quercus* at Din Moss (Hibbert & Switsur 1976). This pattern is likely also at Yetholm Loch (Section 3.3: lpaz Yetholm C), where *Ulmus* had become established by *c* 7650 cal BC but *Quercus* was probably locally present only after *c* 6850 cal BC.

Spatial variation is enhanced by differences in the distributions of birch, hazel, oak and elm trees (Turner & Hodgson 1979, 1983). Both oak and elm were most common in the lowlands, where together with hazel, they comprised the principal tree types. Birch was effectively ousted from lowland dryland soils, although it persisted in lake edge and fen communities where it had competitive advantages. At upland sites in the region, hazel and birch maintained their position as co-dominants in the woodland, as oak found it difficult to compete (Innes & Shennan 1991). Oak probably colonised the inner recesses of the Bowmont Valley at Sourhope (Section 4.3: lpaz Sourhope A), but was delayed by *c* 800 cal years from its establishment in the lowlands 15km downvalley (Section 3.3: lpaz Yetholm C). *Ulmus* (elm) appears not to have grown at all abundantly deep within the valley.

Exceptions to the regional pattern are few, but one might have been the local presence within the Cheviot Hills of *Pinus* (pine). The tree was suggested (Section 3.3: lpaz Yetholm Ab) to have colonised the Yetholm Loch catchment in low numbers in the earliest Holocene, possibly having a competitive advantage for a time on dry soils. Mannion (1978) thought that *Pinus* grew as scattered trees around Linton Loch at this time, although pollen percentages at both sites are less than accepted as indicating local presence (Huntley & Birks 1983; Bennett 1984), as they are at all sites in the Bowmont Valley. Rare stands of *Pinus* may nevertheless have grown and persisted in the hills deep within the valley, at Sourhope until *c* 4600 cal BC (Section 4.3: lpaz Sourhope B) and *c* 3500 cal BC at Swindon Hill (Section 5.3: lpaz Swindon A), but there is no evidence for local growth on the summit ridge at Cocklawhead (Section 6.3). North of the Cheviot Hills, very few localities have demonstrated from wood remains the growth of pine trees in the Holocene period (Dickson 1988, 1992; Ramsay & Dickson 1997). To the west in the Southern Uplands, neither Tight (1987) or Innes & Shennan (1991) thought pine had become established. Tipping (1997b, 1997d, 1998c) suggested that pine could compete with deciduous trees only in the coldest and wettest northerly valleys of the Moffat Hills (Figure 8.7). East of the Cheviot Hills, Moyle (1980) suggested the presence of pine woodland at Black Lough, near Edlingham (Figure 8.7), undated but estimated at around 7450 cal BC. Trees may have colonised only the surfaces of mires (Innes & Shennan 1991), although it is likely that pine did not colonise the consistently dry surface of the mire at Sourhope (Chapter 4). Within the Carboniferous Fell Sandstone uplands south-west of Rothbury at Cauldhope Moss, a *Pinus* stump in peat has been ^{14}C dated to 5206–4943 cal BC (P Frodsham pers. comm.) and more continuous growth suggested by pollen analyses (Manning & Tipping unpublished). In the uplands of northern England, pine was locally abundant at a few localities, not necessarily on the poorest soils (Turner & Hodgson 1979) but in disturbed contexts within upper Teesdale (Turner *et al* 1973) and on the steep unstable slopes of the River Derwent at Pow Hill (Turner & Hodgson 1981) (Figure 8.7).

8.5c Disturbance and the establishment of alder (Alnus)

The last tree to colonise the region in the early to middle Holocene was *Alnus* (alder). There is little spatial patterning within the region: establishment as an important component of the woodland occurred at any time between *c* 6150 and 5250 cal BC (Innes & Shennan 1991; Tipping 1994, 1995a, 1997b, 1997d). For alder trees to have gained some competitive advantage within the deciduous woodlands, niche creation through landscape disturbance was probably necessary (Bennett & Birks 1989; Chambers & Elliott 1990; Tallantire 1992). There were potentially innumerable disturbances, singly or in combination.

One of these was almost certainly the activities of beaver (Chambers & Price 1985). However, the fluctuations in lake sediments possibly generated by beaver at Yetholm Loch (Section 3.3: lpaz Yetholm C) occurred prior to the establishment of alder. The expansion of alder pollen at Yetholm Loch was either very rapid at *c* 5140 cal BC, or more likely the shape of the pollen curve is confounded by an hiatus in lake sedimentation (Section 3.3: lpaz Yetholm D). The apparent reduction in lake level represented by this hiatus was the final and most significant fluctuation recorded, because lacustrine sediments at the sampling site were permanently replaced between 5600 and 4600 cal BC by a fen peat. At Linton Loch the rapid rise in alder pollen percentages was, as at Yetholm Loch, affected by an apparent hiatus in sediment accumulation at the lake margin (Mannion 1978), a lake level lowering which Mannion (1982) dated by pollen stratigraphic correlations with the Din Moss sequence to between 5400 and 4250 cal BC, synchronous with that at Yetholm Loch. Above Hawick, at Wester Branxholme Loch (Figure 8.7), Tight (1987) also recognised a fall in lake level inferred to have occurred at around 5350 cal BC, during a gradual rise in alder pollen. This event has been one of the most consistently recognised changes in lake level at sites throughout northern Britain and throughout northern Europe (O'Sullivan 1975; Boyd & Dickson 1987b; Digerfeldt 1989; Whittington, Edwards & Cundill 1990; Magny 1992; Harrison & Digerfeldt 1993; Milburn 1996; Tisdall 2000). This period of relative aridity, or rather the end of the event and the shift from dry to wet raised moss surfaces, is also recognised in the region at Walton Moss (Hughes *et al* 2000) and Bolton Fell Moss (Barber *et al* 2003), at *c* 5600 cal BC (Figure 8.5).

At Sourhope the local expansion of alder was synchronous with that in the lowlands at *c* 5240 cal BC (Section 4.3: lpaz Sourhope B), and again was rapid. Alder colonised a dry peat surface here, and there is little evidence for waterlogging. Because there are no data for rates of lateral peat spread, it is not known whether the valley floor was extensively converted to a soil preferential to alder growth, but it is unlikely that alder trees colonised drier steeper slopes at Sourhope.

At Din Moss (Hibbert & Switsur 1976) the increase in alder pollen was closely comparable in age to the event at Yetholm Loch, occurring between *c* 5700 and 5550 cal BC. The synchroneity in alder colonisation within the northern Cheviot Hills is exceptional, and at Akeld Steads in the Milfield Basin (Figure 8.7), pollen analyses by Borek (1975) were ^{14}C dated by Tipping (1998), and across the probably extensive valley floor peats in this basin the local colonisation by alder was earlier than within the Cheviot Hills, from *c* 6300 cal BC.

However, this wet valley floor had been available for colonisation by alder from *c* 9500 cal BC (Section 7.7; Tipping 1998), but it colonised only 3000 cal years later. Some workers have argued that alder trees grew in the British Isles from or before *c* 9500 cal BC (Chambers & Elliott 1990; Tallantire 1992), but had been unable to successfully compete, and if this is true then their failure to expand onto substrates that existed, but which they later succeeded on, suggests strongly that a climatic trigger was more important for alder establishment than pedological constraints. The broad synchroneity in the region becomes more impressive in the light of this observation. It suggests that regionally significant climatic factors were causal in the establishment of alder, and that site specific factors were much less significant. Both relative aridity before 5600 cal BC and the subsequent increase in precipitation may have aided establishment. Alder may have colonised fen and valley floor peats in a wetter environment following the recovery of lake levels, but following a period of low lake levels during which lake and fluvial sediments had been carpeted in peat substrates on which alder had competitive advantages.

8.6 Landscape stability and change 5200–3900 cal BC

8.6a Altitudinal limits to tree growth

By 5200 cal BC it is likely that most slopes in the northern Cheviot Hills had evolved mature brown forest soils beneath complete covers of woodland. There is no evidence from Yetholm Loch or from Sourhope (Chapters 3, 4) for the maintenance of grasslands or for the occurrence of heather communities (Section 8.6a). There are no data in the northern Cheviot Hills for this period from the highest slopes and summit ridges (Chapter 6; see below Section 8.7f), although the absence of evidence for blanket peat growth prior to *c* 3800 cal BC is perhaps significant in itself for soil and vegetation development to have been comparable to lower altitudes.

Altitudinal limits to tree growth on the Cheviot Hills in the middle of the interglacial remain speculative. Elsewhere in the region this period is thought to represent the fullest expression of woodland cover, density and arboreal diversity (Tipping 1994). Pennington (1970) and Turner and Hodgson (1979) considered that a substantial woodland cover extended to at least 750m OD in northern England, and Turner (1984) suggested that tree growth was possible on the summit of Cross Fell in the northern Pennines, at an altitude of 893m OD (Figure 8.7). Birks (1972) suggested that in Galloway the tree line lay higher than 460m OD, and although Bennett (1989) and Spikins (1999) implied hills above around 500m asl in northern Britain would have remained unforested, Tipping (1997b; 1999c) suggested that birch, hazel and even oak grew at Rotten Bottom at 620m asl in the Moffat Hills in open but recognisable woodlands. It is probable that trees could have grown to the summit of The Cheviot itself. Only alder is likely to have been constrained by altitude to below 300–350m asl (McVean 1955).

8.6b Geomorphological changes

There were frequent periods of soil erosion from the Yetholm Loch catchment in the early and middle Holocene (Chapter 3; Figure 7.8). Most seem to have been generated by the fragmentation of plant communities and the creation of bare ground during periods of relative aridity. The mid-Holocene disturbances tentatively associated with beaver activities also generated smaller amounts of soil loss or reworking of lake edge sediment. However, these episodes were local to that catchment. The peat sequence at Sourhope (Chapter 4) has no evidence for soil loss despite lying beneath very steep north-facing slopes.

At *c* 5200 cal BC the fen peat that had begun to grow on the delta into Yetholm Loch received another distinct band of inwashed fine grained sediments. This inwashing persisted until *c* 3900 cal BC. There is little evidence that dryland soils were disturbed in this episode (Section 3.3: lpaz Yetholm D), and the greater transport of minerogenic sediment, either from catchment soils or the valley floor, may have been associated with the increases in precipitation that encouraged alder establishment (Section 8.5c). Unlike earlier soil erosion events, it is possible that this event was significant throughout the catchment. Downvalley from Yetholm Loch, sediments deriving from the River Glen at Akeld Steads become more minerogenic after *c* 5500 cal BC (Section 7.7; Figure 7.8), as the river transported and deposited silts and fine sands, perhaps as overbank floods (Tipping 1998).

Within the northern Cheviot Hills there is no other evidence for this phase. Although most upland localities examined are likely to have lost by fluvial erosion any evidence of this early period (Lewin & Macklin 2003), there is currently no evidence that the valley floor peat on the Wooler Water at Earle Mill was disturbed (Section 7.5; Clapperton *et al* 1971). In

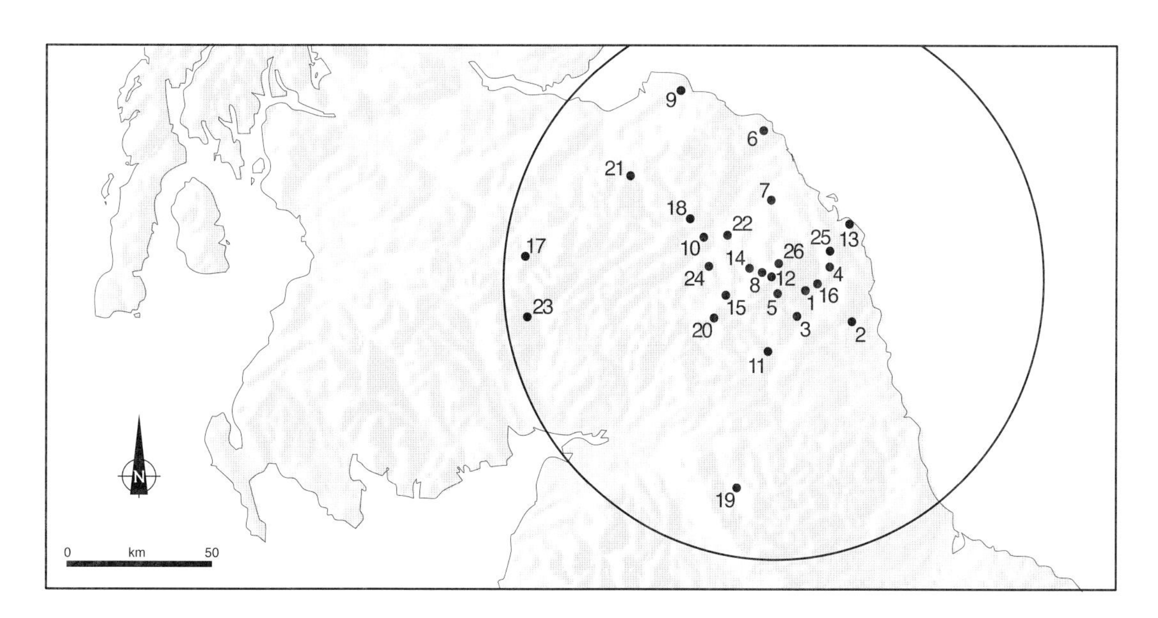

Figure 8.8

Archaeological and archival localities in the region mentioned in this chapter, numbered on Figure 8.6 and listed below in alphabetical order: (1) Alnhamsheles (Dixon 1985); (2) Bolam (Waddington 1999); (3) Callaly Moor (Macklin *et al* 1991); (4) Chatton Sandyford (Jobey 1981); (5) Chew Green (Richmond & Keeney 1937); (6) Coldingham Priory (Dixon pers. comm.); (7) Coupland (Waddington 1999); (8) Crock Cleugh (Steer & Keeney 1947); (9) East Barns (Current Archaeology 2004); (10) Eildon Hill North (Owen 1992); (11) Hallshill (van der Veen 1992); (12) Hayhope Knowe (Piggott 1948); (13) Howick (Waddington forthcoming); (14) Hownam (Piggott 1948); (15) Hut Knowe North (Halliday & Hill unpublished); (16) Linhope Burn (Topping 1993); (17) Lintshie Gutter (Terry 1995); (18) Rink Farm (Mulholland 1970); (19) Simy Folds (Coggins *et al* 1983); (20) Southdean (RCAHMS 1994); (21) Soutra Hill (Moffat 1989); (22) Springwood (Dixon 1998); (23) Stanshiel Rig (RCAHMS 1997; Halliday 1999); (24) The Dunion (Rideout 1992); (25) Titlington Mount (Topping 1998); (26) Whitelaw (Jeffrey 1855).

the region (Figure 8.6), most systems examined are similarly biased to depicting more recent geomorphic events, but the gentler gradient valley of the North Tyne near Otterburn retains evidence of heightened fluvial activity from some time before and after *c* 5000 cal BC (Moores *et al* 1999), around the Solway Firth the Annan Water continued to carry eroding sediment (Tipping 1999b), as did for a short time around 4750 cal BC the much smaller Kirtle Water (Tipping 1995c), and south of the region in the Bowland Fells, upland valley floors were also being altered by increased gravel aggradation (Harvey & Renwick 1987). Rhind (1969) suggested that the aggradation of extensive terrace fills along the River Tweed was of Mesolithic age from the occurrence at Rink Farm, near Selkirk (Figure 8.8) of diagnostic flint scatters (Mulholland 1970), but the *in situ* nature of the assemblages remains uncertain (Warren 2001), and their derivation by erosion from dense scatters on higher, Devensian Lateglacial, terrace surfaces above is more likely.

This is the first time since the beginning of the Holocene period (Section 8.3b) that several river systems had been synchronously active. A link with increasing precipitation after *c* 5600–5400 cal BC has been made. The increased rates of geomorphic change appear to have been modest, and this event is not comparable to those exceptional valley floor transformations described in later periods. There is little evidence, for example, of significant landscape change, and it is likely only that river channels created more minerogenic floodplains to replace valley floor peat. There is currently no evidence at this time for the erosion, transport or deposition on the river beds of gravels. Whether this absence of evidence for the substrate preferred by salmonid fish has implications for the developing thesis that rivers in the region were major resources for salmon (Waddington 1999; Warren 2001) remains to be explored. These fine grained silt and sand floodplains may in turn have encouraged the growth of trees like alder on them, modifying river behaviour in a complex set of feedback constraints (Brown 1988). The apparent modesty of this event may be one reason why, although regionally marked, it appears not to be matched by records in other regions (Macklin 1999; Macklin & Lewin 2003).

8.6c A landscape of trees

In discussion of the early to mid-Holocene landscape evolution of the northern Cheviot Hills so far, human activity has not been seen to have played any part. The lowland landscapes along the foothills of The Cheviots were not undisturbed in this period. Sections 8.4 to 8.6 have discussed often pronounced disturbances to soils, vegetation and river systems. However, none need be attributable to the impacts of hunter-gatherers on their environment. The recognition that there are many naturally occurring factors that can lead to landscape disturbance, and in particular the recognition that climate shifts have been more complex, frequent, rapid and intense (National Research Council 2000) than often conventionally portrayed (Lamb 1985), provide very real competing hypotheses to human activity for landscape change (Tipping 2004). Abrupt fluctuations between relatively arid and wetter climates characterised the early Holocene period (Sections 8.4a, 8.4c, 8.5c). Lest this interpretative scheme be seen as obsessively paradigmatic, there is as yet no evidence from any stratigraphic sequence in the region for landscape disturbance coinciding with the largest phase of climatic deterioration so far detected in the amphi-Atlantic region, at *c* 6200 cal BC (Alley *et al* 1997; Bond *et al* 1997, 2001; Stager & Mayewski 1997; Klitgaard-Kristensen *et al* 1998; von Graffenstein *et al* 1998).

Spikins (1999) explored with great delicacy the environmental opportunities and constraints afforded by the changing woodlands from the early postglacial to the middle of the Holocene period. This development, involving the migration of different trees, their adaptation to environmental constraints and to each other, the closure of the woodland and increasing spatial differentiation, can be seen in the northern Cheviots (Section 8.5b).

There is little evidence that open landscapes persisted into or within the Holocene period. Turner and Hodgson (1983) found only one of their thirty-eight sites with exceptionally high percentages of wild grass pollen, in North Yorkshire, and in general grass pollen was weakly positively correlated with base rich soils in their study, but they argued that it was more likely that such areas were sites of anthropogenic clearance rather than being natural grasslands. Interpretations that natural grasslands persisted on base rich substrates from the earliest postglacial on the Yorkshire Wolds (Bush 1988, 1989) have met with trenchant and valid criticisms (Thomas 1988). The most recent suggestion in support of such grassy enclaves in northern England, by Skinner and Brown (1999) from a complex and undated sink hole stratigraphy near Kirkby Stephen (Figure 8.7) is almost certainly incorrect, and grass rich Devensian

Lateglacial sediments have probably been mistaken for a Holocene stratigraphy.

In detail the altitudinal zonation of woodland types (e.g. Tallis & Switsur 1990) driving Spikins' model is too simplistic (Turner & Hodgson 1983). In walking through this landscape, with its small scale mosaics of sunlight and shade, warm and cold, wet and dry soils, each hillside or plateau surface would have presented different mixes of tree species over very short distances (Topping 1999a; Austin 2000; Tipping 2002a). This vital aspect is inadequately described in its subtlety and diversity from previous sections and the data from Yetholm Loch and Sourhope (Chapters 3 and 4), but we can explore more imaginatively this landscape.

Walking into the Bowmont Valley 10 000 cal years ago (*c* 8000 cal BC) would have provided few contrasting views in woods dominated everywhere by hazel, birch, willow and increasingly uncommon juniper. It is unlikely that the density of the closely spaced trunks beneath the still surprisingly airy canopy changed significantly between lowland and upland, between north and south-facing slopes or between steep slopes and plateaux. This woodland, seemingly not differing whichever way you walked, would have been with you to the coast (Coles 1998), near where the extraordinary early Mesolithic 'houses' at Howick and East Barns (Figure 8.8) have been found (Current Archaeology 2004; Waddington 2008).

Walking in 2000 cal years later (*c* 6000 cal BC) would have been to move from one landscape to another. In the lowlands, the view from cliff tops still above the trees would take in mature oak, elm, ash and hazel trees on nutrient rich soils on gentle slopes and fluvioglacial gravel terrace surfaces, probably maintaining a continuous tall canopy to the grasses beneath. The cliffs below would support those remnants of the earliest postglacial pioneers, junipers, hawthorns and willows. The valley floor, clearly demarcated below the gravel terraces and glistening with open water and channels and clothed in thick peat, supports very dense but unstable and dynamic stands of alder, birch, ash and willow. The edges of these carr communities are

Plate 8.1

In the middle of the Holocene period, trees filled the landscape. As you climbed higher onto the summit ridge, woodlands would have thinned somewhat, and views across the densely wooded lowlands north to the probably forested Eildon Hills might be glimpsed. This photograph from Mow Law asks you to substitute the 20th-century conifer plantations for a birch-hazel woodland but perhaps to accept the density of modern woods as valid for those in the middle of the interglacial near valley floors, and to imagine all the slopes and ridges with a mosaic of different woodlands.

vulnerable to wind throw because of their rooting in peat, and small patches of open ground are continually created at the ecotone between dry and wet soils, making stream banks collapse and adding to the river small packets of sediment. Little of this instability is seen in the centre of the carr, but these trees do not live for long without decay and gap creation.

This thin ribbon of peat and alder carr threads its way along the valley floor, but as the valley sides steepen and narrow the increasingly frequent shallow slope failures promoted by increasing precipitation have pushed sand and silt across the valley floor, providing a firmer footing on floodplains and allowing hazels and oaks to grow with the alders and birches on the valley floors. The scars left by soil loss are rapidly covered with birches and hazels and by occasional pines, so that the woodland patches on the hillsides move around over decades. Oaks grow but on these steep slopes are not as tall as downvalley by the lake. Oaks grow best on the stable soils of the plateaux. Elm trees are very rare. Higher, and the alder trees on the valley floor begin to give way to birches and willows and pines, and on the slopes oaks are less common than hazels and birches. Towards the summit ridges the valley floor itself narrows and fades and the valley floor begins to look like the slopes above, but however high you go you are accompanied by some trees. The trees become more scarce, and the gaps between them allow you views across the lowlands to the Eildon Hills (Plate 8.1), and grasslands become more abundant, but you are never above or outside the woods.

8.6d Woodland disturbance in the Late Mesolithic

In this interpretation, openings in the woodland canopy were inevitable. It is not surprising to identify such openings. They are tentatively recorded in the woods around Yetholm Loch after *c* 4600 cal BC (Section 3.3; lpaz Yetholm D) from the rare occurrence of open ground herbs and by increases in ash (*Fraxinus*), normally regarded as a shade-intolerant tree that is palynologically difficult to detect unless the tree canopy is more open. There is no evidence at this site to indicate that these very small changes are representative of significant vegetation modification, or that such openings were purposeful. Fire frequency and/or intensity, which has been criticised in its frequent use as the sole indicator of Mesolithic human impact (Section 8.4c), was very low, and fires were seemingly very rare in this mature mid-Holocene wooded landscape. At Sourhope, deep within the valley, evidence for an increasingly open woodland canopy is synchronous with that at Yetholm Loch, from *c* 4625 cal BC (Section 4.3: lpaz Sourhope C). Trees such as birch, hazel and ash that would have been shaded by a dense canopy are better represented, and there are distinctive increases in pollen from grasslands, either growing more luxuriantly beneath a lighter tree cover or within larger gaps between trees. Partial woodland regeneration occurred after *c* 4000 cal BC, but the open canopy phase in muted form appears to have persisted for some 1500 cal years until *c* 3150 cal BC. The pollen taxa that increase are suggestive of grazing pressures (Section 4.3: lpaz Sourhope C). Proxy data for fire frequency/ intensity were not recorded in sediments of this age at Sourhope.

The pollen recruitment areas of Yetholm Loch and Sourhope are not shared (Sections 1.6, 2.2), so that this synchroneity suggests that modifications to the woodland occurred throughout the valley. The changes appear to have been more substantial in the upper part of the valley, where the evidence for tree loss is more compelling. Palynological contrasts between the two sites can have a variety of reasons. Vegetation changes may have occurred at different distances from the pollen site, perhaps closer to the valley floor at Sourhope, or the density of the alder carr around the site at Yetholm Loch screened the effects of change on dryland soils. If the differences were real, then it is possible that contrasts in woodland composition between upland and lowland determined the location or the intensity of stresses. However, these contrasts may also determine the ease of palynological recognition of the same impact: the oak and elm woods of the lowlands may not have been as expressive of change as the more open woods of the interior.

It is difficult to interpret these records. Tipping (1996a) argued that these disturbances were anthropogenic. It needs to be appreciated that the purpose and consequent subsampling strategies in the pollen analyses were focused on impacts by farming communities that were expected to have been more enduring than those of gatherer-hunters. The temporal resolution of analyses (Sections 3.2, 4.2; Figure 8.2) are inadequate to resolve the detail of vegetation dynamics so beautifully captured by Innes and colleagues south of the region on the North York Moors (Simmons 1993, 1996; Simmons & Innes 1987, 1988a, 1996; Turner, Simmons & Innes 1989; Turner, Innes & Simmons 1993). Nevertheless, Tipping's (1996a) interpretations in the northern Cheviot Hills were influenced by the well known model of Mesolithic woodland manipulation from farther south (Simmons 1996) in which manipulation of the tree canopy cover, often by burning, is intended to encourage the abundance and quality of grasses browsed by wild animals. Indeed, the greater vegetation impacts occurring at the upland site of Sourhope accord well with models that stress disturbance in upland settings, at the ecotone between woodland and moorland (Simmons & Innes 1987), although the likelihood that the valley at Sourhope was probably well below this ecotone was acknowledged. The absence of a distinctive altitudinal zonation to plant communities in the uplands needs now to be emphasised because the concept of ecotonal manipulation was pivotal to the early theoretical analyses of Simmons (1975) and Mellars (1976). It is probable, from the discussion of mid-Holocene tree lines in Section 8.6a, that well investigated contexts in areas like the North York Moors (Simmons & Innes 1988a, 1988b, 1996) were equally not at or near the upper limit to tree cover.

Mesolithic flint assemblages are recorded throughout the region (Spikins 1999; Waddington 1999; Warren 2001), but they have a lowland distribution, and are rarely recorded from the hills, in contrast to the uplands of the central Pennines. The distortions on distribution patterns induced by biases in collection strategy, inaccessibility, blanket peat growth and geomorphic change have been explored by these workers. Within the northern Cheviot Hills, flint assemblages may be underrepresented by limited antiquarian interest, the only limited amount of excavation and the concerns of fieldworkers in recording upstanding monuments (RCAHMS 1956; Mercer & Tipping 1994), but findspots lost by blanket peat growth, or their discovery being biased to areas of peat now being eroded (Spikins 1999), can have impacted on distribution patterns only on parts of the Cheviot Hills above 500m asl where blanket peat occurs (Section 1.5), a very small area of the Cheviot Hills.

It is very likely that site specific gatherer-hunter impacts operated at the decadal scale rather than as deflectors of vegetation succession over centuries (Edwards & Ralston 1984). This very fine temporal patterning to woodland dynamics, however, makes it extraordinarily difficult to separate natural from purposeful gap creation (Tipping 2004). This difficulty affects the interpretation of a series of short and comparatively poorly defined disturbances from around 6550 cal BC at The Dod (Innes & Shennan 1991), or east of the Cheviots at Black Lough (Moyle 1980) (Figure 8.7).

This might also mean that the recognition of long-lived gaps in woodland, if that is what is seen in the poorly temporally resolved sequence at Sourhope (Section 4.3: lpaz Sourhope C), seemingly persisting for some sixty human generations, is less likely to signify human disturbance. Indeed, the very synchroneity of this event between Yetholm Loch and Sourhope (above), and the same type of woodland disturbance in these two contrasting environments, might also undermine the probability of human impact. Synchronous events within a region are more likely to have been induced by large scale natural disturbances, with climate change most likely. Bonsall *et al* (2002) and Tipping and Tisdall (2004) have recently focused attention on the role of climate change in determining the acceptance of agriculture by communities in northern Britain. In particular, Tipping and Tisdall have emphasised the evidence emerging in northern Scotland for a short lived phase of climatic deterioration at the Mesolithic–Neolithic transition, between *c* 4500 and 3800 cal BC. This event is seen as a major disturbance to ocean and ice core records in the North Atlantic (O'Brien *et al* 1995; Bond *et al* 1997, 2001). It appears to be poorly resolved in palaeoclimatic records from southern Scotland and northern England, but may be apparent at Temple Hill Moss on the east of the country (Figure 8.5) (Langdon, Barber & Hughes 2003). In northern Scotland this event seems to have triggered partial woodland collapse, particularly in upland and montane pine dominated woods, and the expansion of open ground communities (Tipping & Tisdall 2004). This may have happened in some upland woods in southern Scotland and northern England also (Williams 1985; Tallis & Switsur 1990; Simmons 1996), and may be what is detected at Sourhope. This event may explain why upland environments were more affected than lowland environments (Simmons & Innes 1987), and account for what some workers have seen as an increasing frequency of woodland disturbance in the few hundred years before 4000 cal BC (Simmons & Innes 1987; Zvelebil 1994; Simmons 1996).

Entirely speculative at present is what Tipping and Tisdall (2004) argued would have been the likely response of gatherer-hunters to landscapes in which grasslands were increasing through woodland degeneration, but a shift to more intensive pastoralism might be anticipated. At sites like Sourhope, where grasslands were through climatic stresses more abundant, these natural openings might then have been maintained by continued grazing.

8.6e Woodland loss, grazing regimes and climatic stresses: general cautions

The vulnerability to climatic stress of oak rich woods has recently been demonstrated for whole regions of north-west Europe by astonishing dendroecological analyses (Kelly *et al* 2002; Leuschner *et al* 2002; Spurk *et al* 2002), and these new data potentially undermine many of the interpretations of anthropogenic impacts on trees developed by palaeoecologists. These workers have identified abrupt episodes in the Holocene when populations of oak trees throughout north-west Europe died off, synchronously and over large regions. The oak trees that died occupied bog surfaces and river floodplains, and may not have been representative of oak trees growing on dryland soils, but by their nature most pollen diagrams reflect these environments. The inference is that oak rich woods collapsed infrequently. Table 8.3 defines the calibrated ages of events defined from dendroecological analyses. These are brief events, lasting 50–100 years, and most are followed by the rapid regrowth ('germination' phases) of trees. They are most common in the Holocene after *c* 5000 cal BC, and because of this, at local scales, anthropogenic deforestation has not been dismissed (Spurk *et al* 2002). However, such impacts cannot explain regionally synchronous events. The insecurity this gives to palynological interpretations of woodland loss has barely been raised amongst palaeoecologists as yet.

Grazing indicator taxa (Behre 1981) are recorded in later prehistory at all sites in the Bowmont Valley (Chapters 3 to 6), but the data are not so easily interpreted in terms of human impact as they once were (Mercer & Tipping 1994; Tipping 1996a). The herbs that palaeoecologists describe as grazing indicators (Behre 1981; Groenman van Waateringe 1986) are not strictly archaeophytes (present only because of human activity). They must have grown on the woodland floor within natural grass rich communities. They are rare in pollen diagrams from wooded landscapes partly because the plants were more scarce, partly because their pollen production beneath a closed tree canopy is very low, partly because their pollen production is astonishingly low compared to that of trees, and partly because pollen dispersal to a sediment body through a woodland is less effective for these herbs than across open ground. It is difficult to demonstrate that grass and herb communities increased in extent because of grazing pressures unless it is assumed that trees were being lost by the same grazing pressures (Buckland & Edwards 1984). In reality, trees might be lost and the canopy cover reduced for reasons other than grazing pressures, permitting grassland herbs to be more easily detected in pollen analyses.

It has been simplest to assume that woodland loss was causally connected with the spatial expansion of

Table 8.3

The relation between troughs in the relative abundances of *Quercus* pollen at sites in the Bowmont Valley with regionally synchronous 'dying-off' events in the dendroecological record of *Quercus* in north-west Europe (Kelly *et al* 2002).

'Dying-off' event	*Trough in relative abundance of* Quercus *pollen*				
	Yetholm Loch	*Sourhope*	*Swindon Hill*	*Cocklawhead*	
(1)	5090 cal BC	No	No	not recorded	not recorded
(2)	4400 cal BC	No	Yes	not recorded	not recorded
(3)	4020 cal BC	Yes	No	not recorded	not recorded
(4)	2870 cal BC	No	Yes	not resolved	No
(5)	2570 cal BC	No	No	not resolved	No
(6)	2050 cal BC	Yes	Yes	Yes	Yes
(7)	1600 cal BC	Yes	Yes	Yes	Yes
(8)	1000 cal BC	not resolved	not resolved	No	No
(9)	770 cal BC	No	not resolved	not resolved	No
(10)	100 cal BC	Yes	No	not resolved	Yes
(11)	540 cal AD	Yes	Yes	not resolved	No

grasslands. However, the observation that populations of oak, the dominant north-west European lowland tree, periodically collapsed through mechanisms other than grazing pressures (Leuchner *et al* 2002; Spurk *et al* 2002) shatters the assumed relation between woodland loss, increases in grassland herbs and grazing pressure. Such interpretative issues are explicit in thinking about the elm decline (Smith 1981), and the investment in this problem as well as the failure to resolve it are more than faintly disconcerting if we now have to apply the same rigorous tests to later Holocene events, but we probably have to.

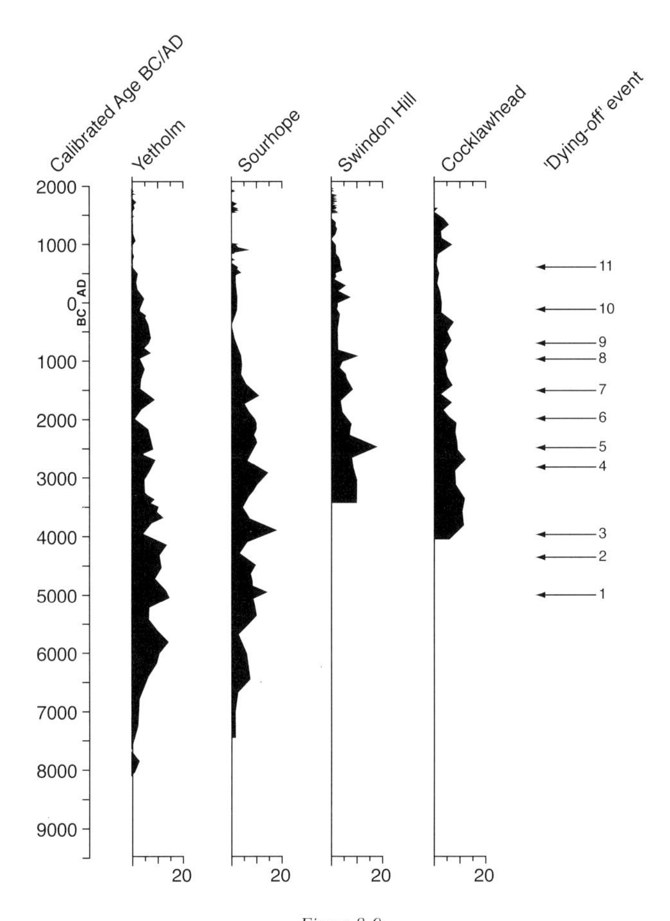

Figure 8.9

Percentages of *Quercus* (oak) pollen (% tlp) plotted against calibrated age BC/AD at Yetholm Loch, Sourhope, Swindon Hill and Cocklawhead (see Chapters 3 to 6 for construction of timescales), showing the relation between the relative abundances of *Quercus* pollen and regionally synchronous 'dying-off' events in the dendroecological record of *Quercus* in north-west Europe (Kelly *et al* 2002).

For example, Section 8.6d reassessed what had been assumed (Tipping 1996a) to be evidence for later Mesolithic grazing regimes at Sourhope by placing a greater emphasis on the synchroneity of events with Yetholm Loch, and considering that grazing indicator herb pollen taxa were more readily detected from a climatically modified open tree canopy. If this is correct, then the idea of repeated climatic impacts on oak woodland needs to be addressed. Figure 8.9 presents in a crude way the correlations that palynologists might need to pursue in resolving these issues. Percentages of oak pollen (% tlp) at Yetholm Loch, Sourhope, Swindon Hill and Cocklawhead are plotted against calibrated age BC/AD. The numbered arrows at different periods depict the ages of synchronous European 'dying-off' events in oak trees presented by Kelly *et al* (2002). The pollen curves are instructive in illustrating the different temporal resolutions of analyses, which determine the sensitivity to change and the frequency of fluctuations, and suggesting how much more rigorous future analyses may need to be to clarify regionally synchronous events. Thus a number of abrupt shifts in oak populations defined from the dendroecological record cannot be resolved in all pollen records from the Bowmont Valley (Table 8.3), but this should not as yet be taken to question the universality of the 'dying-off' events. Currently it seems wise not to dismiss the possibility that some apparent anthropogenic impacts on oak rich woods in later prehistory were of quite different origins, discussed in subsequent sections.

8.7 The transition to an agrarian economy 3900–2500 cal BC

8.7a From Mesolithic to Neolithic economies

It is common among archaeologists nowadays to see the change from gathering and hunting to farming as having occurred gradually, almost imperceptibly, as process rather than event (Whittle 1996, 1999, 2003; Edmonds 1999; Thomas 1999). The first full commitment to agriculture may have been delayed until the Early Bronze Age, after *c* 4500 cal BC (Richmond 1999). This model supposes that external stresses on wild resources did not exist to force this change. It suggests that social mechanisms of increasing familiarity, preference and power relations made the farming economy gradually more attractive.

This gradualist approach led in the 1980s to search for the 'invisible' Neolithic before the first monuments, on the basis that concepts seen as Neolithic, including those of food production, would have emerged or been taken up slowly within the later Mesolithic period. This idea has not borne fruit (Williams 1989). In the same context, it became acceptable to recognise cereal type pollen grains in stratigraphic settings from before the Neolithic (Groenman van Waateringe 1983; Edwards & Hirons 1984; Edwards 1988, 1989a, 1989b). The elm decline was downplayed as the critical marker for the introduction of agriculture because crop growing preceding this event was thought to have been demonstrated (Tipping 1994; Parker *et al* 2002). Macroscopic remains of early cereals have not been reported, however. Criticisms of the pollen record focused on the critical identification of these grass pollen grains as demonstrably of crops (O'Connell 1987; Tipping 1994: Section 2.3f) and the stratigraphic integrity of individual pollen sequences (Tipping 1994). Very few new analyses supporting this idea have emerged in the last twenty years, although some sequences still provide food for thought as most recently on the Isle of Man (Innes, Blackford & Davey 2003).

It is probably fruitless to look back beyond what we know is Neolithic to look for its origin. Instead, the abruptness of the introduction of agricultural elements can be dated to *c* 4200 cal BC. Whether this sharp boundary to the beginning of the Neolithic represents migration of farmers from the continent (Richards 2003) cannot be answered from this work. The rapidity of substitution of wild for domesticated resources has been best argued for coastal communities by Schulting (1998), Richards and Hedges (1999a, 1999b), Bonsall *et al* (2002) and Schulting and Richards (2002). Tipping and Tisdall (2004) have argued how climatic deterioration during the transition (above: Section 8.6d) could have impacted deleteriously on coastal and marine resource availability but advantageously to pastoral herders in inland areas by the creation of grasslands within decaying woods. However, it remains likely that once introduced the rate of adoption of agricultural elements and the speed and confidence with which it was fitted to existing patterns and concepts varied between regions in the British Isles (Richmond 1999; Whittle 1999; Barclay 2001).

8.7b The Mesolithic–Neolithic transition in the northern Cheviot Hills

The rejection now of later Mesolithic anthropogenic impacts on the vegetation in the uplands of the Bowmont Valley (Section 8.6d; cf. Tipping 1996a) does not negate the possibility of a Mesolithic human presence (Waddington 1999). Gatherer-hunters almost certainly moved throughout the different landscapes, but they did not necessarily purposefully modify them. Partial woodland regeneration at Sourhope after *c* 4050 cal BC (Section 4.4: lpaz Sourhope C) is seen as representing recovery from partial fragmentation of upland woods following alleviation of climatic stresses (Tipping & Tisdall 2004). A similar pattern of reduced disturbance was recognised for the uplands of northern England by Simmons and Innes (1981, 1988a), although explained by a loss of human interest in upland areas through soil deterioration following repeated burning. However, highly spatially resolved pollen analyses (Turner *et al* 1993; Simmons 1996; Simmons & Innes 1996) suggest that burnt areas were small, and whether such effects would have operated at the regional scale is very unclear. There is no evidence in the Cheviot Hills for soil deterioration at this time from either the establishment of acid heath vegetation (cf. Caseldine & Hatton 1993; Simmons 1996) or from geomorphological measures (Chapter 7).

Edwards (1988, 1990) suggested that the loss of human interest in upland environments at the Mesolithic–Neolithic transition in south-west Scotland might be demonstrated by a regionally significant diminution of burning, a feature called the charcoal fall. This thesis assumes, of course, that fires were of anthropogenic origin, acknowledged by Edwards (1988). Tipping and Milburn (2000) demonstrated that where seen, however, the fall in charcoal abundance occurred in both lowland and upland contexts and was anyway not a synchronous event. The only record of fire frequency/intensity available in the northern Cheviots, from Yetholm Loch, shows neither high amounts of charcoal in the Late Mesolithic period or, therefore, a subsequent fall (Section 3.3: lpa zones Yetholm D, E).

8.7c The primary elm decline in the northern Cheviot Hills

At Yetholm Loch there were two elm (*Ulmus*) declines. The first is dated to between 3825 to 3540 cal BC; the second occurred much later at around 2640 cal BC. Discussion in this section is confined to the first or primary elm decline. There is no evidence for the loss of other trees during the first elm decline: reductions in oak (*Quercus*) occurred *c* 300 cal years after this, at *c* 3550 cal BC (Section 3.3: lpa zones Yetholm E, Fa). At Sourhope the low numbers of *Ulmus* pollen grains make identification of a decline more problematic, but percentages increase with those of oak at *c* 3400 cal BC (Section 4.3: lpaz Sourhope D), declining abruptly at *c* 2900 cal BC (lpaz Sourhope E). Table 3.3 lists the ^{14}C assays obtained by Hibbert & Switsur (1976) at Din Moss on the beginning of the single elm decline at *c* 4295 cal BC and its end at *c* 4180 cal BC, significantly earlier than at Yetholm Loch. Although very clear at Akeld Steads, the single elm decline was not directly ^{14}C dated (Tipping 1998).

Tipping (1997b) evaluated the many assays from sequences in southern Scotland west of the Cheviot Hills (more numerous than Parker *et al* (2002) collated in their review) which suggest primary elm declines ranging in age from *c* 4150 cal BC to *c* 3500 cal BC, a range supported by new data in the west of the region (Tipping & Milburn 2000; Cayless & Tipping 2002) and within the northern Pennines (Parker *et al* 2002). There are seemingly gradual declines, abrupt falls and rarely, multiple declines (Whittington, Edwards & Cundill 1991a) at Burnfoothill Moss (Tipping 1995b), Over Rig in the Southern Uplands (Boyd unpublished; Tipping 1997b) and at Yetholm Loch (above; Figure 8.7). Events are diachronous within small parts of the region (Tipping & Milburn 2000), as outwith the region in Scotland (Tipping 1994) and northern England (Turner *et al* 1993). They are diachronous between Din Moss, Yetholm Loch and Sourhope at the foot of the northern Cheviots. While large scale synchroneity might be stressed in some reviews (Smith & Pilcher 1973; Parker *et al* 2002) this can conceal instructive site specific delays in response to overriding causes. Nevertheless, the broad scale synchroneity in the elm decline is impressive. Cayless and Tipping (2002) and Parker *et al* (2002) have both turned to climate change to explore how this might have mediated the partial collapse of populations of trees that were robust earlier in the interglacial. These links are complex and unproven but focus on the response of elm to aridity at the end of the Mesolithic period. Data from the northern Cheviots cannot be used to develop this further in the absence of independent palaeoclimatic evidence.

Human impacts as causal in the elm decline have not been rejected (Smith 1981; Tipping 1994; Parker *et al* 2002) despite the difficulties that large scale synchroneity presents for this hypothesis. However, although an absence of evidence, the elm declines at Yetholm Loch (above), at Steng Moss in the northern Pennines (Davies & Turner 1979), Wester Branxholme and Kingside Lochs (Tight 1987) in the Southern Uplands and the primary decline at Burnfoothill Moss near the Solway Firth (Tipping 1995b) (Figure 8.7) suggest no human activity. Purposeful woodland reductions with the first occurrences of grazing indicator pollen taxa can occur at the elm decline, but where the temporal resolution of analyses permits observation these most commonly follow it. Tipping (1994) commented on the comparative frequency in Scotland with which single cereal type pollen grains also follow closely the elm decline, but the evidence for this from around the Cheviot Hills is not strong. Hibbert and Switsur (1976) recorded cereal type pollen from several spectra at the end of the elm decline at Din Moss (*c* 4000 cal BC), but it is not known on what criteria the identifications were based. No such grains accompany the first elm decline at Yetholm Loch.

8.7d Increasing lowland arboreal diversity after the elm decline

The northerly limit to the growth of lime (*Tilia*), or correctly the pollen production of lime since vegetative growth is common, is conventionally placed in southern Cumbria (Pigott & Huntley 1978, 1980; Birks 1989; Greig 1996; Ramsay & Dickson 1997). Its northerly limit has been explained in terms of thermal constraints. To this latitude and temperature regime the tree was able to compete successfully with oak, elm and hazel. Pigott and Huntley (1981) demonstrated the establishment of lime in southern Cumbria by around 5050 cal BC. At Yetholm Loch the pollen records for lime suggest, using similar criteria for local presence to those of Pigott and Huntley (1980), that lime trees colonised this part of The Merse after *c* 3750 cal BC (Section 3.3: lpaz Yetholm E). By this time, and possibly earlier, it is likely that lime had migrated farther north than conventionally thought. Whittington *et al* (1991b) argued for the local growth of lime in the lowlands of north Fife for a short period after *c* 3700 cal BC. There is no evidence that lime migrated directly north from Cumbria onto the northern shore of the Solway (Tipping 1995b, 1997d), and migration probably took place on the less exposed eastern side of Scotland. There is no convincing palynological evidence for local growth at Linton Loch (Mannion 1978) or at Din Moss (Hibbert & Switsur 1976), however, and no evidence from Sourhope (Chapter 4), or from the pollen records at Swindon Hill and Cocklawhead (which commence at this time: Chapters 5, 6; Section 8.7e below) that lime penetrated into the interior of the Bowmont Valley.

These data suggest that the thermal maximum in the Holocene was reached after 3700 cal BC. At these latitudes it was likely that lime could become established only on base rich soils. It may have been very difficult for lime to compete on these soils with already established deciduous trees, and its occurrence immediately after the elm decline may have considerable significance. Lime has similar edaphic demands to elm, and its establishment at a time when elm populations were being reduced may not be coincidental. There is also a need for openings in the woodland canopy cover for successful regeneration of lime (Pigott 1975). Pigott and Huntley (1980) and Birks (1982) noted increased representation in southern Cumbria of lime pollen coincident with the elm decline, attributing this to increased flowering in an increasingly open woodland (see also Pennington 1979). This may have been the case around Yetholm Loch, but direct replacement of stands of elm trees by lime trees is also possible. The pollen record at Yetholm Loch suggests that lime did not necessarily persist for more than a few hundred years, until *c* 3250 cal BC. However, in an archaeological context this is close to the dating of the Ashgrove food vessel in Fife (Dickson 1978) with its distinctive pollen content from lime trees, and the possibility that this pot or its contents was locally made should now be reconsidered.

8.7e Peat inception on the Cheviot plateaux

Between 3800 and 3550 cal BC the peat stratigraphies at Cocklawhead and Swindon Hill started to form (Sections 5.4: lpaz Cocklawhead 7A; 6.4: lpaz Swindon A). This can be regarded as a synchronous single event given the resolution of the dating technique. However, this is not evidence for the widespread and instantaneous expansion of peat throughout the upper Bowmont Valley. The peat that began to form at Swindon Hill was within a small enclosed depression in the bedrock, and there is no suggestion that peat spread across the plateau at this or any later time: a comparable peat basin on the same plateau at Quarry Knowe formed only much later (Sections 5.8: lpaz Quarry A; 8.11b below). On the summit ridge between Windy Gyle and King's Seat at 520m asl, 160m above the Swindon Hill plateau, the peat at Cocklawhead is an unconstrained blanket mire, but pollen stratigraphic correlations across this blanket indicate that peat spread across the bedrock surface only slowly, probably taking several thousand years more to cover the broad col (Section 6.4: lpaz Cocklawhead 7A).

Higher altitudes may have developed a peat cover earlier than this, emphasising further the diachroneity of the pattern and also the important control that temperature has on organic matter decay, because Durno and Romans (1969) dated by regional pollen stratigraphic correlation a peat on the summit of The Cheviot at 815m asl to the Atlantic phase, perhaps around 5000 cal BC. Unlike the analyses at Cocklawhead, this single core cannot capture the complexity and possible age range of upland peat growth (Edwards & Hirons 1982), but it is typical of most analyses of upland peat inception and spread within the region (Tipping 1997b). In the Moffat Hills, farther west and at 620m asl, Tipping (1999b) demonstrated from multiple core ^{14}C dating that these high altitude plateaux were covered in peat between 9800 and 5250 cal BC, and even steep slopes were buried by 3500 cal BC. Tallis (1998) suggested that throughout the British Isles, the period 4000–2000 cal BC was the period of greatest growth, but recognised considerable regional and local diachroneity.

The reconstructions from Cocklawhead and Swindon Hill (Chapters 5, 6) indicate that peat inception in the early Neolithic did not represent a major change in how the landscape looked. There is no evidence that peat inception distorted the spatial distributions of woodland and moorland in the Cheviot Hills in the way that Tallis (1991, 1999) and Simmons (1996) have suggested for the region, with upland woods yielding to extensive peat moors and heath. *Calluna* (ling heather) communities formed an insignificant proportion of upland and lowland Cheviot landscapes in this period. Although growing at Cocklawhead from peat inception (Section 6.4; lpaz Cocklawhead A), *Calluna* heath became prominent at Sourhope and Swindon Hill only after *c* 850 to 800 cal BC (Section 4.3: lpaz Sourhope Gb; Section 5.4: lpaz Swindon B). The upland woods on Cocklawhead are described below (Section 8.7f). Peat inception probably represents a tendency for soils in the uplands to accumulate organic matter, so that some differentiation between brown forest soils and peaty gleys on plateau surfaces is likely at this time, increasing the patchiness of plant communities.

It is not possible to define at either Cocklawhead or Swindon Hill what triggered peat inception, because this has left no stratigraphic record. At neither sequence, paradoxically, are the basal layers of peat thought to have been waterlogged. There is evidence from proxy measures of peat decay at Cocklawhead that this peat was dry and well drained. There are no sediment stratigraphic changes or other proxy measures from the peat sequence at Sourhope that might suggest increases in effective precipitation at this time (Section 4.3: lpa zones Sourhope C, D), although the topographic setting at the base of a slope is not one from which such measures might be confidently defined (Blackford & Chambers 1991). Sediment stratigraphic and other changes indicating lake level shifts at Yetholm Loch are not registered within the fen peat that formed after 5150 cal BC (Section 3.3: lpaz Yetholm D). More reliable palaeoclimatic records from the region similarly record no increase in effective precipitation at this time, and most sequences suggest that regional climate was dry (Rowell & Turner 1986; Chambers *et al* 1997; Barber *et al* 2003; Tipping 1999c). Only at Temple Hill Moss in the Pentland Hills (Langdon *et al* 2003) was the peat surface consistently wet (Figure 8.5). There is no evidence in the region for increases in rainfall to have promoted organic matter accumulation between 4000 and 3500 cal BC. Reductions in temperature can produce the same effect on soils, but we have no unambiguous records of temperature change in the region by which to test this. Perhaps the best estimates for this period, from pine tree ring records in Scandinavia (Helama *et al* 2002), do suggest sharp reductions in summer temperatures at 2850 cal BC.

Peat inception through reductions in soil porosity from the accumulation of charcoal is commonly argued for (Mallik *et al* 1984; Moore 1993; Tallis 1999), but there is no stratigraphic evidence for local burning of the vegetation at Swindon Hill or at Sourhope (Section 5.4: lpaz Swindon A; Section 4.3: lpaz Sourhope D), despite the dry peat surfaces: charcoal abundance was not recorded at Cocklawhead (Chapter 6). Almost by elimination, it remains most likely that disturbance of plant communities on the plateau surfaces led to slight hydrological changes and organic matter accumulation (Section 8.7f below), but not necessarily by anthropogenic modification because there is no convincing evidence at either Cocklawhead or Swindon Hill that grassland communities were encouraged by grazing, and at Sourhope there is evidence for increasing closure of the tree canopy beginning at *c* 4050 cal BC (Section 4.3: lpaz Sourhope C).

8.7f The upland woods

With peat inception at Cocklawhead it is possible to depict the upland woods in some detail (see Section 8.6a). No wood remains were recovered in the blanket mire, and at this exposed site there are difficulties in establishing local presence of plants from pollen data (Hicks 2001). Thus the elm decline at *c* 3700 cal BC probably reflects regional reductions in the wind blown pollen (Section 6.4: lpaz Cocklawhead 7B). Nevertheless, a diverse if open canopy deciduous woodland of hazel and birch, but with oak, ash and willow, and some alder, may have grown on the plateau. In this high altitude wood was yew (*Taxus*), possibly occupying a comparable location to its present day stands in the central Cumbrian fells. The uncertainty over the native status of yew has been discussed in detail by Dickson (1994) and Dickson and Dickson (2000), and the finds from Cocklawhead need to be confirmed.

The openness of the woodland canopy at Cocklawhead probably allowed the survival of some grassland communities and some dry *Calluna* heath. There is no clear evidence that the Cheviot uplands were used by human communities in the early Neolithic period or that grass and heath communities were anthropogenic in origin (Section 8.7e). The evidence in lowland contexts for the continued northward migration of lime (Section 8.7d) suggests that significant reductions in temperature were not at this time leading to the fragmentation of upland woods, but at Sourhope the palynological evidence for a more open woodland canopy through climatic deterioration after *c* 4500 cal BC, closing gradually after *c* 4000 cal BC (Section 8.6d), suggests that woods at higher altitudes may have been more vulnerable and more open, with grass and heath more abundant, immediately prior to local peat growth.

8.7g Early farming communities in the Cheviot Hills

The strongest palynological evidence for agricultural activity is the identification of pollen grains of *Avena/Triticum* (oats or wheat) or *Secale* (rye). The earliest grains of oats/wheat are of Iron Age date, at Sourhope, considered in Section 8.9a. *Secale* (rye) is not recorded until the late Iron Age (Section 8.9d below). The *Hordeum* type (barley type) pollen taxon contains several grass species that grow wild, notably in wetland areas, and is less convincing evidence for agriculture, but the association of this taxon with bare ground herbs can suggest arable plant communities (Behre 1981). The earliest *Hordeum* type grains are found at Swindon Hill, dated to the Later Neolithic (*c* 2850 cal BC) but are not clearly associated at this time with possible weed pollen types (Section 5.4: lpaz Swindon A; see Section 8.7h). Cultivation of barley is more confidently asserted between *c* 1800 and 1350 cal BC at Sourhope (Section 4.3: lpaz Sourhope F).

The evidence for early to mid-Neolithic cereal cultivation anywhere in the Bowmont Valley is thus not strong. One possible cereal type pollen grain, too crumpled to be measured, is recorded at *c* 3450 cal BC at Yetholm Loch but its significance is unclear (Section 3.3: lpaz Yetholm Fa). Cereal type pollen was not identified by Mannion (1978) at Linton Loch. The early Neolithic records of undefined cereal type grains at Din Moss (Section 8.7c) cease before this pollen record was truncated, above *c* 3550 cal BC (Hibbert & Switsur 1976; Birks 1993). This record remains exceptional but ambiguous among the pollen sequences in the region.

Oak pollen percentages at Yetholm Loch decline after the primary elm decline, from *c* 3550 cal BC for around 400 to 500 cal years (Section 3.3: lpaz Yetholm E). Limited amounts of minerogenic sediment were washed into the loch, which may represent some soil erosion, but this need not signify substantial disturbance. Gradual woodland regeneration following partial fragmentation continued at Sourhope after *c* 4000 cal BC. These opposing trends at a time not characterised by regional 'dying-off' events (Section 8.6e; Table 8.3) suggests that lowland oak and lime rich woods were disturbed by human activities, presumably at least partly through increased grazing pressures. There is no unambiguous evidence for settlement, no crops and no use of fire. The pollen data from Din Moss (Hibbert & Switsur 1976) may suggest that people had visited the lowlands for several hundred years before this (Tipping 1996a). Human modification of the lowland woods was negligible, although detectable for the first time. These were not substantial clearings. It is not at all clear from the temporal resolution of analyses at Yetholm Loch that this period of disturbance was sustained. People may have visited the interior of the Bowmont Valley on occasions or as part of a seasonal round (Edmonds 1999), but did not inhibit or slow down the re-establishment of a complete tree canopy around Sourhope. Woodland regeneration at both Yetholm Loch and Sourhope, though not commencing synchronously, occurred at both sites by *c* 3050 cal BC. Around Sourhope, woodland regrowth was sufficient to allow the establishment of elm as well as oak.

8.7h *Woodland disturbance, climate change and human activity in the Later Neolithic*

Further losses of some trees are recorded at both Yetholm Loch (Section 3.3; lpaz Yetholm Fa) and Sourhope (Section 4.3; lpaz Sourhope E) at *c* 2900–2800 cal BC. These are not now seen as representing anthropogenic woodland clearance. Synchronous elm declines are recorded (Section 8.7c) at Yetholm Loch at 2850–2550 cal BC and at Sourhope at *c* 2890 cal BC. Lime trees that had grown around Yetholm Loch (Section 8.7d) seem to have died or ceased to produce pollen. Oak trees were better represented around Yetholm Loch, perhaps because they expanded into areas yielded by elm and lime trees or because their pollen production benefited from woodland losses, but at Sourhope oak pollen values declined briefly as elm values fell. The synchroneity of these elm declines is suggestive, as at the primary elm decline (Section 8.7c above), of a regionally synchronous event. Whittington *et al* (1991a) date the second of three elm declines in north Fife to this time. This period also equates to Event (4) in the chronology of oak 'dying-off' events in north-west Europe (Kelly *et al* 2002; Table 8.3). The trees seemingly affected in the Bowmont Valley were the more thermophilous types, suggesting a link with the short lived suppression of summer temperatures at 2850 cal BC reported in Section 8.7e (Helama *et al* 2002). Trees like hazel, birch and alder seem not to have been disturbed. It was this unstable, partly fragmented woodland that is reflected in pollen sequences around both Swindon Hill and Cocklawhead on local peat inception (Section 8.7e).

In the Bowmont Valley, only at Cocklawhead were quantitative analyses obtained of peat surface wetness. This record (Section 2.3b; Section 6.4) shows from *c* 2750 cal BC a series of extreme but short lived waterlogging events, persisting until *c* 2200 cal BC or *c* 1900 cal BC (lpa zones Cocklawhead 7B, 7C). These flooding events are thought to have been climatic in origin, and are not associated with human impact. They suggest that climatic deterioration was episodic, and that these episodes may have collectively been instrumental in shifting the vegetation on the summit ridge from open woodland to wooded heath. The data do not necessarily imply that precipitation increased during these episodes because falls in temperature would also have promoted greater soil wetness through reduced evapotranspiration, but the tentative interpretation (Section 6.4: lpaz Cocklawhead 7B) that the newly formed blanket mire was cut by eroding gullies at this time would make increased precipitation a more likely cause. Some support for this shift to a wetter climate is seen from the long peat stratigraphic records around the Solway Firth (Figure 8.5) at Bolton Fell (Barber *et al* 2003; Hughes & Barber 2004), Walton (Hughes *et al* 2000) and Burnfoothill Mosses (Tipping 1995a) at *c* 2600 to 2400 cal BC, and in the Moffat Hills (Tipping 1999c) between *c* 3100 and 2500 cal BC.

Tipping (1996a) emphasised an intensification of farming activity after *c* 2850 cal BC in the Bowmont Valley. The Swindon Hill sequence (Section 5.4: lpaz Swindon B) shows that *Hordeum* type pollen grains are consistently recorded (Section 8.7g). Although these grains need not represent barley, and although few arable weeds are present, this pollen type is not recorded from earlier grassland communities at nearby Sourhope and is not recorded after *c* 1150 cal BC at Swindon Hill, suggesting that they are indeed from barley crops. Van der Veen (1992) and Harding (1981) reported carbonised grains of barley from probably Neolithic contexts at sites in the Milfield Basin. The upland setting and the absence of evidence for farming on the valley floors at Sourhope and Yetholm Loch contrasts with the suggestion (Moores *et al* 1999) that floodplains provided *foci* for early Neolithic agriculture, but small fields, perhaps within woodland (Goransson 1986; Edwards 1993; Kristiansen 1993) may have been cultivated on the Swindon Hill plateau. This in turn contrasts with the fleeting or ephemeral presence of human communities identified from the palaeoecological record earlier in the Bowmont Valley and in the region (Annable 1987; Davies & Turner 1979; Richmond 1999). This activity at Swindon Hill appears to have taken place despite climatic deterioration, or possibly because gaps in the woodland promoted by climatic deterioration were then used by farmers (Davies, Tisdall & Tipping 2004).

8.7i Seeing the Neolithic in the Cheviot Hills

The palaeoecological reconstruction of Neolithic environments presented above is less emphatic than presented in 1996 (Tipping 1996a), but closer to the pattern of small patches of farmland within the woods suggested by Mercer and Tipping (1994). Human communities were present in the interior of the valley, on well drained plateaux, from 2850 cal BC, tending small patches of barley but seemingly not purposefully creating by fire or axe spaces in the woodland, and seemingly not managing sufficient numbers of livestock that might have done the same job. People were apparently not interested in the wet and cold valley floors of the interior, typified by the Sourhope pollen sequence. At the foot of the Bowmont Valley around Yetholm Loch, communities appear to have grazed animals (Stallibrass & Huntley 1996) sufficient to alter woodland composition, but not to create permanent gaps (Section 8.7g). There is little evidence for a zonation in land uses between lowland and upland (cf. Topping 1997) in this reconstruction.

How much this view is influenced by new paradigms of Neolithic activities (Edmonds 1999; Richmond 1999; Thomas 1999) is hard to estimate. The palynological evidence at Swindon Hill still contrasts with the absence of upland settlement evidence in the archaeological record (Burgess, Ovens & Uribe de Kellet 1981; Burgess 1984; Waddington 1999). It is probably wrong, of course, to have to associate human activity with archaeologically demonstrable domestic structures. The flimsy Neolithic tent at Bolam (Figure 8.8) excavated by Waddington (1999) may have been typical of a mobile society (Edmonds 1999). Interpretations of rock art on the sandstone outcrops of the Cheviots (but rarely on the andesite of the Cheviot massif itself; Waddington 1996) suggest human interest in upland places without the need to think people stayed there (Beckensall 1996, 2001; Bradley 1996, 1997; Waddington 1996). The spatial patterning of rock art is, however, as positively skewed by the occurrence of rock outcrops on steep upland slopes as the negative biases in evaluating upland distributions of lithic scatters and stone axes (Burgess 1984; Spikins 1999).

The current emphasis in the Neolithic economy on mobile resources like cattle (Ray & Thomas 2003; Richards 2003) is tenuously supported by palaeoecological data in the northern Cheviots. The very restricted evidence for grazed grasslands (Sections 8.7g, 8.7h) implies, however, that Waddington's (1996, 1999) suggestion of summer transhumance to extensive communal grazed areas in upland valleys (see also Lelong and Pollard (1998) west of the Cheviot Hills) is overstated. Transhumance has as a major function the separation of herds from crops, and the comparative insignificance of crop growing in the Bowmont Valley in the Neolithic suggests that such patterns of animal movement would have been unnecessary.

In the Later Neolithic, probably when people began to grow crops at Swindon Hill, the positioning of stone circles at entrances to upland valleys and henges on the Milfield Basin assume symbolic importance in Topping's (1997, 1999a), Waddington's and Harding's (2000) phenomenological landscape reconstructions (see also Evans 1999). The henge at Coupland (Figure 8.8) may indeed be an early Neolithic feature (Waddington 1999). Views of The Cheviot itself from these points are imbued with an almost mythic potency in these models, although the broad dome can hardly have been the most captivating landscape feature. But pedantic though it probably appears, there are as always (Young 1987) rather prosaic but real problems in assuming that long vistas could be gained in and through later prehistoric woodlands. Tests of such ideas using palaeoenvironmental data 'and the like' (Harding 2000, 268) are needed if archaeologists are not to evoke landscapes in an unconstrained way (Chapman & Gearey 2000; Bradley 2002; Tipping *et al* 2004). Such intimate patterns of woodland development cannot realistically be assessed from the only published pollen analyses near the Milfield henge complex, from Akeld Steads (Borek in Tipping 1998), because this diagram reflects plant communities on the floodplain as well as the gravel surface above. It is in the wrong location to characterise what was happening around the monuments, and if pollen recruitment areas are more restricted than we have thought (Section 2.2), location is everything. However, the potential for reconstructing the fine spatial structure of woods around monuments from soil pollen analysis appears also to be very limited (Long *et al* 2000).

8.8 The emergence of the Cheviot archaeological landscape 2500–250 cal BC

8.8a Palynological evidence for later prehistoric crop cultivation

Cultivation of barley was maintained at Swindon Hill from *c* 2850 cal BC, into and almost throughout the Bronze Age, ceasing only after *c* 1150 cal BC (Section 5.4: lpaz Swindon A). At Sourhope the growing of barley is suggested between 1800 and 1350 cal BC (Section 4.3: lpaz Sourhope F). At Cocklawhead (Section 6.4: lpaz Cocklawhead 7C) it is more tentatively suggested that this high altitude plateau supported barley crops between *c* 2100 and 1250 cal BC. It is plausible, though unlikely because of the very low dispersal properties of cereal pollen, that such grains could have been transported from lower altitudes, but even were this to be the case, it would be grounds for suggesting a very high commitment after *c* 2000 cal BC in cereal cultivation throughout the interior of the Bowmont Valley. For a period in the middle of the Bronze Age it is probable that soils at Swindon Hill, Sourhope and Cocklawhead (in short every setting that was examined) supported crops of *Hordeum* (barley). There is, however, no evidence at Yetholm Loch for crop growing in the later prehistoric period (Section 3.3; lpaz Yetholm Fa).

8.8b Woodland loss and grazing pressures

The interpretation of woodland loss is again complicated by the likelihood that some events were not anthropogenic in origin (Section 8.6e). Broadly synchronous reductions in oak pollen percentages at Yetholm Loch after *c* 2100 cal BC (Section 3.3: lpaz Yetholm Fa) may then be correlated with similar reductions at Sourhope from *c* 1950 cal BC (Section 4.3: lpaz Sourhope F), at Swindon Hill after *c* 2350 cal BC (Section 5.4: lpaz Swindon A) and at Cocklawhead after *c* 2100 cal BC (Section 6.4: lpaz Cocklawhead 7c) (Figure 8.9) and with regional 'dying-off' event (6) in Table 8.3. The sustained reductions in woodland at Yetholm Loch and Swindon Hill may, because of the low temporal resolution of analyses, encompass a later regional event (7: Table 8.3). Only at the deltaic infill of Yetholm Loch was woodland loss associated with intermittent episodes of minerogenic sediment inwashing, between *c* 2100 and 1350 cal BC.

Later reductions in oak pollen were not so clearly synchronous (Table 8.3) but that may be because analyses at individual sites are comparatively poorly resolved (Figure 8.9). Alternatively, it may have been that localised anthropogenic modifications to woodland structure and abundance were distorting the simplicity of former patterns. Reductions of oak pollen occurred at *c* 850 cal BC at Sourhope (Section 4.3: lpaz Sourhope Ga) and *c* 800 cal BC at Swindon Hill (Section 5.4: lpaz Swindon B) but there is no evidence at either site for significant woodland loss. On the valley floor at Sourhope, perhaps on the peat surface, alder and willow trees were partly replaced by *Calluna* (ling heather) communities, but this may have been a response to changing peat surface wetness, not through grazing pressures (Section 4.3: lpaz Sourhope Gb). The palynological evidence for even limited grazing pressure on the birch dominated wood at Swindon Hill declines after *c* 800 cal BC. This may, however, have been through the encouraging of woodland around or on the peat basin, and not because this part of the plateau was entirely neglected (Section 5.4: lpaz Swindon B).

Woodland reductions are small at the timescales and resolutions of the pollen analyses, which may indicate only that 'dying-off' events were rapidly followed by the germination of seedlings, but this also implies that grazing pressures were low enough to permit regeneration. Increases in the representation of grazing indicator herb taxa are seen to accompany woodland reductions, but these palynological changes need not have been ecologically linked (Section 8.6e).

It is probable that grazing animals moved throughout the valley, but it is difficult to identify any substantial expanse of grassland throughout later prehistory.

Away from the Bowmont Valley, patterns at other sequences in the region have not been examined for these short lived regional impacts, but in general the poor temporal resolutions and lack of dating controls do not encourage such analyses. The majority of sites suggest that woodland persisted until well after 2550 cal BC. Early Bronze Age woodland clearance, from around 2350 cal BC, is interpreted to have occurred at both Fellend Moss (Davies & Turner 1979) and Fozy Moss (Dumayne 1992) in the south of the region (Figure 8.7), but these early clearances are comparatively rare (Tipping 1997b; Richmond 1999). Throughout the region, later prehistoric anthropogenic activity has remained difficult to identify from pollen records (Tipping 1997b, 1997d; Cayless 2000). The possibility that this is a palynological problem, with small scale clearance around pollen sites being only fuzzily resolved because with clearance woodland pollen is transported from a larger region, remains a possibility but increasingly less likely as our understanding of pollen recruitment improves (Section 2.2). We can with more confidence argue that extensive clearances were very rare in the region.

8.8c *Accelerated geomorphic activity in the Early Bronze Age and the destruction of Neolithic landscapes*

The major landscape transformation at around 2500 cal BC is a geomorphological one, with substantial changes in the appearance and behaviour of rivers on upland valley floors (Chapter 7). At *c* 2500 cal BC the floor of the Halter Burn was transformed by the erosion of gleyed soils and the rapid aggradation of very coarse gravels obtained, probably, by erosion from fluvioglacial gravel terrace deposits (Section 7.4). Within 100 to 200 cal years the peaty valley floor of the Wooler Water at Earle Mill had been overwhelmed by the rapid deposition of similarly coarse gravels (Section 7.5) (Figure 7.8). At Earle Mill it can be shown that this was the first such transformation of this valley floor in the Holocene period, the first time that upland Cheviot valleys had looked the way they do now. It is difficult to demonstrate that all upland Cheviot valleys responded in the same way. In the upper Bowmont Valley the lateral and vertical erosion in subsequent events has destroyed almost all trace of earlier phases. A phase of gravel deposition dated to the Iron Age at Powburn in the Breamish Valley (Section 7.6) suggests that not all valleys were affected by accelerated fluvial activity in the Early Bronze Age. Close to The Cheviot at Callaly Moor near Rothbury, the earliest of two fine grained alluvial fills in a small stream formed after *c* 2450 cal BC and before *c* 800 cal BC (Macklin *et al* 1991), possibly before *c* 1750 cal BC. Farther afield, few comparable upland river systems have sediment sequences preserved from this time, again because of subsequent erosion, but this event is not identified in sequences that do, from the Howgill Fells (Harvey *et al* 1981), the northern Pennines at Thinhope Burn (Macklin *et al* 1992a, Macklin *et al* 1992b) (Figure 8.6) or south of the region in the Bowland Fells (Harvey & Renwick 1987)

Soil inwashing occurred during episodic woodland losses at Yetholm Loch (Section 3.3: lpaz Yetholm F), and on the River Glen at Akeld Steads the supply of fine grained mineral sediments to the peat floodplain was by this time more or less constant (Section 7.7; Tipping 1998a). Similar low energy floodplain construction can be seen on Yorkshire lowland rivers (Macklin *et al* 2000). However, it is likely that minerogenic sedimentation and fluvial activity was very limited on the River North Tyne at Otterburn (Moores *et al* 1999), the South Tyne (Macklin *et al* 1992a, b; Passmore & Macklin 1997, 2000, 2002), below the confluence of these rivers at Scotswood (Passmore *et al* 1992) and in the west of the region in upper Annandale (Tipping *et al* 2000) (Figure 8.6).

This phase of fluvial instability and rapid landscape change may have been selective to the Cheviot Hills. Because of this, and because the palynological evidence for upland Early Bronze Age cereal cultivation is exceptional in the region (Sections 8.8a above), Tipping (1992) argued that Early Bronze Age agriculture had been sufficiently intense to lead to substantial landscape instability, promoting higher than average river flows that were capable of eroding and transporting coarse gravels as well as finer grained sediments. Supportive of this link is the pollen stratigraphy from Earle Mill (Clapperton *et al* 1971) which suggests woodland clearance to have occurred immediately prior to the deposition of fluvial sediments, but pollen sequences from valley floors can reflect vegetation changes that are responses to rather than causes of change (Tipping 2000a). However, cereal cultivation seems to have been widespread in the Bowmont Valley only after *c* 2000 cal BC (Section 8.8a above). Climatic deterioration was probably more significant than recognised by Tipping (1992) (Section 8.7h above). This impacted locally on the high altitude blanket peat at Cocklawhead (Section

6.4: lpaz Cocklawhead 7B), although here there is no stratigraphic evidence that this led to mineral soils being locally eroded.

Tipping (1996a) suggested that this exceptional phase of geomorphic instability could explain the absence of archaeological evidence for Neolithic settlement in the Bowmont Valley. This is likely only for the deeply incised upland valley floors, and increased sediment transfer from slopes may account for the locations of some portable finds, such as Neolithic stone axes, on piedmont and lowland valley floors (Jobey 1961; Burgess *et al* 1981; Topping 1997). But this cannot have been true for the extensive plateau surfaces within the Cheviot Hills (Section 1.6). The peat stratigraphies at Sourhope, Swindon Hill and Cocklawhead (Chapters 4, 5, 6) contain no evidence at all for Early Bronze Age soil erosion. It is likely that most sediment erosion and movement was confined to the active gravel valley floors themselves. Soils on slopes above these seem to have been more stable.

8.8d Early Bronze Age upland colonisation?

The interior valleys of the Cheviot Hills appear to have been used for cereal cultivation extensively after *c* 2000 cal BC (Section 8.8a). Grazing of animals must have played a role, but there is little evidence for extensive grassland, even at high altitudes within the most climatically stressed woodlands (Section 8.8b). Burgess (1984) identified this horizon in the archaeology of the Cheviot uplands, endorsed in many analyses throughout the British Isles (Fleming 1978; Ashmore 1996, 2001; RCAHMS 1997; Richmond 1999; Topping 1999a).

Burgess (1984) argued that Early Bronze Age climatic amelioration would have induced settlers to colonise new landscapes in the hills, but there is abundant evidence that from 2750 to 2500 cal BC that climate deteriorated (Section 8.7h) throughout northern and western Europe through falling temperatures (Gear & Huntley 1991; Rothlisberger 1986; Eronen *et al* 2002), increasing effective precipitation (van Geel 1978; Barber 1982; Dupont & Brenninkmeier 1984; Aaby 1986; Middeldorp 1986; Haslam 1987; Charman 1990; Barber, Chambers & Maddy 1994, 2003; Tipping 1995a; Chambers *et al* 1997; Hughes *et al* 2000; Langdon *et al* 2003) and increasing storminess (Orford *et al* 2000; Wilson *et al* 2001). It is unlikely that people were drawn to the uplands by climate improvement, but on the other hand it is clear that they were not actively discouraged or they had the capacity to overcome the problems (Topping 1999a). Burgess (1984) further suggested that population pressures and a failing lowland agricultural economy, through soil impoverishment, led to abandonment of areas like the Milfield Basin and the lowland river valleys, although evidence for their abandonment has not been forthcoming from either archaeological or palaeoecological data (Harding 1981; Bartley *et al* 1976; Tipping 1998a, 2002b; Richmond 1999; Waddington 1999). This is true even if some of the purportedly Later Neolithic pottery from lowland archaeological monuments is actually of middle to late Bronze Age date (Gibson 2002).

Quantifiable archaeological data are very hard to find, however, and if there is no evidence for significant population movement apparent in the Early Bronze Age, there is equally little evidence from which to assess postulated demographic expansion (Burgess 1989; Waddington 1999). We do not know what encouraged communities to work more extensively in the Cheviot uplands. In the Scottish context, Tipping (2002b) has argued that populations are unlikely to have been pushed into the hills either by population pressures or the failure of lowland farming economies, and an elegant if complex hypothesis has been developed for northern Scotland by Davies (1999; Davies *et al* 2004) in which the fragmentation of upland woods following climatic stresses created new opportunities for farmers, particularly pastoral farmers, by creating natural grasslands. The applicability of this to the Cheviots is unclear, however, not least because the palynological evidence (Section 8.8a) stresses the enthusiasm with which the cultivation of barley rather than livestock production was practiced.

8.8e Bronze Age settlement densities in the uplands

The house type most likely to relate to Bronze Age upland settlement is the unenclosed settlement (Burgess 1980, 1984; Gates 1983; Halliday 1985; Jobey 1985; Mercer & Tipping 1994; RCAHMS 1997; Topping 1999a; Ashmore 2001). Few such sites have been excavated and securely dated, but collectively those that have span the duration of the Bronze Age and early Iron Age (Gates 1983; Jobey 1980, 1983; Terry 1993, 1995). There are difficulties, however, in assuming that unenclosed platform settlements excavated in one part of the region have a relevance in age or function to those in another (RCAHMS 1997). Continuity of occupation cannot be demonstrated (Ashmore 2001).

Topping (1999a) indicates that unenclosed platform settlements are most often single houses in the southern

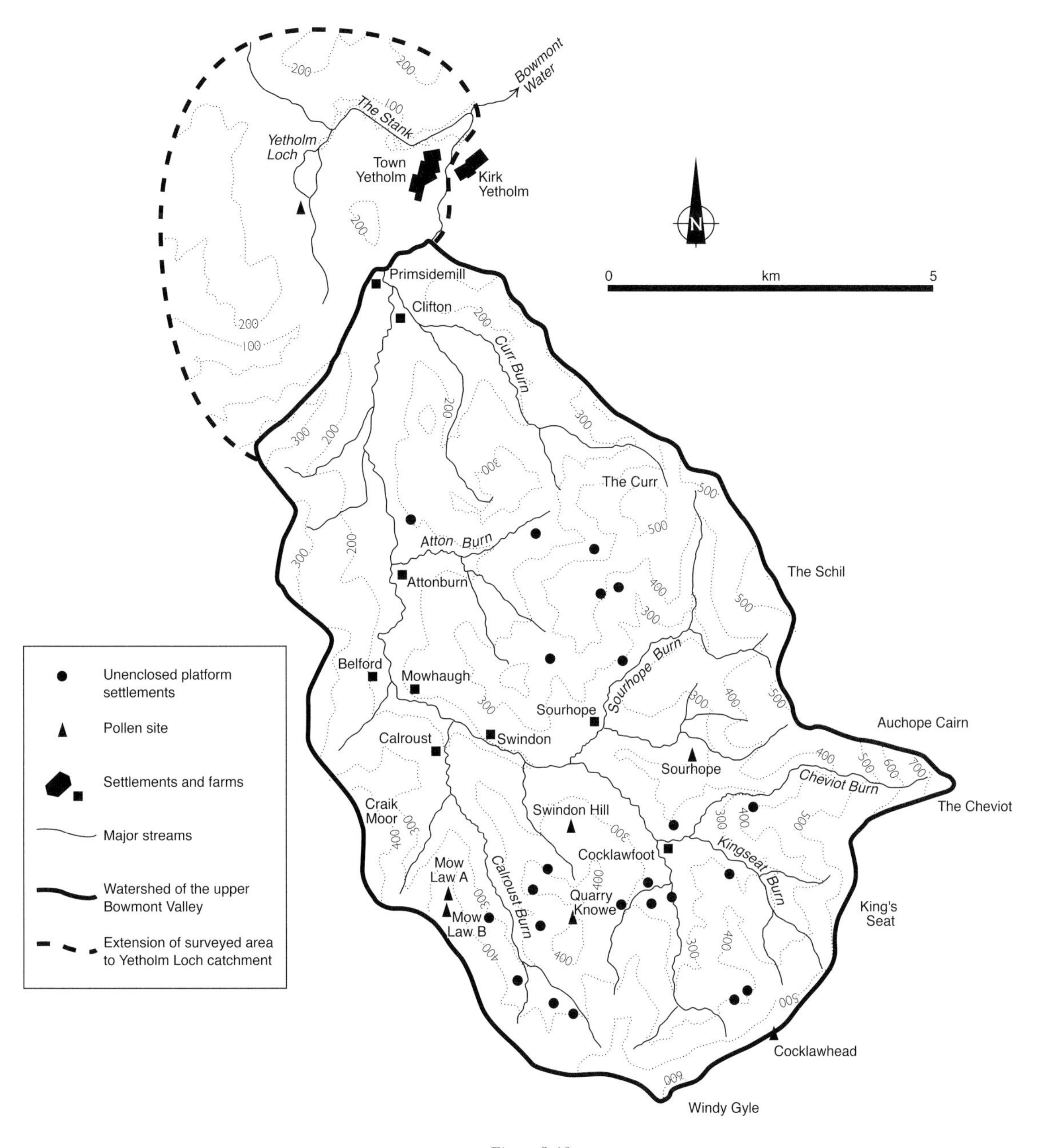

Figure 8.10
Distribution in the archaeologically surveyed area of the upper Bowmont Valley of later prehistoric unenclosed platform settlements (from Mercer & Tipping (1994) figure 1.5).

Cheviot Hills, and that concentrations (Gates 1983) are rare. This is one difference with their distribution in the uplands to the west (Terry 1995; RCAHMS 1997). Unenclosed platform settlements are common above upland valley floors up to 400m asl (Gates 1983; Topping 1999a). Halliday (1985) wondered whether the highest settlements were part of a transhumant system, as did Waddington for the Later Neolithic (1996) (Section 8.7i). However, the palynological evidence for Bronze Age crop growing on Cocklawhead at 520m asl and at Swindon Hill at 360m asl (Section 8.8a) suggests that farming communities did not reserve for pasture the upland parts of the landscape. This might imply that unenclosed platform settlements were more alike in function than we have thought. People seem to have done the same things everywhere in the upper

Bowmont Valley, unconstrained by initial climatic deterioration.

Most unenclosed settlements are in the English Cheviots on south- and east-facing slopes (Topping 1997). This may be a bias induced by the radial drainage pattern of valleys around The Cheviot. Twenty-three examples were reported by Mercer and Tipping (1994) from the surveyed area in the upper Bowmont Valley (Figure 8.10), ranging as elsewhere in the Cheviot Hills between 290 and 380m asl, and as high as 426m asl. These settlements will be analysed in detail by Mercer (in prep.): as with all discussion of the archaeological monuments in the upper Bowmont Valley the data-set used is only that published by Mercer and Tipping (1994). Of the sites on slopes, nine (43%) face east to south, and only one faces west, but eleven (52%) face north because this is the way the land lies in the upper Bowmont Valley. Only two sites are on level ground (Figure 1.4; Section 1.6): however, probably by definition platform settlements will be on slopes. Eight sites (35%) are on steep slopes, three of which are north facing, indicating that little direct sunlight would have shone on them (Topping 1981).

Gates (1983, 110) interpreted the distribution pattern of unenclosed platform settlements as one of farmsteads 'scattered singly or in small groups separated by large expanses of apparently "empty" landscape', and this view is supported by Topping's (1999a) reconstruction. Both are in apparent contrast to Burgess' (1984, 143) reconstruction of 'considerable tracts, as yet undefined in area, ... cleared and tilled up to 400m', but Burgess was not discussing settlements in that passage but the extent of farmed land. The minimalist descriptions of Gates (1983) and Topping (1999a) accord well in some aspects with the pollen records from the Bowmont Valley. There is no evidence that Bronze Age woodland loss occurred on larger scales than in the Neolithic (Section 8.8b). Spaces in the woodland, created naturally or by grazing, were small, isolated and ephemeral, and this is typical of most upland pollen sequences in the region (Turner 1970; Davies & Turner 1979; Wilson 1981; Tipping 1994, 1997b), although not for particular localities (Chambers 1978; Davies & Turner 1979; Higham 1986; Moores *et al* 1999) which, problems of temporal resolution notwithstanding, appear to record episodes of grazing pressure for many hundreds of years without woodland regeneration.

In other aspects Burgess' (1984) descriptions remain attractive in that they describe the widespread, extensive nature of land use. There is no paleoenvironmental evidence from the upper Bowmont Valley that Bronze Age farming was intensive. So although Gates (1983) reported that over 85% of Northumbrian unenclosed platform settlements had evidence for land clearance in the form of organised plots, often small fields, there is no requirement for this investment to have occurred within a few hundred years of communities seemingly discovering that the hills could be lived in. Models of increasing organisation and investment in land clearance have been developed, from cairns to the construction of irregular fields (Topping 1981, 1983; Halliday 1999; Johnston 2002), and to the suggestion (Vyner 1994; Topping 1999a) that there were larger scale territorial structures, but almost none of this developmental sequence is underpinned by a secure chronology (Bradley 2002). Johnston (2000) suggests an Early Bronze Age date for Northumbrian cairnfields, early in the sequence of upland archaeological monuments, although how typical these very few radiocarbon assays are, sometimes from distinctive cairns within cairnfields, remains to be demonstrated. It is unclear that stone removal in cairnfields consistently represents cereal cultivation (Burgess 1984; Halliday 1999; Johnston 2000). Pasture improvement is as likely, with the elaborate triradial cairns of the Northumberland Cheviot seen as shelters for animals (Adams 1999; Ford, Deakin & Walker 2000). In the west of the region, pollen analyses from a small diameter peat basin within a complex of cairns and small fields at Stanshiel Rig (RCAHMS 1997; Halliday 1999) (Figures 8.7, 8.8) failed to provide evidence for crop growing, or indeed for significant woodland clearance (Cayless 2000). The relation between cairnfields and the archaeological evidence for preserved tree throw holes (Halliday 1995) remains unknown, and indeed the relation between what the archaeologist perceives as major and instantaneous events in woodland removal is not seen in the pollen analyses in the Bowmont Valley.

Into this later prehistoric sequence must be placed cultivation terraces and lynchets, probably also early (Burgess 1980; Topping 1983, 1987, 1993). Cultivation terraces are best seen as having an arable function, maximising the surface of a ploughed slope (Topping 1983). At Linhope Burn, the earliest plough marks beneath a lynchet are suggested, from pollen analyses in contexts difficult to interpret, to indicate the cultivation of cereals on a partly open grassy slope within a pastoral economy (Topping 1993). The Lintshie Gutter group of unenclosed platform settlements produced evidence for the growing of barley (Terry 1995), though not necessarily on nearby cultivation terraces (Ashmore 2001). An arable component to the mid-Bronze Age cairnfield system on Callaly Moor was suggested by Macklin *et al* (1991), and also around the mid-Bronze Age burnt mounds constructed at Titlington Mount south of Beanley (Innes in Topping 1998) and later in the Bronze Age at the unenclosed settlement at Hallshill in Redesdale (van der Veen 1985, 1992) (Figure 8.8).

8.8f Later Bronze Age cessation of crop growing and climatic deterioration

Between 1300 and 1150 cal BC the growing of barley appears to have ceased in the deep set valley at Sourhope, on the higher but better drained plateau of Swindon Hill and on the increasingly peat covered summit ridge at Cocklawhead (Section 8.8a). Establishing this with confidence is not easy because of the need to make much of an absence of evidence. Interpretation is made more difficult because cereal type pollen has very limited pollen dispersal, so that new cultivated areas more distant from pollen sites will appear as a cessation of crop growing. However, this pattern is seen at three localities (the Yetholm Loch record is poorly resolved at this time; Chapter 3), and is taken to be real for the upland part of the valley.

This is not necessarily evidence for settlement abandonment of the Cheviot uplands. For this to be demonstrated palaeoecologically, woodland regeneration would need to be shown to have been complete. This cannot be demonstrated, although there are a number of reasons why this test can be seen as too rigorous: the effects of long term climate deterioration may have constrained the potential for complete woodland regrowth, and the more abrupt but short lived impacts on oak populations may over time have weakened their ability to regenerate; progressive blanket peat growth, though slow and restricted, may have deterred woodland re-establishment. The very limited evidence for any emphatic woodland loss in later prehistory in the Bowmont Valley (Section 8.8b) is itself difficult to interpret (Section 8.8e), but there is argued to be no consistent evidence for natural woodland regeneration. Substantive woodland regeneration occurred only at Swindon Hill (Section 5.4: lpaz Swindon B), where, unusually, only birch trees grew, and this has been interpreted as representing woodland management (see also Section 8.9c below). At Cocklawhead (Section 6.4: lpaz Cocklawhead 7C) the increasing proportions of the grazing sensitive tall herb *Filipendula* (cf. meadowsweet) after *c* 1000 cal BC may indicate that grazing pressures were reduced, but woodland did not recolonise. The interpretation here is that communities did not abandon the upland slopes of the Bowmont Valley, that they continued to use the hills for grazing, at low stocking densities or in a largely mobile system, but either collectively or individually, groups decided that the growing of barley was not to be a part of the upland economy.

There is evidence from the valley, and elsewhere, that climatic deterioration may have been an important factor in decision making. At the most exposed site at Cocklawhead, bare ground herbs like *Artemisia* (mugworts) were more common after *c* 1000 cal BC despite the apparent cessation of crop growing. Soil erosion became common on the summit ridge after *c* 850 cal BC, and the peat surface became substantially wetter between *c* 600 and 400 cal BC (Section 6.4: lpaz Cocklawhead 7C). At *c* 950 cal BC groundwater levels rose substantially within the previously free-draining peat at Sourhope (Section 4.3: lpaz Sourhope Ga). These changes agree with abundant evidence for what was probably a complex series of shifts to greater precipitation, and probably lower temperatures, in the region and across north-west Europe between 1200 and 800 cal BC (Aaby 1976; Barber 1981, 1982; Dupont & Brenninkmeier 1984; Rowell & Turner 1985; Haslam 1987; van Geel *et al* 1996, 1998a, 1998b; Wimble 1986; Chambers *et al* 1997; Hughes *et al* 2000; Langdon *et al* 2003; Blaauw, van Geel & van der Plicht 2004), and perhaps further instability after *c* 500 cal BC (Dickinson 1975; Aaby 1976; Rowell & Turner 1985; Wimble 1986; Haslam 1987; van der Molen & Hoekstra 1988). Recovery may not have happened until *c* 150 cal BC (Lamb 1981). There is little uncertainty now in the intensity and longevity as well as the complexity of the climatic change (Tipping 2002b). None of these changes, however, can be linked to Icelandic volcanic activity, as much hypothesised (Baillie 1989; Parker Pearson 1993; Richmond 1999): see Buckland, Dugmore & Edwards (1997) and Dodgshon, Gilbertson & Grattan (2000).

Although both phases of climatic deterioration at *c* 850 and 500 cal BC are defined by Macklin & Lewin (2003) as major flood episodes in Britain there is only limited evidence for this from the region, from the North Tyne at Otterburn and in upper Annandale (Moores *et al* 1999; Tipping *et al* 1999) (Figure 8.6). Section 7.6 and Figure 7.8 suggested that the exceptional phase of braided river development and gravel aggradation on the River Breamish at Powburn may have commenced after *c* 800 cal BC, earlier than estimated by Tipping (1992). Macklin *et al* (1991) linked later Bronze Age climatic deterioration with accelerated fluvial sedimentation at Callaly Moor (Figure 8.6), but alluviation may have been within the mid-Bronze Age if the ^{14}C dated burial cists at *c* 1400 and *c* 1750 cal BC provide a *terminus ante quem* date for agricultural activity (Cowley in Hedges *et al* 1992).

The relevance of this climatic deterioration to settlement in Scotland has been discussed since Piggott (1972) initiated debate, and the Cheviot Hills have been central (Lamb 1981; Burgess 1984, 1985, 1989, 1990, 1995; Gates 1983; Jobey 1980, 1985; Higham 1986; Mercer & Tipping 1994; Tipping 1994; Young 2000; Young & Simmonds 1995; Tipping 2002). Yet within the Cheviots, there is no unambiguous archaeological evidence for abandonment. In different contexts, Pryor (1995), McCulloch and Tipping (1998) and Caseldine (1999) have argued that it is extremely difficult to demonstrate abandonment from this sort of evidence. Away from the Cheviots, Owen (1992) suggested that climatic change might account for apparent abandonment after *c* 950 cal BC of the later Bronze Age hilltop settlement of Eildon Hill North (Owen 1992) (Figure 8.8), but Jobey (1980, 1985), Hill 1982a, Triscott (1982), Gates (1983) and van der Veen (1992) have argued for continuity of more domestic settlements, although the difficulties of demonstrating settlement continuity from archaeological data are perhaps as demanding as establishing abandonment.

From the palaeoecological evidence in the northern Cheviot Hills, it is argued that later Bronze Age farmers understood that cereal cultivation, even of barley, was inappropriate at altitudes above 300m asl. This suggests a flexibility in decision making which we should expect (Barber 1997; Bruck 2000; Young 2000; Tipping 2002b). At some upland sites in southern Scotland and northern England, cereal type pollen (undefined further) continues to be recorded into the Iron Age, at Steng Moss in the northern Pennines (Davies & Turner 1979) (Figure 8.7), although this example is unusual. From securely ^{14}C dated sites throughout the Scottish uplands, Tipping (2002b) could not identify consistent palynological evidence for later Bronze Age settlement retreat, although reappraisals and shifts in how the uplands were managed were common. The overwhelming majority of sites, however, show the maintenance of pasture at varying levels of intensity.

8.8g Later prehistoric soil quality

Jobey (1981) and Payton (1987) suggested that soils at Chatton Sandyford, on the Carboniferous Fell Sandstone east of the Cheviot Hills (Figure 8.8), were becoming too acidic for cultivation from before and during the later first millennium BC, through woodland clearance accelerating a tendency to podsolisation. Several points suggest, however, that andesitic soils on the Cheviots (Section 1.6) maintained a comparatively high nutrient status throughout later prehistory. *Calluna* (ling heather) rich communities at Cocklawhead were growing, albeit sparsely, from peat inception at *c* 3800 cal BC (Section 6.4: lpaz Cocklawhead 7A), and only after *c* 100 cal BC were they dominant on the then extensive blanket peat (lpaz Cocklawhead 7D). Phases of soil erosion may have retarded acidification here through nutrient replenishment (cf. Askew, Payton & Shiel 1985). Comparable plant communities had been present at Sourhope and Swindon Hill from *c* 850 cal BC (Sections 4.3: lpaz Sourhope Gb; 5.4: lpaz Swindon B), again probably on already nutrient poor peats, but the expansion of *Calluna* heath away from these peat surfaces was not significant until the later historic period (Section 8.10c below): at Yetholm Loch *Calluna* has never been important (Chapter 3). There is in addition no palaeoecological evidence for extensive or long lived woodland clearance to induce soil deterioration (Section 8.8e). Birch was by far the dominant tree in the upper valley by the middle of the Iron Age (Chapters 4, 5, 6; Section 8.8b), and this may have played a significant role in maintaining and restoring nutrient status of soils (Miles 1985, 1988). In the northern Cheviots, Kerr (1977) linked later prehistoric settlement to the highest quality, brown forest soils, but this observation may have no real significance if, as suggested here, soils were then more uniform than present day distributions would suggest.

8.8h Yetholm Loch and lowland landscapes in later prehistory

Attention has been focused in this section on the upland Cheviot landscape, partly because the combined evidence from the three pollen sequences at Sourhope, Swindon Hill and Cocklawhead provides more insights than in published studies into the temporal and spatial variability of later prehistoric environments and land uses, partly because archaeological data from field surveys are so rich, and partly because the debate concerning continuity of occupation has been concerned with stresses likely to have been most effective at higher altitudes.

However, this focus has also developed because the lowland pollen record at Yetholm Loch (Chapter 3) yields no clear evidence of later prehistoric human impacts. There are difficulties in interpretation of this record. First is the low temporal resolution of analyses at Yetholm Loch in this period (Section 3.2; Table 3.4), and yet analyses at Swindon Hill in the same time period are at lower resolutions (Section 5.3; Table 5.4) and more information has been recovered (above). One interpretation of this is that more changes occurred at Swindon Hill than at Yetholm Loch. A second difficulty at Yetholm Loch is that the pollen sampling site may have been insensitive to land use change throughout later prehistory because it lay deep within a dense alder carr into which the pollen of dryland plants rarely penetrated. Although probably true, interpretative circularities notwithstanding, this only emphasises the extraordinary human impacts on the landscape after *c* 250 cal BC discussed next

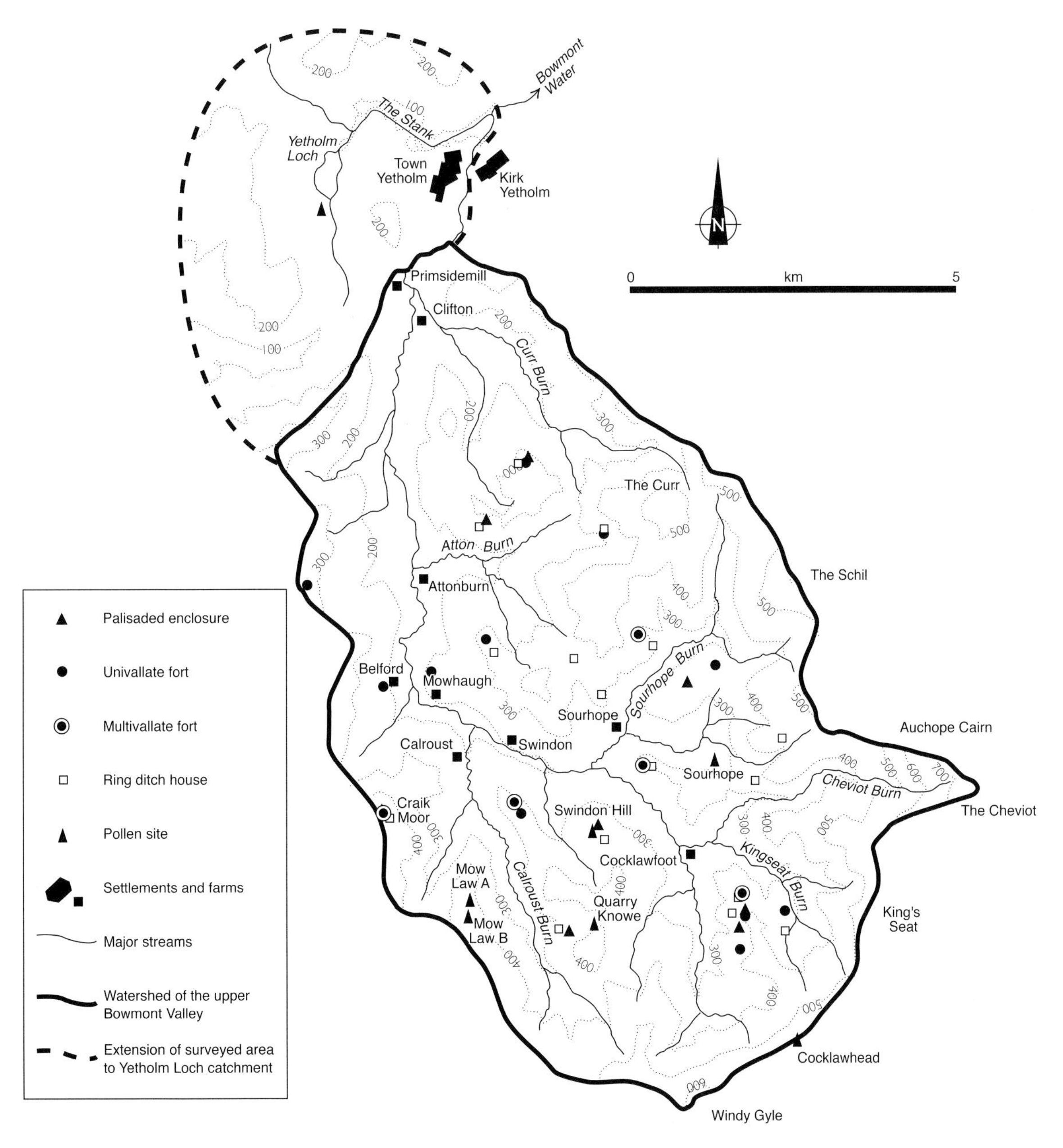

Figure 8.11
Distributions in the archaeologically surveyed area of the upper Bowmont Valley of later prehistoric palisaded enclosures, univallate and multivallate hilltop defended enclosures (forts) and ring-ditch houses (modified from Mercer & Tipping (1994) figures 1.2 and 1.3).

(Section 8.9a), which are better seen at Yetholm Loch than at upland sites. For a number of reasons, then, the sequence at Yetholm Loch reveals little of the activities of human communities that must have been there: Dent and McDonald (1997) describe the Bronze Age hoard of three shields placed into Yetholm Loch. For similar reasons the pollen data of Borek (1975) reinterpreted and ^{14}C dated by Tipping (1998) at Akeld Steads in the Milfield Basin are also poor descriptors of later prehistoric lowland environments. The growth of dense fen and carr woodlands on lowland valley peats undoubtedly distorted the deposition of pollen from farmed landscapes across the region (Tipping 1997b, d). This issue presents a problem of

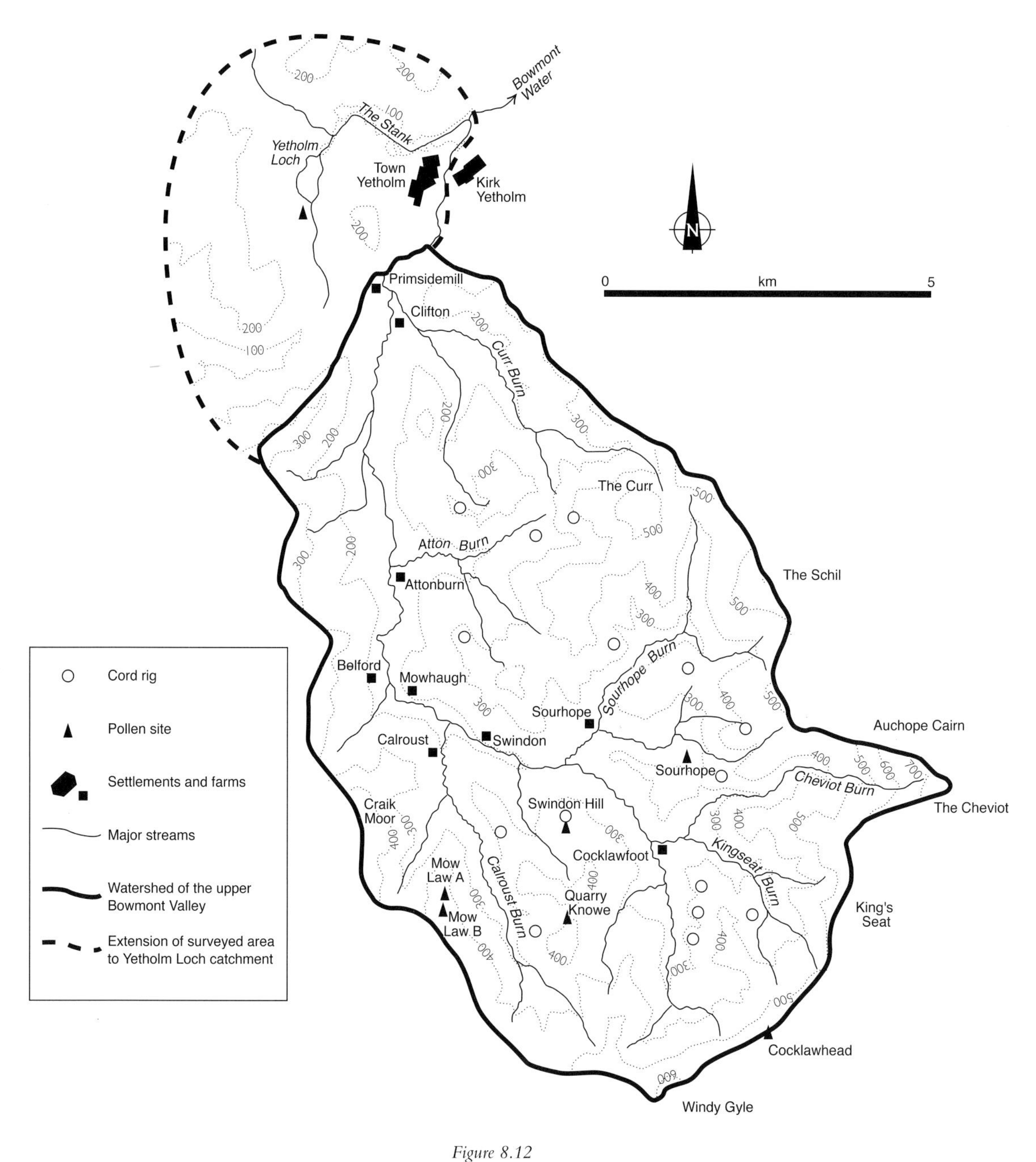

Figure 8.12
Distribution in the archaeologically surveyed area of the upper Bowmont Valley of later prehistoric cord rig cultivation traces (modified from Mercer & Tipping (1994) figure 1.6).

misrepresentation as serious as that seen in the limited survival of lowland archaeological sites and landscapes (Haselgrove 2002).

8.8i Later prehistoric palaeoecological and archaeological records in the Bowmont Valley

The overturning of the 'Hownam' (Piggott 1948) chronology of later prehistoric settlement in south-east and southern Scotland, more by careful observation of stratigraphic relations during field survey than by detailed excavation (Hill 1982a, b; RCAHMS 1997; Armit 1999; Welfare 2002), has undermined our ability to explain the archaeological record. Two effects are critical, the stretching into the Bronze Age of what was thought to be a short late Iron Age chronology and the consequent long period in which settlement types, open and enclosed, could come and go and come again. A simple developmental sequence, however stretched, cannot explain the relations between archaeological monuments, and we as yet have no schema to replace this. The archaeological monuments of broadly later Bronze Age and Iron Age date recorded by Mercer and Tipping (1994) in the upper Bowmont Valley are depicted in Figure 8.11, but no attempt without extensive excavation can be made to assess the chronology of this record. The current miasma is further muddied because it is probable that no single horizon within later prehistory, before 250 cal BC (Section 8.9 below) can be defined from the pollen records at Sourhope, Swindon Hill and Cocklawhead (Chapters 4, 5 and 6) as representing a significant phase of land use intensification or monument construction (Sections 8.8a, b above). Before we can understand why these communities remain almost ghostlike in terms of their impacts on the landscape yet so visible archaeologically, we urgently need to understand the chronology of monument construction on a landscape scale.

8.8j Cord Rig and the Cheviot palaeoenvironmental record

The cultivation trace known as cord rig, with characteristically narrow (1–1.5m) widths between ridges, occurring in small plots, not necessarily walled, is very widely recognised in the uplands of the region (Topping 1989a, b; 1993; Halliday 1993, 2003; Mercer & Tipping 1994; RCAHMS 1997). Traces are found to 420m asl but also almost to sea level. Cord rig is convincingly prehistoric in age, and is associated with later prehistoric settlement types in the region, though the interpretation that it is demonstrably of Iron Age date (Topping 1989a, b) is hampered by the lack of stratigraphic associations *termini ante quem* and the recognition that elsewhere in Scotland comparable ridged cultivation can be of late Neolithic and Bronze Age date (Barclay 1983; Carter 1995; McCulloch & Tipping 1998). Halliday and Hill's unpublished excavations at Hut Knowe North in the western Cheviots, and Topping's (1993) excavation of cord rig at Linhope Burn in the Breamish Valley (Figure 8.8) yielded no ^{14}C dating controls.

The Linhope Burn excavation appears to show that cord rig was used in several phases in later prehistory. The palynological evidence from that site is considered by this worker to be equivocal with regard to the association between ridging and crop growing. It seems reasonable, however, to assume that ridging was for a crop or crops, but what sort of crop remains unknown. Fifteen localities within the archaeologically surveyed area at the Bowmont Valley containing small plots of cord rig (Plate 8.2) were recorded (Mercer & Tipping 1994; Figure 8.12). The distribution is at least in part determined by survival of the evidence away from areas later destroyed. Again, only the evidence published by Mercer and Tipping (1994) is used here. In the upper Bowmont Valley, cord rig plots range from 275m asl to 440m asl, with the average at 356 ± 44m asl. This range or even the very high altitude of some plots is not by itself problematic for cereal cultivation, because Section 8.8a has argued that barley was grown above 500m asl. Most plots are on level to moderate ground (cf. Section 1.6: 53%), but the remainder are on moderately steep slopes. Although not quantified here, the steepness of these slopes and the very limited direct sunlight they would have received suggests that what was cultivated did not need long growing seasons and could cope with cold soils. Only three plots are on north-facing slopes, but these include at least one on moderately steep ground above Cocklawfoot (Figure 8.12).

It is dangerous practice to relate too closely the record of land uses from off-site pollen analyses to site specific archaeological records, even when the pollen records define small pollen recruitment areas (Section 2.2). However, one preserved plot of cord rig is within the recruitment area of a pollen record in the upper valley, at Swindon Hill (Figure 8.12). If the pollen record represents what was grown at some time in later prehistory in this plot, and what was grown was a cereal, then it is more likely that the cord rig here is of late Neolithic or Bronze Age date (Section 8.8a): the assumptions in all this discourage further

Plate 8.2

Clear traces of cord rig on the level to gentle ground of a low level plateau surface at Auchope Rig, south east of the Sourhope Valley, looking south to the snow-speckled lower slopes of Score Head on the summit ridge. The scale is Roger Mercer.

speculation. However, within the upper valley there is no palynological evidence for cereal cultivation in the Iron Age, which is probably a more significant point in understanding the local dating and function of cord rig. It is possible, speculating somewhat, that cord rig represented a very limited level of agricultural investment (RCAHMS 1997), at a scale too low to be recorded in these pollen analyses (Chapters 4 to 6), or that what was grown is not recognised in pollen analyses. It is tempting to suggest that these were garden plots for vegetables, notoriously underrepresented in charred plant and pollen analyses.

Speculating further, little discussion has been given to the mechanisms by which cord rig is preserved. The often steep slopes on which it is found would mitigate against its survival, particularly when newly dug or ploughed. While many plots may have been lost through soil erosion, enough survive to wonder how these slopes retain morphological evidence in such astounding detail (Topping 1989a; RCAHMS 1997) unless slope and soil stability were imposed instantly. Exposure of even weed covered fields on steep slopes to winter rains would obliterate the undulating topography of ridge and furrow unless this was preserved under a grass sward within, probably, a few weeks of the last crop, by deliberate reseeding. This issue and the implications from it for intent and planning by prehistoric farmers need to be explored.

8.9 Late Iron Age and Romano-British agricultural intensification 250 cal BC–500 cal AD

8.9a Woodland clearance and agricultural impacts

The undisturbed alder carr woods of the valley floor at Yetholm Loch were then dramatically and lastingly destroyed by an exceptionally complete and abrupt clearance of woodland, totally different in character to all preceding episodes. This event is comparatively loosely dated because the minerogenic lake and floodplain sediments precluded ^{14}C assay and because the sediment accumulation rates were probably both rapid and highly variable (Section 3.3: lpaz Yetholm Fb; Tipping 1992, 1997a). The preferred age of the clearance event is around 175 cal BC, in the late Iron Age. The removal of trees was probably very rapid, but the degree of geomorphic instability created in this act is thought to have pushed very high amounts of tree pollen stored in soils from preceding woodlands into the loch, disguising the abruptness of the event and making it appear that woodland loss occurred later than it did. Because of the extent of sediment and pollen reworking, the relative chronology of woodland loss cannot be reconstructed. It is unknown whether dryland woods were cleared before the valley floor carr. The combined effect was the total removal of any plant community that could be seen as a functioning woodland, one in which local seed sources could assure regeneration. The rapid destruction of woodland around the loch cannot be seen as the product of gradual grazing pressures, and probably not that of an amalgam of separate small scale clearances, but rather represents the establishment of a planned landscape, cleared in one concerted effort over a short time. The totality, rapidity and geomorphic impacts of the event suggest clear felling by axe: fire was not used. The deliberation and scale of the event is shocking in the palaeoecological record at Yetholm Loch, and must have seemed so to the people involved. The devastated hillsides clearfelled in the twentieth century cal AD of their conifer plantations spring to mind as an image of this late Iron Age landscape.

Woodland loss initiated severe erosion of soils, possibly in much the same way as does present day deforestation. Topsoils were lost through clearance, and valley floor floodplain sediments eroded as the river swung across the floodplain unconstrained by carr woodland. Mineral sediment transport was prominent until *c* 50 cal AD and did not cease until *c* 600 cal AD (lpaz Yetholm Ga). Very coarse sediments were transported, and at the sampling site sediment deposition may have led to the rapid building of the delta. The nutrient status of the lake improved significantly, seen in an expansion of aquatic plant communities and algal mats. Farmers established probably extensive fields of crops on well drained soils on the fluvioglacial gravels and on the till and bedrock slopes, and grew oats or wheat and, possibly, rye (lpaz Yetholm Ga: Section 8.9b below). Areas of pasture were created, and were possibly intensively grazed. Hay meadows appear to have been managed, and these are most likely to have been for herds of cattle. The archaeofaunal record in the region is inadequate to assess this (Hambleton 1999).

In the interior of the Bowmont Valley, woodland clearance on a similar scale is seen also at Sourhope, possibly at the same time as the event at Yetholm Loch, at *c* 100 cal BC (Section 4.3: lpaz Sourhope H). Here trees appear to have been totally removed. Grazed ground was common, as were fields planted with oat, probably barley and perhaps rye. At Cocklawhead, from where the destruction of the woods around Yetholm Loch could be seen, there was accelerated soil erosion after *c* 100 cal BC (Section 6.4: lpaz Cocklawhead 7D). As at lower altitude sites (above) there was a sharp reduction in tree pollen. How much this reflects reductions in far-travelled pollen is unclear, but it is likely that local losses occurred as trees were replaced by heath and also by grazed grasslands, and probably by intermittent cereal crops. This woodland clearance is seen throughout the Bowmont Valley at the same time, but the loss of all species precludes the impacts of climatic change on single species (Spurk *et al* 2002). Woodlands were removed by direct anthropogenic impacts except at Swindon Hill (Section 5.4: lpaz Swindon B), where the birch woods established in the early Iron Age persisted. This difference may well be strong evidence that the woodland at Swindon Hill was intended to be there, as a resource managed in its own right (Section 8.9c below).

As is now well understood, the pattern exhibited throughout the Bowmont Valley of abrupt and near complete woodland destruction is seen at many sites in northern England, southern and central Scotland (e.g. Roberts, Turner & Ward 1973; Bartley, Chambers & Hart-Jones 1976; Donaldson & Turner 1977; Turner 1979; Barber 1981; Wilson 1981; Honeyman 1985; Dumayne 1992, 1993a, b; Bartley, Jones & Smith 1990; Fenton-Thomas 1992; Mackay & Tallis 1994; Tipping 1994; 1995b, 1997a, b, d; Dark & Dark 1997; Manning, Tipping & Birley 1997; Wiltshire 1997; Ramsay & Dickson 1997; Dumayne-Peaty 1998a, b, 1999a; Fleming 1998; Dark 2000; Huntley 2000; Campbell, Tipping & Cowley 2003; Oldfield *et al* 2003). The overwhelming majority of extensive clearances are of later Iron Age date, not of Romano-British age. Early clearances occurred prior to *c* 250 cal BC but the extent and rate of clearance, measured by the numbers of sites affected, gathered pace after *c* 150 cal BC. There is the statistical possibility that some clearance events on and near Hadrian's Wall occurred during Roman occupation (Tipping 1997; Huntley 2000), but the majority of those that overlap with Roman occupation commenced earlier (Fenton-Thomas 1992; Tipping 1997b). At some localities woodland regeneration following clearance appears to have occurred prior to the Roman advance into Scotland (Dumayne 1993b). The regional context of this well defined event throughout the uplands south of the Highland Line had nothing to do with Roman invasion, however, and the purpose of clearance was not military (McCarthy 1995; Hanson 1996).

Some major clearances followed periods of apparently negligible human activity, as at Yetholm Loch (above), and represent large scale clearance from scratch, but the majority of sites indicate that woodland clearance became more intense and complete, as at Sourhope (above). Although generally substantial, these clearances are of varying intensity and duration. A few sites suggest that total woodland loss took only a few decades (Tipping 1997). The most dramatic and rapid clearances were not necessarily, however, the most sustained (Dumayne 1992). In addition, some localities show no vegetation change, e.g. Swindon Hill (above) and Tight's (1987) sites of Kingside Loch and Wester Branxholme Loch west of Hawick (Figure 8.7). At Swindon Hill it is argued that the woodland was protected (above): at other sites the limited temporal resolution of analyses precludes detailed discussion.

All landscape elements in the Bowmont Valley were impacted, including the summit ridges. The pollen data at Cocklawhead (Chapter 6) indicate this, as do the undated analyses at Broad Moss to the east (Davies & Turner 1979) and Raistrick's pollen counts (Richmond & Keeney 1937) from the Roman camp at Chew Green high in the southern Cheviots (Figure 8.8), indicating occupation in a treeless heather moor. There appears to be no focus only on lowland contexts, although upland and lowland may have been linked. Vyner (1999) suggested from work in the Stainmore Pass that the northern Pennine moorlands may have developed their exclusively pastoral character in the later Iron Age as the Tyne-Tees lowlands were established as the 'bread basket' of that region (van der Veen 1992). There is no strong evidence that clearance events across the region occurred later in time the farther north they were (cf. Turner 1981a), or that clearance events were less substantial and involved less investment in the region north of the Tyne than in areas south of the Tyne (Tipping 1997b).

8.9b Woodland clearance and the archaeological record

The overriding purpose of the clearances was almost certainly the expansion of farmed land. Woodland removal led in all cases to increases in cultivated and grazed areas. The durations of these activities varied between localities, sometimes over short distances. The complexity of this relation and the driving forces that defined relative success, environmental, social and economic, have not yet been defined. The increasing number of woodland clearance events in the late Iron Age gives the strong impression of an expanding agricultural population after *c* 550 cal BC, but this would be a simplistic interpretation. There is currently no palaeoecological evidence at the regional scale to suggest gradual population pressures. This might have been the case at individual locations where earlier prehistoric activities seem largely to have been accelerated (Fenton-Thomas 1992; Dark 2000), but the often abrupt and complete clearance events in the pollen records suggest that this was a radical restructuring of the agrarian landscape.

A parallel may well be drawn with the processes of amalgamation and enclosure in the post-Medieval landscape (Overton 1996; Williamson 2002), which although in part a response to rising population levels was fundamentally a shift in how land ownership was consolidated and the economic system organised. There need be no requirement to identify an archaeological equivalent to this late Iron Age landscape transforming process, or at least one that can be quantified by survey techniques alone (Ferrell 1995, 1997; Wise 2000; Haselgrove 2002). In the post-Medieval period the major archaeological changes came not in straightforward increases in numbers of domestic structures (Hinton 1990; Newman 2001): enclosure led to an emptier rural landscape (Thirsk 2000). Rather, improvements in status and wealth of a late Iron Age elite might be sought (van der Veen 1992; Hunter 1997).

To associate the palaeoecological evidence for woodland clearance and agricultural intensification with the archaeological record is not easy. This is partly because of the paucity of dated archaeological sites and the uncertainties in defining distribution patterns, trends and chronologies for settlement types (Section 8.8i above). It was the difficulty in identifying later prehistoric settlements at all, rather than an absence of native settlement *per se*, that contributed to Dumayne's (1992, 1993a, b, 1995) association of woodland clearance with much more archaeologically visible Roman occupation (McCarthy 1995, 2000). Ferrell's (1995, 1997) interpretations are dependent on assumptions of contemporaneity between settlements that are as yet undemonstrable, but notwithstanding this, Ferrell argued for a change in settlement structure and cohesion between the later Iron Age and the Romano-British period in the northern Cheviot Hills, from communities that may have functioned in isolation to ones more connected and integrated. This is consistent with the emphasis in the pollen records for late Iron Age communities to have acted collectively in clearing woodland at much larger spatial scales than before, and probably to have made decisions affecting entire landscapes (Tipping 1997b) rather than only within the small areas defined by individual farmsteads (Wise 2000).

Nevertheless, the settlement sites identified with Romano-British consolidation around the Cheviots are individually small (Ferrell 1995). Cowley (2000) has proposed that the complex of

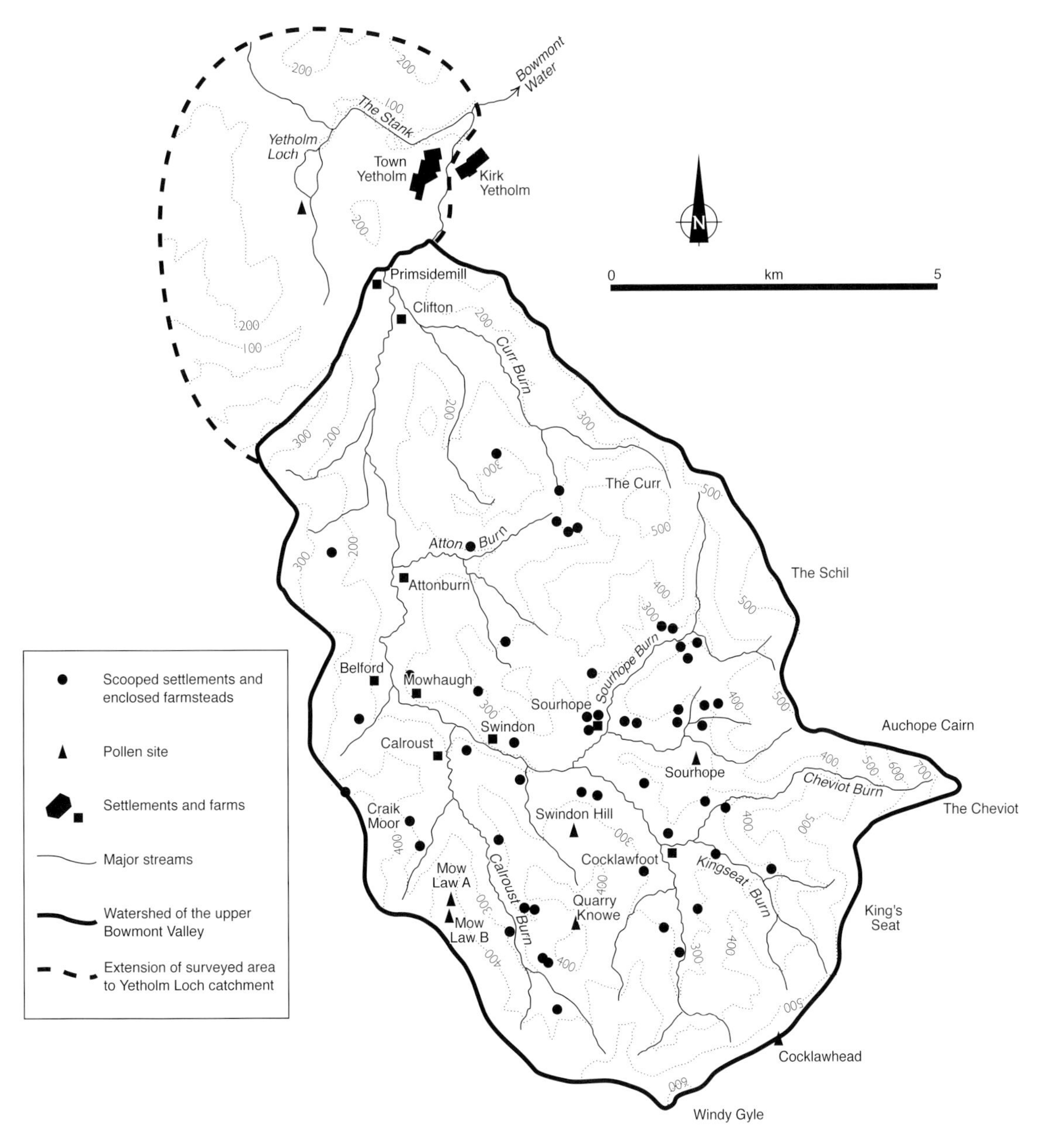

Figure 8.13

Distribution in the archaeologically surveyed area of the upper Bowmont Valley of late prehistoric and Romano-British scooped and enclosed settlements (from Mercer & Tipping (1994) figure 1.4).

small site types defined as enclosed settlements were contemporaneous with extensive woodland clearance. Mercer and Tipping (1994) were more specific, perhaps unjustifiably so, in suggesting that the scooped settlement was the appropriate settlement type. Both may be correct. Figure 8.13 shows the very high concentration of these small farmsteads in the upper Bowmont Valley, from Mercer and Tipping (1994). These were most commonly enclosed or stockaded settlements (Jobey 1964, 1981) within rectilinear or curvilinear palisaded enclosures usually regarded as stock yards. Hundreds of examples are known from lowland and upland contexts (Jobey 1981; Gates 1981; Clack 1982). Scooped settlements appear to have been contemporaneous (Burgess 1970, 1984). Both exist in the Bowmont Valley (Steer & Keeney 1947; RCAHMS 1956; Jobey 1966, 1981; Mercer & Tipping 1994: Figure 8.13). Settlements recorded by Mercer (in prep.) in the Bowmont Valley show a much higher altitudinal limit than the *c* 300m asl reported for the Cheviots by Jobey (1981), up to *c* 425m asl on Craik Moor, with 35% of the fifty-one settlements mapped above 300m OD.

Clack's (1982) model of agrarian organisation for the Cheviots identified a pattern of semi-nucleated or nucleated farmsteads in the lower parts of upland valleys, farms concentrating on arable products and meadow, and dispersed, exclusively pastoral, settlements in the uplands. Both were seen to have functioned as part of one unit. Gates (1981) in contrast found that nearly 30% of farmsteads, even in the uplands, had associated field systems, such as at Crock Cleugh, in the Bowmont Valley (Steer & Keeney 1947) (Figure 8.8), assumed to have been used for crop growing and thus reducing contrasts in land use between lowland and upland. Palynological evidence from the upper Bowmont Valley reveals all the elements of the farming landscape proposed by Clack (1982) (Section 8.9a), but little evidence for altitudinal differentation, in support of Gates' model.

It is most often assumed that the most clearly hierarchical archaeological structures in the Cheviot Hills and across southern Scotland, the hillforts (RCAHMS 1956, 1997; Feachem 1966; Rideout *et al* 1992) (Figure 8.11), were unrelated to this landscape change (Ferrell 1995; RCAHMS 1997) because they went out of use before Roman occupation (Jobey 1978; Hill 1982a), but this has not been demonstrated (Rideout *et al* 1992; Armit 1999; Cowley 2000; Erdrich, Giannotta & Hanson 2000). The extent of major woodland clearances clearly extended far beyond the upland concentration of hill forts, but these may have continued to represent central authority and control (Hunter 1997).

The association of centralised landscape change with hillforts in south-east Scotland needs to be tested further. It cannot be extended to northern England with its the near absence of hillforts (Feachem 1966; Higham 1986). Places such as the Stanwick *oppidum* were not necessarily comparable (Haselgrove 2002). Using analyses of charred plant remains from ^{14}C dated archaeological sites, van der Veen (1992) identified two types of crop growing regime within the region in the late Iron Age. One regime on the Northumberland coastal plain practiced a high energy, intensive but small scale agriculture, specialised in emmer wheat cultivation and perhaps used spades rather than ploughs. This was characterised as 'traditional', and was seen as 'backward' in contrast to that regime south of the Tyne-Tees, in which fields were much less intensively managed but were much larger. North of the Tyne, the conservatism of the regime suggested to van der Veen (1992) that cereal production had not developed beyond subsistence levels, possibly through social stresses implied by the continued need for fortification. By comparison, the lack of defended settlements south of the Tyne was argued to represent a more centralised political and social system. Fenton-Thomas (1992) attempted to relate the pattern of agricultural production from palynology to this regionality, as has Ferrell (1995, 1997) from the archaeological record. Tipping (1997b) argued from similarities in the chronology and scale of woodland clearances in pollen records that van der Veen (1992) had undervalued agricultural enterprise in southern Scotland, but pollen records are poor at resolving the sophistication of agricultural systems. There are critical weaknesses in assessing the relative balance between arable activities and pasture from palynology, but it is also likely that charred plant analyses from archaeological contexts provide an equally skewed emphasis on crop growing.

8.9c Consumption and conservation of woods

The loss of woodlands was almost certainly because of agricultural demands (Section 8.9a above). Population pressures alone and the consumption of wood for building would have made little impression. This can be explored briefly by developing the analyses of Hanson and MacInnes (1980). They used Piggott's (1949) excavation of timber houses at Hayhope Knowe in the Bowmont Valley (Figure

8.8) to estimate, perhaps rather playfully, that a later Iron Age palisaded settlement (Section 8.8i) of six houses required timber from between 0.72 ha and 1.5 ha of mixed deciduous woodland, dependent on the management of the woodland resource. Recent survey (Mercer 1987; in prep.) has recorded 12–15 house stances at Hayhope Knowe. A minimal area of woodland consumed in construction of this settlement probably exceeded 1 to 2.15 ha of woodland. The pollen record at Sourhope, assuming the pollen catchment at this time to have a radius of 500m (Section 2.2) depicts an area of around 78 ha. If all timbers for consumption at Hayhope Knowe were removed from the Sourhope pollen catchment, this would have amounted to a loss of trees of between 1.28 and 2.75% of this catchment, probably barely discernible in the pollen record. Assuming that each of the seventeen hill forts within the upper Bowmont Valley (Mercer & Tipping 1994) actually consumed twice as much wood as estimated for Hayhope Knowe, itself a conservative estimate, and that wood was supplied for all the forts from the Sourhope pollen catchment, total clearance of the catchment would have taken place. However, the Sourhope pollen catchment is only 1.5% of the archaeologically surveyed area of the upper Bowmont Valley. There were other demands on timber, of course, but this estimate, however simplistic, clearly shows that such large scale timber use for constructional purposes would have made very few inroads into the woodland. The expansion of farmland must be seen as the most significant consumer of former woodland.

So was the late prehistoric and early historic woodland managed? Within the upper Bowmont Valley woodland loss had already altered the structure and composition of the woodland by the late 1st millennium BC to one dominated by birch, hazel, alder and willow (Sections 8.6d–e, 8.7c–d, 8.7h, 8.8b, 8.9b above). Almost no oak trees were left in the upper valley. This range of wood species closely matches that recovered from excavation of later prehistoric settlements in and near the northern Cheviots, although this has not been analysed in any rigorous way. Charred fragments of *Alnus* (alder) and *Salix* (willow) were recovered at Hayhope Knowe (Piggott 1949), *Betula* (birch) and *Corylus* (hazel) at nearby Hownam Rings (Piggott 1948) and the same taxa from modern standard excavations at The Dunion (Rideout 1992) (Figure 8.8). These may not have been typical of larger constructional timbers (Reynolds 1982), but may reflect the limited range of trees locally available. There is no suggestion that trees providing larger timbers were grown in the valley, or equally that they were transported into the valley for use in construction.

However, if not planted, the suggestion is that woods, seemingly monodominant woods of birch, were protected, as at Swindon Hill (Section 5.4: lpaz Swindon B; Section 8.9a above). Establishment of this wood in the early Iron Age may not have been intentional, but by the land-grabbing of the late Iron Age the stability of this wood and the apparent absence of other invading species are anomalous. The trees were removed gradually between *c* 570 and 1000 cal AD, probably by grazing pressures, and there is no palynological evidence from abrupt losses that timber in this wood was cut down. However, perhaps significantly in terms of the woodland resource, communal decision making and the extent of land under control, by *c* 700 cal AD a new birch wood was established on the peat at Sourhope (Section 4.3: lpaz Sourhope J), for probably a single generation of trees before that was cut down. Rackham (1980) suggested that birches were grown as timber trees and as underwood for a range of uses (see also Mackenzie & Callander 1997). We do not know where other woods in the valley were, but the position of these two on and close to wetland and peat surfaces least appropriate for farming suggests considerable centralised authority in land use planning. In a society dependent on timber supplies (Armit & Ralston 2002), woodland conservation might appear an inevitable development, but one which pollen analysts can usually only tentatively invoke (Tipping 1997c).

8.9d Rye cultivation in the late Iron Age

Some cereal type pollen grains at sites in the Bowmont Valley have been identified as of *Secale* (rye). This will always be uncertain using size measurements (Section 2.3f) because slight distortions in the shape of the pollen grain affect determination. Nevertheless, pollen grains assigned to *Secale* are recorded at Sourhope between 102 and 94cm (Table 4.5), between *c* 220 and 20 cal BC, and at Yetholm Loch at 125cm (Table 3.6), at *c* 175 cal AD. It may have been introduced as a crop to the region during late Iron Age agricultural expansion (Hillman 1981; van der Veen 1992), although it is rare but probably underrepresented in van der Veen's charred plant assemblages, in contrast to assemblages on the other side of the North Sea (Kooistra 1996; Henriksen 2003), where it was a significant winter sown crop.

8.9e Agricultural intensification and geomorphic activity

Soon after *c* 750 cal BC the earliest identified braided river gravels in the Breamish Valley began to aggrade (Sections 7.6; 8.8f above). These may initially have been transported and deposited in response to climatic deterioration. However, the river continued to deposit very coarse gravels throughout the Iron Age and the Romano-British period, and the magnitude of this sustained fluvial activity should not be underestimated. Cessation of gravel accumulation is not closely established but predates Medieval cultivation (Section 7.6). Events at this time in other Cheviot valleys remain undated or unexamined (Chapter 7) save for the demonstration of considerable soil erosion at Yetholm Loch in the late Iron Age (Sections 3.3: lpaz Yetholm Fb; 8.9a above), but by the turn of the millennium many valley floors in the region (Figure 8.6) were actively aggrading gravels or undergoing major channel changes (Potter 1976, 1979; Harvey & Renwick 1987; Passmore *et al* 1991; Macklin *et al* 1992a, b, c; Passmore *et al* 1992; Passmore *et al* 1993; Tipping 1995b; Passmore & Macklin 1997; Cotton *et al* 1999; Moores *et al* 1999; Tipping *et al* 1999). The association of floodplain destruction and redeposition with woodland clearance is clear at Yetholm Loch, and at other lowland lacustrine sequences of this age examined in the region, particularly in the Tees lowlands (Bartley *et al* 1976) (Figure 8.7). A correlation between soil erosion and the generally quickening pace and intensity of farming in the late Iron Age seems clear.

Woodland clearance is argued in Section 8.9a to have been rapid within entire catchments, however, and slope and soil instability created during clearance would have been short lived. In the Breamish Valley (Figure 8.7) the age and rapidity of woodland loss is unclear because the continuous pollen record at Broad Moss (Davies & Turner 1979) on the flanks of the Cheviot at 390m asl (Figure 8.7) was not ^{14}C dated and pollen analyses from prehistoric archaeological contexts (Figure 8.8) reflect small areas of ground (Topping 1993, 1998). On Wether Hill above Ingram, woodlands had been lost by *c* 430 cal AD when peat began to accumulate in a cross-ridge ditch (Topping 1999b; Davies & Dixon 2007), and associated archaeological sequences imply that deforestation was late prehistoric in age. Continuing fluvial instability in valleys like the Breamish was probably closely related to the longevity of late prehistoric and historic agriculture. Simmons (2003) has suggested that the shift to winter sown crops like rye in the later Iron Age (Section 8.9c above) may have been particularly significant in terms of increasing landscape instability, as fields were ploughed and made vulnerable to soil erosion at the wrong time of year.

The continued instability of river systems throughout the early historic period should not, however, be taken to imply that agricultural practices were necessarily damaging to soils everywhere in these catchments. Rivers access much of the sediment they transport from stream banks, not from eroding fields. Other important sources are gullies and alluvial fans which transfer water and sediment between valley side slopes untouched by erosion. Only south of the region at Gormire Lake in the North York Moors have sophisticated sediment analyses defined that most sediment eroded during late Iron Age deforestation not from eroding topsoils but from subsoils and bedrock being eroded in gullies or by deep seated slope failures (Oldfield *et al* 2003). The accelerated fluvial activity at this time was a response to increasing water flow but probably not to extensive topsoil losses. At Yetholm Loch (Section 3.3: lpa zones Yetholm Fa & Ga), for example, the maintenance of cereal cropping during the phase of late Iron Age soil erosion might imply that while discrete parts of the landscape actively changed, slopes did not.

Management of erosion may also have included the emergence of walled fields in the later Iron Age and Romano-British period (Gates 1981; Jobey 1981). Walls can be as important in constraining soil losses, by reducing effective slope length, as they are in corralling herds or defining ownership (Mercer & Tipping 1994), as are cultivation terraces which Mercer (1991) argues reappeared in the Bowmont Valley in the later Iron Age. Later prehistoric plots of cord rig are not normally associated with walled boundaries (Topping 1989; Halliday 1993), but Romano-British fields when identified have stone walls.

8.9f External pressures on farming economies

The restructured agricultural landscape of the Bowmont Valley was some 200 years old when the Romans marched into southern Scotland. Many parts of southern Scotland and northern England had likewise been cleared and reorganised (Section 8.9a). There is no requirement to assume that Roman occupation triggered agricultural expansion in southern Scotland or northern England.

There is no indication in the lowland landscape at Yetholm Loch that agricultural productivity waned at all in the *c* 2000 years of the historic period (Section 3.3: lpa zones Yetholm Ga to H). Agricultural modifications and improvements characterise this long period, discussed in later sections. Hidden in the interior, the hills around Sourhope similarly show no evidence for diminished human activity: vegetation changes defined in lpa zones Sourhope I to L (Section 4.3) reflect shifts in peatland plants or agricultural innovations. This description is true also for the summit ridge at Cocklawhead (Section 6.4: lpa zones D and E), although agrarian changes at this altitude in the historic period were few. Over some 500 cal years after *c* 570 cal AD the woodland at Swindon Hill was lost, probably by sustained grazing pressures, and possibly because protection of the trees was deemed no longer necessary or was no longer enforcible, but at more or less the same time a comparable birch wood was established at Sourhope for a single generation of trees (Section 8.9c above). There is no indication throughout the historic period that this upland plateau was abandoned or ceased to be a focus for agricultural activity (Section 5.4: lpa zones Swindon C to E). The agricultural transformation at the end of the Iron Age in this valley was a permanent and extraordinarily successful one.

The regional distribution of surviving Romano-British farmsteads (Jobey 1981) suggests that a greater density of native settlements developed near Hadrian's Wall (but see Jones & Walker 1983 for a critique), either emerging from a pre-existing but archaeologically difficult to see late Iron Age pattern (Allason-Jones 1989; McCarthy 1995; Dark & Dark 1997; Manning *et al* 1997) or as a response to Roman markets (Manning 1975; Snape 1989), implying some reorientation of native settlement. The scant archaeofaunal data from archaeological sites in northern England suggest that regionally diverse cattle raising economies developed on either side of the Pennines (Stallibrass 1998).

The attraction of this market may have led to native population movement towards the frontier, seen in the construction in southern Scotland of exotic buildings (Dunwell 1999; Cowley 2000). However, the Bowmont Valley and the northern Cheviots were not marginalised. Surpluses of meat and grain may have gone to the troops (Hanson 1997): all these resources were grown within the northern Cheviot Hills (Section 8.9a). It is likely, however, that the one item native communities could not supply was timber (Section 8.9a above; Hanson 1997). This is true also for later periods, and the northern Cheviot Hills were not a source for what Hope-Taylor (1977, 334) recorded from seventh century cal AD Yeavering, of 'a high proportion of long, straight [oak] timbers of massive section'.

The agrarian achievement seen so clearly in the Bowmont Valley may not have been so enduring elsewhere in the region, however. A few pollen sequences at sites furthest north of Hadrian's Wall (Figure 8.7) seem to indicate that woodland regeneration occurred within a century or so of Roman occupation (Dumayne 1993a, 1998b, 1999b), although reconstructions from the immediate vicinity of second century cal AD Roman sites on the Antonine Wall suggest open and farmed landscapes (Hanson & Maxwell 1983; Boyd 1984, 1985a, 1985b; Keppie *et al* 1997; Dunwell & Coles 1998; Dickson & Dickson 2000). Whittington and Edwards (1993) have suggested an antagonistic relation between native and Roman farther north still, but their chronologies of events cannot be as precise as they suggest.

The very strong evidence for continuity in land use in the northern Cheviot Hills is seen in a period when the temporal resolutions of all pollen analyses are very high (Figure 8.2), and there is little likelihood that significant periods of abandonment or economic stagnation have gone unrecognised. There is no reason to suggest that farming in the northern Cheviots suffered when Roman control ended, whether this was in the middle of the third century cal AD (Fowler 2002) or as conventionally placed at the beginning of the fifth century cal AD (Jones 1996). The data in the northern Cheviots are supportive of a tradition of interpretations that stress settlement continuity and economic stability after Roman retreat (Reece 1980; Turner 1979; Bennett 1984; Fulford 1990; Dark 2000; Wilmott 2001).

Similar patterns of land use continuity are seen in the western and eastern Cheviot Hills (Campbell *et al* 2002; Davies & Dixon 2007) (Figure 8.7). The suggestion from published palynological data by Dark and Dark (1997; Dark 2000) that farming activity was reduced near Hadrian's Wall on Roman withdrawal needs to be reassessed given that, as Huntley (2000) argued, most pollen sites in this area depict large and rather ill defined pollen catchments, and that Dumayne-Peaty and Barber (1998) recognised that these very large peat mosses will themselves have periodically supported woodland covers, distorting the palynological depiction of agricultural activity and dry woodland regeneration.

8.10 Continuity and innovation in the rural economy 500–1400 cal AD

8.10a Continuity

The identification of event boundaries within the pollen sequences in the Bowmont Valley (Table 8.2; Figure 8.3) as significant landscape transforming divisions (Section 8.2) breaks down now. The near synchronous local pollen assemblage boundaries at Sourhope and Swindon Hill that draw the eye in Figure 8.3 define vegetation changes that are site specific, almost certainly only affecting the peat surfaces at each site. At Swindon Hill (Section 5.4: lpaz Swindon C) the birch woodland that had hidden the agricultural landscape from palynological view was gradually cleared after *c* 570 cal AD, over some 400 cal years, by grazing pressures (Section 8.9c), to be replaced by grassland. At Sourhope the valley peat surface was covered in a *Calluna* heath after *c* 425 cal AD (Section 4.3: lpaz Sourhope I), possibly because peat cutting had disturbed the hydrology of the mire, and then at *c* 710 cal AD (lpaz Sourhope J) the probably drier (drained?) mire surface was used to grow a single generation of birch trees (Section 8.9c). The mire continued to be impacted by peat cutting and the abrupt flooding events that followed their abandonment (lpaz Sourhope K). These vegetation changes give us remarkable insights into how this upland economy was functioning in early history, with both peat and wood resources being integrated parts of a thriving rural economy. But they are small scale insights.

Throughout the valley, the palaeoecological evidence shows that the diversified but spatially uniform structure of pasture and crop growing established in the late Iron Age continued (Section 3.3: lpaz Yetholm Ga; Section 4.3: lpa zones Sourhope H to K; Section 5.4: lpaz Swindon C; Section 6.4: lpaz Cocklawhead 7D). No assured estimate of the proportions of pasture to arable fields can be made from pollen analyses, but all the sequences suggest that cereals were part of the farming economy.

This interpretation of a vibrant landscape finds little support from some interpretations of early historic Cheviot and southern Scottish archaeology (Burgess 1984; RCAHMS 1997) although the dearth of excavated sites limits analysis (Morris 1995). The enclosed farmstead of Crock Cleugh (Figure 8.8) on the west side of the Swindon Hill plateau (Steer & Keeney 1947) may span the early historic period. Sunken dwellings represent a second possibly contemporaneous small settlement type (Gates & O'Brien 1988), and at a higher hierarchical level some forts were reoccupied, or continued to be occupied into the seventh century cal AD (RCAHMS 1956; Higham 1986, 1993; Morris 1995). Most recently, O'Brien (2002) has attempted to trace the early historic origins of large estates within the northern and eastern Cheviots, arguing that multiple estates or their equivalent existed throughout the Cheviot valleys from before the time of Bede (687 cal AD). This interpretation of difficult archival data is much closer to the reconstruction developed from palaeoecological evidence. There is a need to address the apparent archaeological invisibility of post-Roman settlement.

A significant hiatus in agricultural activity was suggested in the region from the mid-sixth century cal AD by Turner (1979), or earlier (Dark 2000), from increases in tree pollen percentages in often poorly temporally resolved pollen analyses. The assumption, however, that increases in the proportions of trees in a pollen diagram necessarily represent woodland regeneration on agriculturally abandoned land is increasingly untenable as palaeoecologists begin to recognise the implications for landscape change of woodland management described by historians (Rackham 1980; Vera 2000; Smout 1997, 2002). This applies not only to the early historic period, of course, but is more readily understood to be an issue here because it is but a short time before contemporaneous details of this comprehensive resource management can be gleaned from archival sources (Tipping 1997c; 2002a; Tipping & McCulloch in press). In this regard the interpretation of tree taxa in pollen analyses at both Swindon Hill and Sourhope (Section 8.9c) suggests the role of woodland conservation, and this point may have considerable relevance to the interpretation of woodland change at sites in the Solway Firth described by Dumayne-Peaty and Barber (1998). The pollen analyst needs to recognise the present paucity of interpretative models by which to understand the cultivation of the woodland resource, and this is critical for understanding our interpretation of the agricultural landscape. The suggestion from the upper Bowmont Valley (Section 8.9c) is that people were selecting those soils low in agricultural potential to grow trees: these are the peats that so frequently provide the material for pollen diagrams. As discussed in Section 8.8h with regard to the Yetholm Loch pollen stratigraphy, it is very difficult palynologically to 'see' through trees to the landscape beyond.

At Cocklawhead blanket peat spread was probably complete by or in the early historic period (Section

6.4: lpaz Cocklawhead 7D). Erosion of exposed mineral soils had stopped by *c* 650 cal AD, probably because these were now sealed by peat. The rapidity of lateral peat spread at this late stage was not measured, but between *c* 300 and 650 cal AD the peat surface at site 7A was very significantly wetter, and peat may have spread more rapidly in this period across the ridge. This may represent responses to the first major climatic deterioration in the region since the Iron Age, persisting until, perhaps, between 850 and 950 cal AD (Lamb 1981; Dupont 1986; Heidinga 1987) or as late as *c* 1100 cal AD (Barber 1981). It is recorded as an increase in effective precipitation throughout the region (Figure 8.5) and beyond (e.g. Dickinson 1975; Barber 1981; Hafsten 1981; Blackford & Chambers 1991; Tipping 1995b; Charman, Hendon & Packman 1999; Mauquoy & Barber 1999; Chiverrell 2001; Hendon, Charman & Kent 2001; Barber *et al* 2003). Increased storminess was likely (Clarke *et al* 2002). Increasing fluvial activity (Figure 8.6) is attributed to this climatic instability in the northern Pennines (Macklin, Rumsby & Heap 1992), but in the North Tyne the river seems to have become measurably less active (Moores *et al* 1999). The short lived but regionally significant impact at 540 cal AD on oak populations has long been recognised (Baillie 1989; Spurk *et al* 2002; Section 8.6e) but cannot be distinguished in woodlands in the Bowmont Valley because no oak trees remained, and because anthropogenic manipulation was by this time overwhelming (Section 8.9). This event has formed the focus for catastrophist interpretations of population change (Baillie 1999; Gunn 2000), but there is no clear reason to see abandonment and agricultural recession in the uplands of northern Britain.

If we can no longer be confident of trends in tree cover as representing such abandonment in pollen analyses, we can work on either the absence of apparent regeneration or positive indicators of agricultural activity. These indications are, of course, dependent on the ability to 'see' landscapes through trees, so that the identification at Swindon Hill of possible cereal type pollen grains between *c* 400 and 750 cal AD (Section 5.4: lpaz Sourhope C) is possibly a reflection of being able to 'see' already existing fields as trees were thinned. However, more consistent patterns of possible cereal type pollen finds in areas like upper Teesdale (Figure 8.7) (Turner *et al* 1973; Chambers 1978; Fenton-Thomas 1992) and the Southern Uplands (Tight 1987) might relate to an expansion of arable agriculture in the uplands, despite climatic deterioration, perhaps associated with the enclosures at upland settlements like Simy Folds (Coggins, Fairless & Batey 1983).

It is this economic expansion (Fowler 2002) that may form the background to the political expansion northward to southern Scotland of Northumbrian rule after *c* 600 cal AD (Nicolaisen 1964). Colonisation was not without conflict (Higham 1993). Interpretation that expansion was political, without the British population being displaced (Hope-Taylor 1977), is uncertain. Morris (1995) described Ian Smith's views that the line of Dere Street may represent the border between Anglian consolidation and British survival, and from pollen analyses at Stanshiel, close to Woden Law and Dere Street (Figure 8.7), Campbell *et al* (2002) have noted the longevity and stability of late Iron Age farming practices in contrast to the dynamism apparent at sites in the northern Cheviot Hills (Tipping 1999a; this volume).

In or around 655 x 670 cal AD, Oswin of Deira (Hart 1975) or Oswy of Bernicia (Morris 1977) granted to the monks of Lindisfarne the upper Bowmont Valley and the various *villae* within it. This was one of the earliest gifts of land to the Lindisfarne Community, and their holdings included part of the Kale Valley, closely corresponding to the bounds of the present Morebattle parish. The gift of an already defined large estate would fit well with O'Brien's (2002) reconstructions for the northern Cheviots. Such grants would have been for land 'whose potential was either already realised or easily assessable' (Morris 1977, 90), and this accords well with the palaeoecological reconstructions in this section. The Bowmont Valley was already a highly productive 'estate'. The places named in the grant, like those at Yetholm and Sourhope, had been settled and farmed continuously since well before the Roman incursion, and the gift of the valley to Lindisfarne symbolises the high regard placed by the king and the monks on these agriculturally rich lands.

The dominance of Anglian place names in the Bowmont Valley (Nicolaisen 1964) is not evidence for it being an empty landscape (Higham 1986, 1992). Continuity in the pollen records from the valley endorses this view. The suggestion from archaeofaunal data at sixth-century Yeavering (Hope-Taylor 1977) that the Cheviots maintained an economy dominated by cattle can be challenged by recognising the ceremonial nature of consumption at this site (Higham 1986), but a transhumant cattle economy in the early historic period is also central to how O'Brien (2002) saw the Cheviot estates to have functioned. This is unclear from the palaeoecological evidence. It is very likely that transhumance cannot be demonstrated or disproved from pollen records save in the definition developed in Section 8.8e, that landscape elements were reserved exclusively for pasture. With this rather unsatisfactory definition it can be argued that the early historic upland economy, like that in later prehistory, had not developed a specialist function. Cattle may well have been grazed in upland pastures throughout the valley. All parts of the interior, the deep valley at Sourhope, the plateaux and the summit ridges, were grazed. Grazing may have been extensive rather than intensive. However, at least intermittently, crop growing was also maintained on all landscape elements, upland as well as lowland.

There is also no indication that the sward was grazed or the soils were tilled to the extent that soil erosion was accelerated in the early Medieval period. The two least stable landscape elements in the Romano-British period, the lowlands and the summit ridges, were stable by the early historic period. Gravel aggradation continued in the Breamish Valley for some hundreds of years, but there is currently no geomorphic evidence in the Cheviot Hills for the degree of increased slope and river channel instability reported from the sixth to the twelfth centuries cal AD in uplands to the west and south-west of the region (Figure 8.6) by Harvey *et al* (1981) in the Howgill Fells, Harvey and Renwick (1987) Tipping (1995c, 1999b), Tipping and Halliday (1994), Tipping *et al* (1999) and Dunsford (1999) in the Southern Uplands, Wild *et al* (2002) in Cumbria, Passmore and Macklin (2002) in the Tyne Valley, Dunsford (1999) in the Southern Uplands and northern Pennines, and farther south in the Bowland Fells (Harvey & Renwick 1987) and eastern Yorkshire (Hudson-Edwards *et al* 1997; Macklin *et al* (2002) (see also Brown 1998).

8.10b Innovation and intensification in arable agriculture

By the twelfth century cal AD, the Bowmont Valley was divided into two parishes (*tenementum*: Dixon 2003); the upland area in the south was known as Mow or Molle (from the Celtic *Moel*, conical hill), with Morebattle parish lying north of Belford (Figure 1.3). Mow was held partly as monastic holdings, principally of Kelso and Melrose, and by a number of individuals, including one Eschina, wife of Walter, one of the great Anglo-Norman lords, and Steward to David I. Eschina was 'found for him' (Barrow 1980, p. 65) by Malcolm IV, and since Malcolm appears to have overridden the inheritance rights of male heirs to Eschina's property, her dowry may have been of as much interest as the lady herself, intimating how highly valued was the upper Bowmont Valley.

The valley was well populated and intensively cultivated, a 'highly developed area of land' (Gilbert 1979, p. 236; Moffat 1985; Barrow 2003). Grants and perambulations (Innes 1854; Jeffrey 1855), depict a well organised farming landscape. In *c* 1250 cal AD, Cicely of Mow granted parcels of arable land and meadow (probably on the haughlands) throughout the parish. Kelso Abbey owned arable land, meadow, common pasture in the uplands, and access to coppiced woodland. Cereal cultivation was clearly of importance, and in the late twelfth century cal AD the parish contained at least one mill and one malt kiln. Comparably diverse Border landscapes were reconstructed from archival data by Gilbert (1983).

The agrarian landscape described from contemporary documents is readily identifiable in all its complexity and vigour from the pollen record (Chapters 3 to 6). More significantly, the pollen records show that after *c* 1100 cal AD farming practice in the valley was sharply modified, for perhaps the first time in more than a thousand years, a major restructuring not recorded in archives. Around Yetholm Loch (Section 3.3: lpaz Yetholm Gb) a greater proportion of land may have been planted, with oats certainly, rye probably, and barley possibly grown. Some of the ploughed land may have been given over to winter sown cereals. This might suggest some specialisation in farming practice, because spring sown crops are most common in pasture dominated economies where overwintering stock need all available resources (Jones 1981). However, pasture continued to be important around Yetholm Loch.

A new crop was introduced to the lowlands around Yetholm Loch, *Cannabis sativa* (hemp), grown for textile production. This crop may have been introduced to the interior at Sourhope at some time between *c* 875 and 1675 cal AD (Section 4.3: lpaz Sourhope K). How abundantly it was planted in the valley is unclear. Pollen grains of hemp are found at Mow Law B at 420m asl from peat inception at *c* 1100 cal AD (Section 6.11: lpaz Mow Law B–A), but the crop was most likely to have been introduced to the plateaux only after *c* 1650 cal AD (Sections 5.4: lpaz Swindon Db; 5.8: lpaz Quarry B; 6.8: lpaz Mow Law A–A). The timing of this introduction is necessarily imprecise, but it is difficult to avoid correlation with either Anglo-Norman landownership or perhaps more likely, monastic holdings as suggested at Soutra

Hospital (Moffat 1989), in lowland Fife (Whittington & Jarvis 1986; Whittington & Edwards 1990) and at Coldingham Priory (P J Dixon pers. comm.) (Figure 8.8). Associated with hemp cultivation at Yetholm Loch, and perhaps later at Sourhope, is the pollen of *Reseda*, probably *R. luteola* (Dyer's Rocket), grown for its yellow dye. Both crops may have gone into the preparation of canvas, but the dye may have been used in the burgeoning wool trade (Moffat 1985; below).

Dixon (1985) presented archival evidence for upland Medieval cultivation on the Northumbrian side of the Cheviots, and excavated one such farmstead at Alnhamsheles in the upper Breamish valley (Figure 8.8), at around 200m asl, which was thought to have

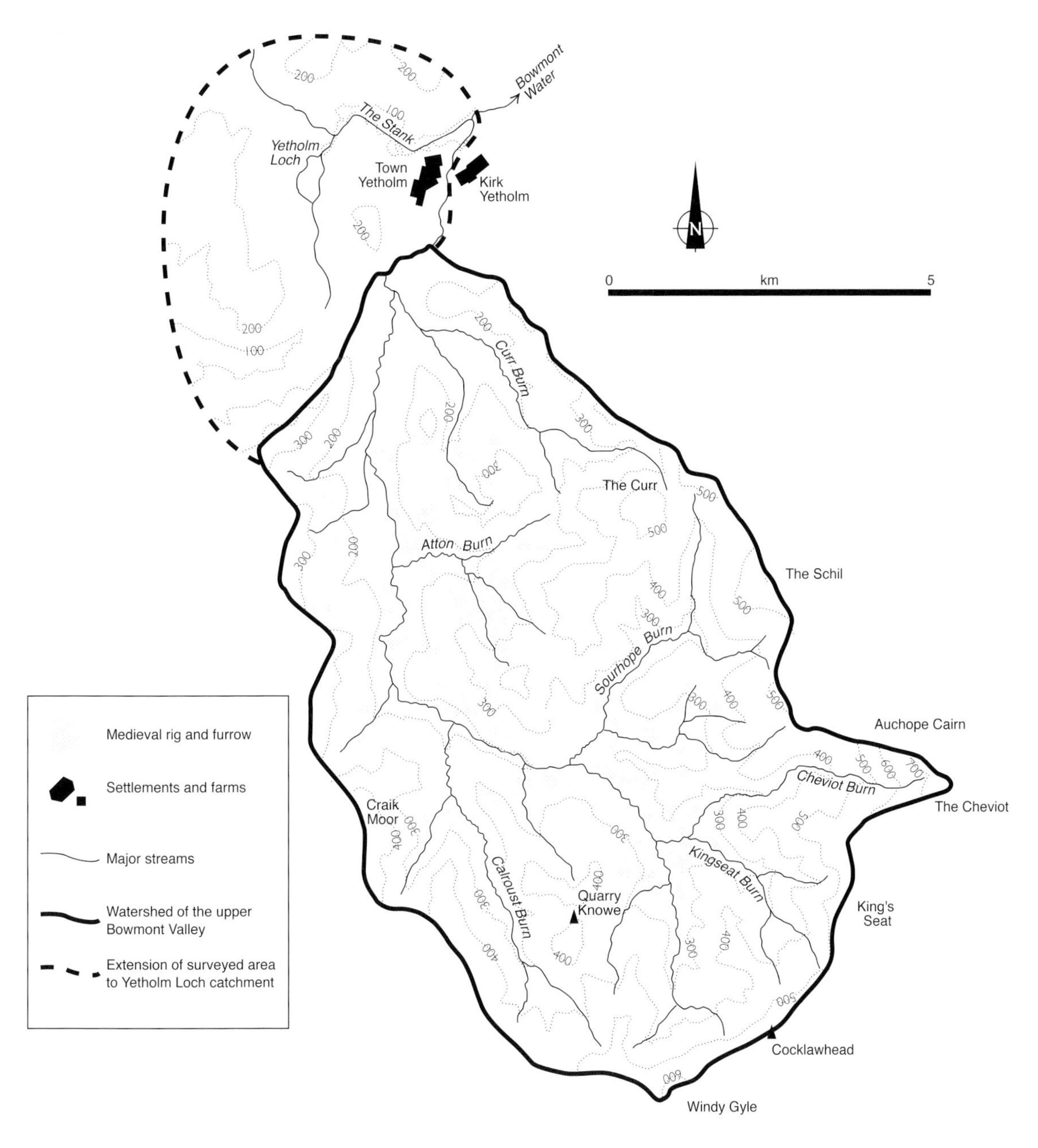

Figure 8.14
Distribution in the archaeologically surveyed area of the upper Bowmont Valley of purportedly Medieval broad rigged cultivation and the extent of subsequent (post-improvement and modern) cultivation (after Mercer & Tipping (1994) figure 1.6).

been permanently settled and ploughed in the thirteenth to fourteenth centuries cal AD. Within the Bowmont Valley, Kelso Abbey was granted in 1234 x 1249 cal AD a 'toft and croft', implying cultivation 'on the moors near to the outlet at *Wytelawe* [Whitelaw]' high on the Border ridge (Figure 8.8) at 350–400m asl (Jeffrey 1855, 274–5). Similar suggestions have been made for the large farm complex at Southdean, west of Carter Bar (Figure 8.8) (RCAHMS 1994), and across The Merse in the Lammermuir Hills, Parry (1978) suggested the Medieval upland expansion of crop growing to altitudes up to 425m asl.

Davies and Turner (1979) argued from palynological data in upland Northumberland for this also, but their sequences are either loosely or not dated, temporal resolutions are comparatively low and cereal type pollen grains not closely defined. These controls are much better for the sites of Sourhope, Swindon Hill and Mow Law B in the upper Bowmont Valley (Sections 4.2, 5.3, 6.10; Figure 8.2), though not for Cocklawhead (Chapter 6). Nevertheless, establishing continuity in cereal cultivation from pollen analyses can only tentatively be made (Tipping 1998b) and little can be made of apparent absence. At Sourhope cereal type pollen including oat or wheat is recorded from *c* 1100 cal AD until *c* 1675 cal AD (Section 4.3: lpaz Sourhope K). At Swindon Hill (365m asl) cereal type pollen including oat or wheat was infrequently recorded between *c* 1150 and *c* 1300 cal AD, but then not again until *c* 1475 cal AD (Section 5.4: lpaz Swindon Da). However, at Mow Law B (420m OD) cereal type pollen is not confidently identified between *c* 1100 and 1300 cal AD (Section 6.11; lpaz Mow Law B–A and B–B). Later intensification of upland crop growing (Tipping 1998b) is evaluated in Section 8.11d below. These data are difficult to interpret, but it seems likely that upland plateaux in the Cheviots were used for cereal cultivation in the agrarian intensification after *c* 1100 cal AD. Crops included barley, and either or both oats and wheat: all plus rye (not found at this time in the Bowmont Valley pollen records) were recorded as plant remains in the lowland settlement at Springwood, near Kelso (Figure 8.8) (Nye & Turner in Dixon 1998). In the Bowmont Valley these crops need have been for no more than subsistence consumption, but it supports contemporaneous descriptions in showing that the landscape was far from given over to grazing animals.

The piecemeal scattering of arable, described in both the documents (Barrow 2002; Dixon 2003) and inferred from the pollen data (above), does not necessarily accord with the blocks of single use land inferred from our understanding of the infield-outfield system, however, and it remains uncertain how we should imagine these functional units (Dodgshon 1983; Dixon 1994; Barrow 2002). The identification of broad rigged cultivation alone (Mercer & Tipping 1994; Mercer in prep.) cannot define the system (Dixon 1994), even if it can be dated. Halliday (2003) has suggested that few remains of broad rig can be shown to predate the eighteenth century cal AD. Figure 8.14 depicts the pattern of broad rigged cultivation in the upper valley identified from archaeological survey (Mercer & Tipping 1994), indicating a concentration in valleys, but not at all solely on the broader haughlands of the larger rivers. Broad rig tends to occur on the gentler valley side slopes of the hills above the cliffs falling to the valley floor, and is found on north as well as south-facing slopes. Occasional isolated patches lie high up on the summit ridges, and if of Medieval age, support the documentary and palaeoecological evidence for there to have been no significant agrarian specialisation with altitude.

Parry (1978) attributed the extension of settlement and arable farming to high altitudes to the milder climate of the early Medieval period (Lamb 1977, 1985). This may be true, although our understanding of year to year variability of the weather has undermined this concept (Hughes & Diaz 1994), and there are interpretative circularities in using land use patterns to infer climatic amelioration. Tree ring records may by this time also reflect land use histories rather than throw light on them (Crone 1998; Crone & Mills 2002). However, it seems most likely that from *c* 900 cal AD, if not demonstrably warmer, soils in the region were drier and more amenable to cultivation. This can be inferred in the upper Bowmont Valley at Cocklawhead where the peat surface was demonstrably dry until *c* 1370 cal AD (Section 6.4: lpaz Cocklawhead 7E), and can be inferred from peat stratigraphic changes suggesting increased waterlogging after *c* 1400 cal AD at Swindon Hill (Section 5.4: lpaz Swindon Da) and at *c* 1585 cal AD at Mow Law B (Section 6.11: lpaz Mow Law B–B), and seen also at lowland mires in the region (Figure 8.5) (Tipping 1995b; Mauquoy & Barber 1999; Barber *et al* 2003).

8.10c Innovation and intensification in pastoral agriculture

Although cattle are most commonly mentioned in connection with pasturing rights in the Bowmont Valley (Innes 1854; Jeffrey 1855), and Donkin (1978) has emphasised the significance of cattle in the monastic economy in general, sheep were overwhelmingly dominant in the uplands of the Bowmont Valley from the twelfth to thirteenth century cal AD. If the Anglian pastoral economy was indeed significantly weighted towards cattle production (Hope-Taylor 1977), it remains unknown when sheep began to assume the importance in huge ranches it had in the high Medieval period (Moffat 1985). This cannot be satisfactorily explored using pollen analysis. Although sheep are more selective grazers than cattle (Grant *et al* 1985), dietary preferences are primarily between different types of wild grass growing to different heights, and these different grass species cannot be distinguished palynologically. There are suggestions from the palaeoecological records, however, that grazing practice changed markedly though gradually between 1100 and 1400 cal AD (Tipping 2000b).

While peat inception on the highest slopes of the summit ridge commenced at *c* 3800 cal BC (Section 8.7e), the lower plateaux have always been free of this blanket. Instead, isolated shallow basins have been infilled with fens and soligenous mires (Section 1.6). Four basins on two plateaux, Swindon Hill and Mow Law, were analysed (Chapters 5 and 6). Of these, Swindon Hill began to infill with peat at more or less the same time as on the summit ridge at Cocklawhead (Section 8.7e), but the three other basins formed at different times but only in the last *c* 900 cal years. The basin at Mow Law B began to infill at *c* 1100 cal AD (Section 6.11: lpa zones Mow Law B–A and B–B) during a period of dry climate (Section 8.10b). Peat inception may have been caused by large quantities of charcoal restricting drainage (Mallik *et al* 1984), deposited by burning of the local vegetation. This vegetation was a species rich grazed grassland, as it was throughout the upland pastures of the valley. *Calluna* heath had yet to spread from nutrient poor peat surfaces as dry heathland. There is no evidence from other upland pollen records in the valley from this period, where microscopic charcoal was measured (Sourhope; Swindon Hill), that fire frequency or intensity had increased prior to this (Section 4.3: lpaz Sourhope K; Section 5.4: lpaz Swindon Da and Db). Burning became an important aspect of landscape change after *c* 1100 cal AD, and was almost certainly deliberate. Its purpose at Mow Law B was probably to increase the abundance of green plants and to improve nutrient availability of forage grasses.

However, what rapidly replaced the grassland at Mow Law B was a *Calluna* heath (Section 6.11: lpa zones Mow Law B–A and B–B). Grazing pressures alone should not have led to this change if animals were managed under current systems of winter grazing and confinement to patches called hefts (Hunter 1962; Ryder 1983; Armstrong & Milne 1995). Heath is markedly inferior to most grasslands in nutrient status, and Hunter (1962) showed that sheep much prefer bent-fescue (*Agrostis-Festuca*) grassland to heather communities. Only when sheep are on the hill in the winter is *Calluna* consumed and regeneration suppressed. One possibility to explain the appearance of *Calluna* heath in upland grazings from *c* 1100 cal AD is to suggest that it expanded because animals were taken off the hill in the winter, and that it therefore spread by competitive advantage with grasses that were being overgrazed during the summer months. Some evidence that the pressures of overgrazing were recognised, and that sheep were responsible, might be seen in contemporary (*c* 1300 cal AD) protective measures taken to control grazing (Gilbert 1979). On *Berehope*, probably near the Craik Moor–Mow Law plateaux (Figure 1.3), 700 'muttons' could be grazed but between early June and August these had to be removed, and cattle only were allowed.

This measure might also be seen to illustrate an attempt to resolve the competitive tensions between a cattle economy and the new sheep flocks. The sheep may have been taken off the hill during the months that cattle transhumance (shieling) was traditionally practiced (Gilbert 1983), to maintain the old ways. Seasonal transhumance has haunted our interpretations of land use in the upper Bowmont Valley since the Neolithic period (Sections 8.7I, 8.8e, 8.10a), and although the documentary evidence is strong in the Medieval period (Gilbert 1983; McDonnell 1988, 1990; Bil 1990; Winchester 2000; Dixon 2003) this does not help in defining its origins. The archaeological evidence for seasonal settlement is ambiguous, but the palaeoecological evidence and archaeological evidence for upland cereal cultivation (Figure 8.14) suggests, again, that this was a patchwork multi-tasked landscape.

From documentary records (Innes 1854; Jeffrey 1855), the ratio of sheep to cattle varied from 5.8:1 and 7:1, to 25:1 on *Hethou*, *Craeg* (possibly Craik Moor) and at *Mollehope* (modern Mowhaugh) and to 30:1 at *Persouth*. These higher ratios might suggest very considerable pressures on the grazed upland pastures: King and Nicholson (1964) regarded modern sheep:cattle ratios of 11:1 as balanced. However, stocking densities are critical, and these cannot be reconstructed although Trow-Smith (1957) thought they were much lower than today. They cannot be demonstrated from palynological data (Groenman van Waateringe 1993), but the expansion of *Calluna* heath indicates that grazing pressures cannot have been extreme (Hobbs & Gimingham 1987; Tipping 1998b). There is in addition no geomorphological evidence (Chapter 7) for accelerated soil erosion on these hills. The impacts of excessive grazing pressures would come in the eighteenth century (Section 8.11e below) with the loss of this heath vegetation.

Tipping (1998b) explained the development of *Calluna* heath not by grazing pressures. He argued that intensified upland grazing in the northern Cheviot Hills, probably the expansion of sheep ranching, came at a time when grasslands were in decline through falling soil quality, and that the introduction of sheep only encouraged continued deterioration in grazing quality. At Mow Law B, the spread of *Calluna* heath as a consequence of burning may not have been what was anticipated by farmers: they were hoping to promote improved grassland. If farmers thought they knew what they were doing, which is not necessarily the case in innovative practices, then there were unpredictable effects of burning on the andesitic brown forest soils of the Bowmont Valley. One might have been that the frequency of burning was too low to promote grassland species but optimal for *Calluna* establishment (Hobbs 1984), but farmers lacked either the experience or confidence to alter the frequency with which they set fires. Another may have been the accelerated acidification of burnt surface soils, particularly when burnt unskilfully (McVean & Lockie 1969; Maltby, Legg & Proctor 1990).

Acidification may also have reached this threshold without the impacts of local burning. Romans and Robertson (1975) argued that brown forest soils in the Southern Uplands were deteriorating to podsols in the Medieval period, although their chronological controls are poor. But at Swindon Hill (Section 5.4: lpaz Swindon Da) *Calluna* heath expanded after *c* 1400 cal AD despite there being no increase in fire frequency/intensity, and soil acidification is a plausible mechanism. In this model, as well as the likelihood that farmers tried to juggle between the demands of cattle and sheep, declining soil quality also constrained their ambition, and restricted the creation of very high sheep stocking densities in the Medieval period. Attempts to increase productivity by raising stocking densities or by improving grazing quality through burning only made things worse by unintentionally promoting a less productive vegetation cover.

The highest ground at the head of the Bowmont Valley, above Cocklawfoot and including the blanket peat at Cocklawhead (Chapter 6), was a hunting reserve in the Medieval period (Gilbert 1979). The pollen sequence (Section 6.4: lpaz Cocklawhead 7D) shows no significant vegetation changes from the later Iron Age. Changes to this landscape were promoted more by the decline of hunting and the relaxation of regulations after 1400 cal AD (Gilbert 1979; Dixon 2003).

8.11 Stresses and solutions in the rural economy 1400–2000 cal AD

8.11a Political stresses and their recognition in the rural economy

That there were political stresses imposed on the landscape is undeniable. The development of the Anglo-Scottish Border (Mack 1924) and the hostilities between the two countries that later arose are only the most demonstrable features (Ridpath 1848; Bain 1896; Tough 1928; Mares 1972; Dobson 1973; Kershaw 1973; Watts 1975; Dixon 1979; Tuck 1985; Robson 1987; Robson 1989; Goodman 1987; McCord & Thompson 1998). In 1302 cal AD Melrose Abbey were ordered to pay Kelso Abbey tithes and other rights in the Bowmont Valley which they had withheld since 1269: the reassessment, 'considering the devastation of the country', amounted to a devaluation of some 39% (calculated from data in Innes 1854, 416).

Increasingly, some pollen analysts working in the historic period have tried to relate apparent fluctuations in the types, extent and/or intensity of land uses to such political stresses (e.g. Oldfield 1969; Barber 1981; Mackay & Tallis 1994; Dumayne-Peaty 1999b; Chiverrell 1999). However, there are very real difficulties in this (Tipping 2005), not least in the imprecision of chronologies, understood by Dumayne *et al* (1995) but not resolved. It is a moot point whether the historic period should be regarded as inherently more complex than later prehistory. Tipping (2005) argues that behind these attempts at correlation with known historical events is an insecurity among palaeoecologists in defining events independent of archival analyses, and a deferential assumption that archival records are superior. Work in the Bowmont Valley suggested to Tipping (1999a) that at least as much can be learnt about the history of the environment from palaeoenvironmental sources.

A different view of environmental history is to see land use as far freer from political crises (Turner, Roberts & Ward 1973; Oldfield *et al* 2003; Tipping 2005). For example, the Calendar of Border Papers (Bain 1896) shows the high frequency of cross- and inter-border raids (see also Mares 1972), but also how their timing was related to the farming year, commencing after harvest, and so how the provision of food was of utmost importance. In the pollen records from the Bowmont Valley (Chapters 3 to 6), no clear environmental or agricultural changes can be ascribed to short term political or military crises. The link between Anglo-Scottish hostilities and increased burning, seen in elevated amounts of microscopic charcoal between *c* 1370 and 1500 cal AD around Yetholm Loch (Section 3.3: lpaz Yetholm Gb), is made to suggest the emptiness and lack of rigour of such correlations.

8.11b Climatic stresses and impacts

The assumption that climatic deterioration drove the abandonment of upland landscapes in southern Scotland after the fourteenth century cal AD has been highly influential for many years (Parry 1975; 1978; Whyte 1981; Lamb 1985; Tipping 1998b, 1999a). There are strong grounds for recognising the effects of rising precipitation and declining temperature on different landscapes in the region, but it is still very uncertain that this climatic deterioration, loosely known as the 'little ice age' (Lamb 1977, 1985; Grove 1988) had impacts on human beings or the way they worked the land (Section 8.11c below).

To move from the particular to the general, there is abundant evidence in the upper Bowmont Valley that soils became increasingly waterlogged after *c* 1400 cal AD (after *c* 1375 cal AD at Cocklawhead, *c* 1400 cal AD at Swindon Hill and *c* 1585 cal AD at Mow Law B: Section 8.10b above). At Cocklawhead the peat surface became relatively dry again after *c* 1500 cal AD but the measurement of relative peat wetness (Section 2.3b) is complicated by the possible effects of lowered temperatures on evapotranspiration (Section 6.4: lpaz Cocklawhead 7E; below). There were several phases of waterlogging at Swindon Hill, between *c* 1550 and 1600 cal AD, *c* 1675 to 1700 cal AD and *c* 1775 to 1850 cal AD, with the later seventeenth century cal AD substantially wetter when the basin was a pond (Section 5.4: lpaz Swindon Db). The establishment of peat in separate shallow bedrock basins at Quarry Knowe and Mow Law A was synchronous at *c* 1660 and *c* 1670 cal AD respectively. The flooding of the basin at Mow Law A (Section 6.8: lpaz Mow Law A–B) was probably caused by increased effective precipitation because no dryland vegetation change occurred to have triggered this, but peat inception at Quarry Knowe was also linked to comprehensive anthropogenic clearance of an alder wood (Section 5.8: lpaz Quarry B: see Section 8.11d below). The basin at Quarry Knowe was also open water between *c* 1750 and 1800 cal AD. In combination, the synchroneity of events on the Swindon Hill and Mow Law plateaux suggest that the later seventeenth century cal AD was a period of markedly increased precipitation and waterlogging of soils in the Bowmont Valley. Daniel Defoe probably did see a large pond on the summit of The Cheviot (Section 1.1). This peat stratigraphic evidence can be matched with comparable, indeed, more refined but less securely dated evidence between *c* 1400 and 1700 cal AD from peats in the region (Tipping 1995b; Mauquoy & Barber 1999; Hughes *et al* 2000; Barber *et al* 2003) (Figure 8.5) and throughout north-west Europe (Barber *et al* 1999; Mauquoy *et al* 2002; Mauquoy *et al* 2004). Whyte (1981) documents significant changes in precipitation in this period from the archival record in the Southern Uplands. Storminess appears to have increased nationally and locally (Lamb & Frydendahl 1991; Walsh 1995; Wilson *et al* 2001) and sea and land temperatures were highly variable (Plaut, Ghil & Vautard 1995; Ahleit & Hagen 2002). Although the status of the 'little ice age' has been questioned by high resolution analyses that demonstrate year to year variability in weather but few trends (Probert-Jones 1984; Briffa *et al* 1990; Bradley & Jones 1992; Jones & Bradley 1992), Grove (2001) has restated the view (Lamb 1985; Grove 1988) that this was a highly significant climatic downturn, and this is supported by new data that stress the hemispheric if not global extent of this event (Plaut *et al* 1995; Bond *et al* 1997; Kreutz *et al* 1997; Broecker 2000; Meeker & Mayewski 2002).

It is probable that climatic stresses triggered both soil erosion and accelerated fluvial activity in the Bowmont Valley. High on the summit ridge at Cocklawhead the blanket peat has received inwashed mineral sediment incessantly for the last *c* 700 cal years despite a near continuous peat cover and absence of significant vegetation changes or human impacts (Section 5.4: lpaz Cocklawhead 7E). Soil erosion is thought to have been promoted by the gully erosion of the blanket peat from *c* 1300 cal AD which improved drainage and retarded peat growth. This provides a possible time for the onset of peat erosion observed on these slopes by Wishart and Warburton (2001) which would be consistent with analyses of blanket peat erosion in upland landscapes west and south of the Cheviot Hills (Tallis 1985, 1987, 1994, 1995, 1997, 1998; Stevenson, Jones & Battarbee 1990; Archer 1992; Tallis 1994; Rhodes & Stevenson 1997; Simmons 2003).

Increasing soil losses are, however, not apparent on the lower plateaux (Chapter 5) or at the foot of the long north-facing slope at Sourhope (Chapter 4). The grazed grasslands continued to remain intact, unfragmented because grazing pressures were still low and appropriate management strategies employed (Section 8.10c above). Cultivated fields appear to have been maintained without severe soil losses, perhaps through careful soil conservation measures (Sections 8.9e, 8.10b above). However, on the valley floor of the Bowmont Water at Swindon Haugh, and in the neighbouring Calroust Burn, there was severe disturbance to the river regime between *c* 1670 and 1770 cal AD (Section 7.3; Tipping 1992, 1993). This may have happened in one significant catastrophic event within this period, but is more likely to represent a sustained phase of much greater channel mobility. Although only analysed in these two reaches, this event is assumed to have impacted throughout the incised interior valleys of the Cheviots (Archer 1992), and has been identified in upland and piedmont rivers with varying degrees of temporal precision throughout the region (Figure 8.6) and farther afield (Harvey *et al* 1981; Smith & Boardman 1989; Macklin *et al* 1992a, b; Passmore *et al* 1993; Rumsby & Macklin 1994, 1996; Tipping 1995b; Merrett & Macklin 1999; Moores *et al* 1999; Passmore & Macklin 2000, 2002; Macklin & Lewin 2003), although the association with climatic change alone remains unresolved. Locally, Tipping (1993) attributed this extraordinary geomorphic instability on the Bowmont Water to climatic deterioration in the absence of significant vegetation changes or human impacts in the surrounding hills. The palynological evidence at Sourhope is for substantive changes in the representation of heath and grassland communities from *c* 1675 cal AD (Section 4.3: lpaz Sourhope L), but this is interpreted in Section 8.11e (below) as an early example of increasing grazing pressures not seen at other upland pollen sites in the valley until the nineteenth century cal AD, and as such probably unrelated to fluvial activity.

8.11c Agrarian resilience to climatic stresses

There is clear evidence that the series of climatic excursions loosely defined as the 'little ice age' seriously perturbed the soils and fluvial systems of the northern Cheviot Hills. Significant effects on the vegetation system are far less easily recognisable, as they are everywhere in the uplands of Britain. This is partly because we have very few finely resolved or securely dated records of late historic vegetation change and partly because human activities were dominant in disturbing plant communities. Plants that might in early prehistory be associated with disturbance typical of climatically induced soil erosion (solifluction) are also those associated with the maintenance of bare ground under cultivation, so that the two effects are confounded (Ballantyne 1991). In the Bowmont Valley, only at Swindon Hill are there suggestions that climatic deterioration led to vegetation change. Between *c* 1450 and 1700 cal AD heathers that are today associated with snow bed communities (McVean 1958) and the highest montane surfaces of The Cheviot (Ratcliffe 1974) grew 200m lower, and are found with grassland herbs suggestive of arctic-alpine affinities (Section 5.4: lpa zones Swindon Da and Db). However, although the pollen record at Cocklawhead cannot be interrogated in this detail (Section 6.2), there is no suggestion of a coherent vegetation restructuring on the Mow Law Plateau 60m higher than Swindon Hill, and climatic impacts are uncertain.

If the effects of climatic deterioration were at best ambiguous on plant communities, there are greater uncertainties concerning the effects of the 'little ice age' on human communities (Tipping 1998b; 2002b). Parry's interpretations (1973, 1975, 1978, 1981) of archival and cartographic data suggested that Medieval farming communities, who had established farms on the highest areas of the Lammermuir Hills across The Merse from the Cheviot Hills, subsequently retreated from this frontier because climatic deterioration in the 'little ice age' had made the farming economy, and specifically arable productivity, untenable. The thesis was beautifully presented, and was highly influential in defining the marginality of human tenancy in the uplands (Lamb 1985; Burgess 1989). Initially handicapped by the blunt chronological tool of climatic reconstruction at the time (Lamb 1977), Parry and Carter (1985) quickly moved to recognise the extraordinary short term intensity of climatic excursions in this period (Briffa *et al* 1990; Probert-Jones 1984; Plaut *et al* 1995) in suggesting the enduring effects on human populations of several consecutive years of hardship. However, the chronological controls developed by Parry are insufficiently precise to compare with the refinement of, for instance, the Central England temperature record, and to this difficulty are a series of assumptions concerning both the economic reliance on crop growing and the apparent frailty and indifference of the social system which seemingly left farmers exposed on the hilltops (Tipping 1998b).

Even accepting these assumptions, the vulnerability of crop production can be challenged from palynological data, because crops are recorded in pollen analyses. Absences of evidence will be just that, but in the Bowmont Valley there is positive evidence that crops continued to be cultivated at high altitudes until the nineteenth century cal AD. At Cocklawhead, where the measurement of definitive cereal type pollen is least clear (Section 6.3), single grains of *Secale* (rye) are rare from *c* 1500 cal AD until the later nineteenth century cal AD (Section 6.4: lpaz Cocklawhead 7E), although their derivation from fields on this ridge is uncertain. There is the suggestion in 1522 cal AD that crops might be expected at these high altitudes, however (Mack 1924), because the reason for their absence and for the low grazing pressures from cattle was seen to be the extent of wet blanket mire (Section 6.2). The blanket peat was there in its entirety (Sections 8.7e; 8.11b above), was probably a 'great waste' and was probably being dissected at that time to create the morass there today (Section 1.1). What was growing on mineral soils at this altitude has not been identified, but arable farming may intermittently have been a usual component of upland 'tofts and crofts' (Section 8.10b). Whether at Cocklawhead there is a relation between sporadic crop growing after *c* 1500 cal AD and the relaxation of hunting laws (Section 8.10c) is an interesting possibility.

At a lower altitude on increasingly acid brown forest soils, there is abundant evidence for cereal type pollen grains, including oats or wheat, at Mow Law A from peat inception at *c* 1670 cal AD until *c* 1830 cal AD (Section 6.8: lpa zones Mow Law A–B and C). At Swindon Hill, lower still, crops may not have been grown in the Medieval period, perhaps because on parts of this plateau outside the hunting reserve, though easily accessed from farms, grazing stock were encouraged. However, after *c* 1475 cal AD until *c* 1900 cal AD crops including oats or wheat, and perhaps rye, were common (Section 5.4: lpaz Swindon Da to Dc). On this plateau but within the hunting reserve, at Quarry Knowe, pollen data are unavailable until peat inception in the later seventeenth century (Section 8.11b), but oats or wheat pollen is recorded from then until *c* 1830 cal AD (Section 5.8: lpaz Quarry B). Cereal cultivation seems to have declined at Sourhope before *c* 1650 cal AD, however (Section 4.3: lpaz K), suggesting perhaps that the coldest and dampest parts of the uplands were by this time identified as areas of specialised pastoral production.

If we use early cartographic evidence such as Roy's Military Survey (1747–55) to indicate the presence of fields in the middle of the eighteenth century, then the cultivated areas on the Swindon Hill and Mow Law plateaux were well outside established areas of plough cultivation. These were, as with the archaeological remains of broad rig (Figure 8.14), above the haughland, although there is not a perfect correspondence between cartographic and archaeological data. It seems most likely that the high altitude plateaux, exceedingly difficult to access with machinery (Section 1.6), were not ploughed but may have been spade dug, as would have been some areas of cord rig in later prehistory (Section 8.8j above). Tipping (1998b) evaluated some of the ways in which cereal cultivation could routinely have been a part of later historic upland farming practice (Dodgshon 1975; Bil 1990) until the radical restructuring of the agricultural economy in the eighteenth century (Section 8.11e below). Tipping (1998b) also tried to resolve the apparent differences in agriculture between the Lammermuirs and the northern Cheviots by suggesting that crop growing was in the Cheviots not as central to farming, and crop failure not so crippling, but palynological evidence from 325m asl at Johnscleugh, above the montane cleughs of the Whiteadder Water in the Lammermuir Hills (Figure 8.7), suggests that crop growing also continued in the Lammermuirs until the later eighteenth century AD (Hall & Tipping unpublished). There are currently few grounds for accepting Parry's long standing determinist hypothesis, or for a retreat from the margins until much later, after the *nadir* of the 'little ice age', for economic reasons (Dodgshon 1972, 1975, 1976; Devine 1994; Brayshay & Williams 1995).

8.11d Population pressures, woodland resources and Scottish agrarian success

It is not possible to use palaeoecological data in any coherent way to assess population expansion. There are too many unresolved variables in how the intensity or extent of land uses are identified from these techniques, and many of these have been evaluated in this chapter. The extraordinary evidence for agricultural expansion

Plate 8.3
Parts of the high altitude plateaux still have sufficient heath to burn. This photograph is on Craik Moor and shows in the mid distance the line of an old and well set burn. Old growth heather is lower down on the slope. In the foreground, the tussocky clumps of grasses are now invading the heather, as they have done for the last 250 cal years.

and nineteenth century *Calluna* pollen percentages declined, between *c* 1775 and 1825 cal AD at Swindon Hill (Section 5.4: lpaz Swindon Dc), after *c* 1800 cal AD at Quarry Knowe (Section 5.8: lpaz Quarry B) and after *c* 1860 cal AD at Mow Law A (Section 6.8: lpaz Mow Law A–C): the large expanses of valley floor peat at Sourhope (Chapter 4) and blanket peat at Cocklawhead (Chapter 6) show no reductions. What replaced *Calluna* on mineral soils were wild grasses (Gramineae <8μm anl-D) (Plate 8.3). It is not possible to define the species of grass from pollen analyses, but at the same time there were substantial reductions and eventual losses of many grassland herbs, including characteristic grazing herbs such as ribwort plantain (*Plantago lanceolata*) and docks (*Rumex*). These herbs are closely associated in the Bowmont Valley with species rich bent-fescue (*Agrostis-Festuca*) grasslands on well drained brown forest soils (King 1962), and it is thought that their demise was related to the replacement of such grasslands by species impoverished *Nardus* (purple moor grass) and *Molinia* (mat grass) communities (King 1955, 1962). This was a significant loss of plant diversity as well as making the uplands much less attractive to view in late spring.

There were probably site specific factors affecting the character and rate of vegetation change. At Swindon Hill (Section 5.4: lpaz Swindon Dc) the loss of heath is linked to reductions in the frequency or intensity of moor burning, but disentangling cause and effect is very difficult. *Calluna* communities might have collapsed because old growth was not replaced by young shoots in burns that, though moderate, were too frequent. Equally the loss of heath may have dissuaded farmers from the value of setting fires. Reductions in burning would have led to scrub and woodland establishment unless grazing pressures were maintained or intensified (Miles, Welch & Chapman 1978; Simmons 2003): intensification was most likely (Dodgshon 1976; Tipping 1999a; 2000b). Drainage of the mire surface may also have encouraged the spread of grassland at Swindon Hill (Section 5.4: lpaz Swindon E), but the consistency of the changes suggests a common cause on all slopes.

The diachroneity of the changes, however, suggests that common climatic factors (Klanderud & Birks 2003) were unlikely to have provoked these changes, or soil acidification promoted by wind-blown industrial pollutants (Lee, Tallis & Woodin 1988; Jones *et al* 1990). Soil acidification has been suggested to have influenced the development of heath in the upper Bowmont Valley in the later Medieval period (Section 8.10c), and it is unlikely that further acidification would have led to its decline. These diachronous changes were instead most likely to have been provoked by differences in space and time in the intensity of exceptional grazing pressures (Fenton 1935; McVean & Lockie 1969; Patrick *et al* 1990; Stevenson & Thompson 1993; Chambers, Mauquoy & Todd 1999; Simmons 2003). Nevertheless, the shift to species poor grassland represents a significant decline in grazing quality (Mather 1993) so that sheep, though very numerous, were less well fed.

Many workers have thought that the overwhelming burden of sheep farming induced severe soil erosion in the uplands (e.g. Tivy 1957; McVean & Lockie; 1969; Evans 1977; Innes 1983) but there is little evidence for this in the Bowmont Valley. The destruction of the floodplains at Swindon Haugh and the Calroust Burn (Sections 7.3, 8.11b) was complete before the development of this sheep economy. This needs to be contrasted with the very frequent records elsewhere in the region for upland and piedmont rivers to have been highly active in the last *c* 200 years (McEwen 1989; Archer 1992; Rumsby & Macklin 1994; Rowan, Black & Schell 1999; Merrett & Macklin 1999; Macklin & Lewin 2003), but these very frequently originate in valleys affected by lead mining, and may be untypical (Figure 8.6).

There is equally no stratigraphic evidence in any peat in the valley for accelerated soil instability in the last few hundred years except on the Cocklawhead ridge (Section 6.4: lpaz Cocklawhead 7E), but here soil losses were sustained from the Medieval period and enhanced by peat erosion in the 'little ice age' (Section 8.11b). There is no evidence for the unconstrained moor burning suggested to have impacted the Bowland Fells to the south-west by Mackay and Tallis (1992, 1996) in the nineteenth century cal AD. Increasing landscape stability is likely despite the pressures of overgrazing (Kirkby 1967; Whitfield & Furley 1971; Jennings 1981; Douglas & Harrison 1984: Section 1.6), at least on mineral soils (Wishart & Warburton 2001). The dense Cheviot turf remained intact, with sheep scars and terracettes being the only evident disturbance (Section 1.6), and this may be a tribute to the careful management of these flocks.

Pride in the landscape remained, prompted among land owners by the initial profitability of the sheep economy (Dodgshon 1976; Devine 1994). The rebuilding of farms from the mid-eighteenth century cal AD on Medieval sites throughout the lower parts of the upper Bowmont Valley is clear (Mercer in prep.), and around these farms were constructed hedges, shelter belts, avenues as well as blocks of woodland managed for aesthetic and commercial reasons (Section 2.4c: Anderson 1967; House & Dingwall 2003). This more wooded landscape would have been most noticeable in the lowlands, which we have ignored in discussion of the Medieval and post-Medieval agricultural economy because very little appears from the pollen data to have changed (Section 3.3: lpa zones Yetholm Bb and Gc; Section 8.10b above). Small alterations in the way this completely agrarian landscape was used can be suggested, such as the possible demise of hemp cultivation after *c* 1600 cal AD, but in essence this lowland valley developed in this period by processes not recorded by pollen analyses, although the fen was free of trees and the surrounding fields 'visible' to the analyst.

Almost ironically, however, given the way in which the prehistoric landscape remained hidden from view by alder carr (Section 8.8h), the landscape in the last *c* 170 cal years has also been hidden by the tangle of willows that today one fights through to reach the sampling site. Yet this tangle was almost certainly planted in the nineteenth century cal AD, and probably grown to produce withies (Section 3.3: lpaz Yetholm H), a purpose curiously traditional in outlook in this new world. It lingers, almost an anachronisism in a landscape transformed.

REFERENCES

Aaby, B 1976 'Cyclic variations in climate over the past 5,500 years reflected in raised bogs', *Nature* 163, 281–4.

Aaby, B & Berglund, B E 1986 'Characterisation of peat and lake deposits', *in* Berglund, B E (ed) *Handbook of Holocene Palaeoecology and Palaeohydrology*. Chichester: Wiley, 231–46.

Adams, M 1999 'Beyond the pale: some thoughts on the later prehistory of the Breamish Valley', *in* Bevan, B (ed) *Northern Exposure: Interpretative Devolution and the Iron Ages in Britain*. Leicester: Leicester Archaeology Monographs 4, 111–22.

Affleck, T L, Edwards, K J & Clarke, A 1988 'Archaeological and palynological studies at the Mesolithic pitchstone and flint site of Auchareoch, Isle of Arran', *Proc Soc Antiq Scot* 118, 37–59.

Ahleit, J & Hagen, E 2002 'Climate variability and historical NW European fisheries', *in* Wefer, W G *et al* (eds) *Climate Development and History of the North Atlantic Realm*. Berlin: Springer-Verlag, 435–45.

Allason-Jones, L 1989 'Roman and native interaction in Northumberland', *in* Maxfield, V A & Dobson, M J (eds) *Roman Frontier Studies 1989*. Exeter: Exeter University Press, 1–5.

Alley, R B, Mayewski, P A, Sowers, T, Stuiver, M, Taylor, K C & Clark, P U 1997 'Holocene climatic instability: a prominent, widespread event 8,200 years ago', *Geology* 25, 483–6.

Andersen, S Th 1979 'Identification of wild grasses and cereal pollen', *Danmarks Geologiske Undersögelse Årbog* 1978, 69–92.

Anderson, M L 1967 *A History of Scottish Forestry*. Edinburgh: Thomas Nelson & Sons.

Anderson, P 1997 'Fire damage on blanket mires', *in* Tallis, J H, Meade, R & Hulme, P D (eds) *Blanket Mire Degradation. Causes, Consequences and Challenges*. Aberdeen: Macaulay Land Use Research Institute, 16–29.

Andrew, R 1984 *A Practical Pollen Guide to the British Flora*. Cambridge: Quaternary Research Association Technical Guide 1.

Annable, R 1987 *The Later Prehistory of Northern England*. Oxford: BAR.

Applebaum, S 1954 'The agriculture of the British Early Bronze Age, as exemplified at Figheldean Down, Wiltshire', *Proc Prehist Soc* 20, 103–14.

Appleby, P G & Oldfield, F 1983 'The assessment of ^{210}Pb data for use in limnochronology', *Hydrobiologia* 103, 29–35.

Archer, D 1992 *Land of Singing Waters. Rivers and Great Floods of Northumbria*. Stocksfield: The Spredden Press.

Armit, I 1999 'Life after Hownam: the Iron Age in south-east Scotland', *in* Bevan, B (ed) *Northern Exposure: Interpretative Devolution and the Iron Ages in Britain*. Leicester: Leicester Archaeology Monographs 4, 65–79.

Armit, I & Ralston, I 2003 'The coming of iron, 1000 BC to AD 500', *in* Smout, T C (ed) *People and Woods in Scotland: A History*. Edinburgh: Edinburgh University Press, 40–59.

Armstrong, H M & Milne, J A 1995 'The effects of grazing on vegetation species composition', *in* Thompson, D B A, Hester, A J & Usher, M B (eds) *Heaths and Moorlands. Cultural Landscapes*. Edinburgh: HMSO, 162–73.

Ashmore, P A 1996 *Neolithic and Bronze Age Scotland*. London: Batsford.

Ashmore, P 1998 'Single entity dating', *Actes du Colloque ^{14}C Archaeologies* 1998, 65–71.

Ashmore, P A 2001 'Settlement in Scotland during the second millennium BC', *in* Bruck, J (ed) *Bronze Age Landscapes. Tradition and Transformation*. Oxford: Oxbow, 1–8.

Askew, G P, Payton, R W & Shiel, R S 1985 'Upland soils and land clearance in Britain during the second millennium BC', *in* Spratt, D & Burgess, C (eds) *Upland Settlement in Britain: the Second Millennium BC and After*. Oxford: BAR, 5–34.

Atkinson, T C, Briffa, K R & Coope, G R 1987 'Seasonal temperatures in Britain during the past 22,000 years, reconstructed using beetle remains', *Nature* 325, 587–92.

Austin, P 2000 'The emperor's new garden: woodland, trees and people in the Neolithic of southern Britain', *in* Fairbairn, A S (ed) *Plants in Neolithic Britain and Beyond*. Oxford: Oxbow Books and Neolithic Studies Group Seminar Papers 5, 63–78.

Bailiff, I K 1992 'Luminescence dating of alluvial deposits', *in* Needham, S & Macklin, M G (eds) *Alluvial Archaeology in Britain*. Oxford: Oxbow, 27–36.

Baillie, M G 1989 'Do Irish bog oaks date the Shang Dynasty?', *Current Archaeology* 117, 310–13.

Baillie, M G L 1991 'Suck-in and smear: two related chronological problems for the '90s', *J Theoretical Archaeology* 2, 12–16.

Baillie, M G L 1999 *From Exodus to Arthur*. London: Batsford.

Bain, J 1896 *The Border Papers: Calendar of Letters and Papers relating to the affairs of the Borders of England and Scotland, vol. II (1595–1603)*. Edinburgh: Her Majesty's General Register House.

Ball, D F 1964 'Loss-on-ignition as an estimate of organic matter and organic carbon in non-calcareous soils', *J Soil Science* 15, 84–92.

Ballantyne, C K 1991a 'Holocene geomorphic activity in the Scottish Highlands', *Scottish Geographical Magazine* 107, 84–98.

Ballantyne, C K 1991b 'Late Holocene erosion in upland Britain: climatic deterioration or human influence?', *The Holocene* 1, 81–5.

Bannister, P 1964 'The water relations of certain heath plants with reference to their ecological amplitude. III Experimental studies: general conclusions', *J Ecology* 52, 499–509.

Barber, J 1997 *The Archaeological Investigation of a Prehistoric Landscape: Excavations on Arran 1978–1981*. Edinburgh: STAR Monograph 2.

Barber, K E 1981 *Peat Stratigraphy and Climatic Change: a Palaeoecological Test of the Theory of Cyclic Peat Bog Regeneration*. Rotterdam: Balkema.

Barber, K E 1982 'Peat-bog stratigraphy as a proxy climatic record', *in* Harding, A F (ed) *Climatic Change in Later Prehistory*. Edinburgh: Edinburgh University Press, 103–13.

Barber, K E 1984 'A large capacity Russian-pattern sediment sampler', *Quaternary Newsletter* 44, 28–31.

Barber, K E, Chambers, F M & Maddy, D 1994 'Sensitive high-resolution records of Holocene palaeoclimate from ombrotrophic bogs', *in* Funnell, B M & Kay, R L F (eds) *Palaeoclimate of the Last Glacial/Interglacial Cycle*. London: NERC Earth Science Directorate Special Publication 94/2, 57–60.

Barber, K E *et al* 1999 'Proxy records of climate change in the UK over the last two millennia: documented change and sedimentary records from lakes and bogs', *J Geological Soc of London* 156, 369–80.

Barber, K E, Chambers, F M & Maddy, D 2003 'Holocene palaeoclimates from peat stratigraphy: macrofossil proxy climate records from three oceanic raised bogs in England and Ireland', *Quaternary Science Reviews* 22, 521–39.

Barclay, G 1983 'Sites of the third millennium BC to the first millennium AD at North Mains, Strathallan, Perthshire', *Proc Soc Antiq Scot* 113, 122–281.

Barclay, G J 1997 'The Neolithic', *in* Edwards, K J & Ralston, I B M (eds) *Scotland: Environment and Archaeology 8000 BC – AD 1000*. Chichester: Wiley, 127–50.

Barclay, G J 2001 '"Metropolitan" and "parochial"/"core" and "periphery": a historiography of the Neolithic of Scotland', *Proc Prehist Soc* 67, 1–16.

Barclay, G J, Brophy, K & MacGregor, G 2003 'Claish, Stirling: an early Neolithic structure in its context', *Proc Soc Antiq Scot* 132, 65–137.

Barrett, J, Bradley, R & Green, M 1991 *Landscape, Monuments and Society: The Prehistory of Cranborne Chase*. Cambridge: Cambridge University Press.

Barrow, G W S 1980 *The Anglo-Norman Era in Scottish History*. Oxford: Clarendon Press.

Barrow, G W S 2003 *The Kingdom of the Scots: Government, Church and Society from the Eleventh to the Fourteenth Century*. Edinburgh: Edinburgh University Press.

Bartley, D D 1966 'Pollen analysis of some lake deposits near Bamburgh in Northumberland', *New Phytologist* 65, 141–56.

Bartley, D D & Chambers, C 1992 'A pollen diagram, radiocarbon ages and evidence for agriculture on Extwistle Moor, Lancashire', *New Phytologist* 121, 311–20.

Bartley, D D, Chambers, C & Hart-Jones, B 1976 'The vegetational history of parts of south and east Durham', *New Phytologist* 77, 437–68.

Bartley, D D, Jones, I P & Smith, R T 1990 'Studies in the Flandrian vegetational history of the Craven District of Yorkshire: the lowlands', *J Ecology* 78, 611–32.

Battarbee, R W, Anderson, N J, Appleby, P G, Flower, R J, Fritz, S C, Haworth, E Y, Higgitt, S, Jones, V J, Kreiser, A, Munro, M A R, Natkanski, J, Oldfield, F, Patrick, S T, Richardson, N G, Rippey, B & Stevenson, A C 1988 *Lake Acidification in the United Kingdom 1800–1986*. London: ENSIS Publishing.

Beckensall, S 1996 'Symbols on stone: the state of the art', *in* Frodsham, P (ed) *The Neolithic of Northern England*. Newcastle: Northern Archaeology Group, 139–46.

Behre, K-E 1981 'The interpretation of anthropogenic indicators in pollen diagrams', *Pollen et Spores* 23, 225–45.

Bell, J N B & Tallis, J H 1973 'Biological Flora of the British Isles, *Empetrum nigrum* L', *J Ecology* 61, 289–305.

Benito, G, Baker, V R & Gregory, K J 1998 *Palaeohydrology and Environmental Change*. Chichester: Wiley.

Bennett, J 1984 'The North-East in the Second Century', *in* Wilson, P R, Jones, R F J & Evans, D M (eds) *Settlement and Society in the Roman North*. Bradford: School of Archaeological Sciences, University of Bradford, 35–8.

Bennett, K D 1984 'The post-glacial history of *Pinus sylvestris* in the British Isles', *Quaternary Science Reviews* 3, 133–55.

Bennett, K D 1986 'Competitive interactions among forest tree populations in Norfolk, England, during the last 10,000 years', *New Phytologist* 103, 603–20.

Bennett, K D 1989 'A provisional map of forest types for the British Isles 5,000 years ago', *J Quaternary Science* 4, 141–4.

Bennett, K D 1994 'Confidence intervals for age estimates and deposition times in late-Quaternary sediment sequences', *The Holocene* 4, 337–48.

Bennett, K D 1996 'Determination of the number of zones in a biostratigraphical sequence', *New Phytologist* 132, 155–70.

Bennett, K D & Birks, H J B 1989 'Postglacial history of alder (*Alnus glutinosa* (L) Gaertn.) in the British Isles', *J Quaternary Science* 5, 123–34.

Bennett, K D & Fuller, J L 2002 'Determining the age of the mid-Holocene *Tsuga canadensis* (hemlock) decline, eastern North America', *The Holocene* 12, 421–9.

Bennett, K D, Whittington, G & Edwards, K J 1994 'Recent plant nomenclatural changes and pollen morphology in the British Isles', *Quaternary Newsletter* 73, 1–6.

Bil, A 1990 *The Shieling 1600–1840: The Case of the Central Scottish Highlands*. Edinburgh: John Donald.

Birks, H H 1972 'Studies in the vegetation history of Scotland II. Two pollen diagrams from the Galloway Hills, Kirkcudbrightshire', *J Ecology* 60, 183–217.

Birks, H H, Birks, H J B, Kaland, P E & Moe, D 1988 *The Cultural Landscape: Past, Present and Future*. Cambridge: University Press.

Birks, H J B 1970 'Inwashed pollen spectra at Loch Fada, Isle of Skye', *New Phytologist* 69, 807–20.

Birks, H J B 1973 *The Past and Present Vegetation on the Isle of Skye: A Palaeoecological Study*. Cambridge: Cambridge University Press.

Birks, H J B 1982 'Mid-Flandrian forest history of Roudsea Wood National Nature Reserve, Cumbria', *New Phytologist* 90, 339–54.

Birks, H J B 1989 'Holocene isochrone maps and patterns of tree-spreading in the British Isles', *J Biogeography* 16, 503–40.

Birks, H J B 1993 'Din Moss', *in* Gordon, J E & Sutherland, D G (eds) *Quaternary of Scotland*. London: Chapman & Hall, 584–7.

Birks, H J B 1994 'The importance of pollen and diatom taxonomic precision in quantitative palaeoenvironmental reconstructions', *Review of Palaeobotany and Palynology* 83, 107–17.

Birks, H J B 2003 'Developments in age-depth modelling of Holocene stratigraphical sequences', *PAGES News* 11, 7–8.

Birks, H J B & Birks, H H 1980 *Quaternary Palaeoecology*. Cambridge: Cambridge University Press.

Bjorck, S, Rundgren, M, Ingolfsson, O & Funder, S 1997 'The Preboreal Oscillation around the Nordic Seas: terrestrial and lacustrine responses', *J Quaternary Science* 12, 455–66.

Blaauw, M, van Geel, B & van der Plicht, J 2004 'Solar forcing of climatic change during the mid-Holocene: indications from raised bogs in The Netherlands', *The Holocene* 14, 35–44.

Blackford, J 1990 *Blanket Mires and Climatic Change: A Palaeoecological Study based on Peat Humification and Microfossil Analyses*. Unpublished PhD thesis, University of Keele.

Blackford, J J 1993 'Peat bogs as sources of proxy climatic data: past approaches and future research', *in* Chambers, F M (ed) *Climate Change and Human Impact on the Landscape*. London: Chapman & Hall, 47–56.

Blackford, J J & Chambers, F M 1991 'Proxy records of climate from blanket mires: evidence for a Dark Age (1400 BP) climatic deterioration in the British Isles', *The Holocene* 1, 63–7.

Blackford, J J & Chambers, F M 1993 'Determining the degree of peat decomposition for peat-based palaeoclimatic studies', *International Peat J* 5, 7–24.

Bluck, B J 1976 'Sedimentation in some Scottish rivers of low sinuosity', *Trans Royal Soc Edinburgh* 18, 425–55.

Bohncke, S, Vandenberghe, J & Wijmstra, T A 1988 'Lake level changes and fluvial activity in the Late Glacial lowland valleys', *in* Lang, S & Schluchter, C (eds) *Lake, Mire & River Environments in the Past 15,000 Years*. Rotterdam: Balkema, 115–21.

Bohncke, S J P 1993 'Lateglacial environmental changes in the Netherlands: spatial and temporal patterns', *Quaternary Science Reviews* 12, 707–17.

Bond, G, Showers, W, Cheseby, M, Lotti, R, Almasi, P, deMenocal, P, Priore, P, Cullen, H, Hajdas, I & Bonani, G 1997 'A pervasive millennial-scale cycle in North Atlantic Holocene and glacial climates', *Science* 278, 1257–66.

Bond, G C *et al* 2001 'Persistent solar influence on North Atlantic climate during the Holocene', *Science* 294, 2130–6.

Bonny, A P 1976 'Recruitment of pollen to the seston and sediment of some Lake District lakes', *J Ecology* 64, 859–87.

Bonny, A P 1978 'The effect of pollen recruitment processes on pollen distributions over the sediment surface of a small lake in Cumbria', *J Ecology* 66, 385–416.

Bonsall, C, Macklin, M G, Anderson, D E & Payton, R W 2002 'Climate change and the adoption of agriculture in north-west Europe', *European J of Archaeology* 5, 9–23.

Bonsall, C, Sutherland, D, Tipping, R M & Cherry, J 1990 'The Eskmeals Project: Late mesolithic settlement and environment in north-west England', *in* Bonsall, C (ed) *The Mesolithic in Europe*. Edinburgh: John Donald, 175–205.

Borek, M J E 1975 *Pollen Analysis and Vegetational History of the Akeld Basin*. Unpublished MSc thesis, University of Durham.

Bowes, R 1847 *The English Border in the Days of Henry VIII*. Newcastle: Richardson.

Bown, C J & Shipley, B M 1982 *Soil and Land capability for Agriculture: South-east Scotland*. Aberdeen: Macaulay Institute for Soil Research.

Boyd, W E 1984 'Prehistoric hedges: Roman Iron Age hedges from Bar Hill', *Scot Archaeol Rev* 3, 32–4.

Boyd, W E 1985a 'Palaeobotanical evidence from Mollins', *Britannia* 16, 37–48.

Boyd, W E 1985b 'The problem of the time span represented by pollen spectra in podzol turves, with examples from the Roman sites at Bar Hill and Mullins, Central Scotland', *in* Fieller, N R J, Gilbertson, D D & Ralph, N G A (eds) *Palaeobiological Investigations: Research Design, Methods and Data Analysis*. Oxford: BAR, 189–201.

Boyd, W E 1986 'Vegetation history at Linwood Moss, Renfrewshire, central Scotland', *J Biogeography* 13, 207–23.

Boyd, W E 1988 'Methodological problems in the analysis of fossil non-artifactual wood assemblages from archaeological sites', *J Archaeol Science* 15, 603–19.

Boyd, W E & Dickson, J H 1986 'Patterns in the geographical distribution of the early Flandrian *Corylus* rise in south-west Scotland', *New Phytologist* 102, 615–23.

Boyd, W E & Dickson, J H 1987a 'The pollen morphology of four *Sorbus* species, with special reference to the two Scottish endemic species, *S. arranensis* Hedl. and *S. pseudofennica* E H Warb', *Pollen et Spores* 29, 59–72.

Boyd, W E & Dickson, J H 1987b 'A post-glacial pollen sequence from Loch a'Mhuillinn, north Arran: a record of vegetation history with special reference to the history of endemic *Sorbus* species', *New Phytologist* 107, 221–34.

Bradley, R 1978 *The Prehistoric Settlement of Britain*. London: Routledge.

Bradley, R 1996 'Learning from places – topographical analysis of northern British rock art', *in* Frodsham, P (ed) *The Neolithic of Northern England*. Newcastle: Northern Archaeology Group, 87–100.

Bradley, R 1997 *Rock Art and the Prehistory of Europe: Signing the Land*. London: Routledge.

Bradley, R 2000 *An Archaeology of Natural Places*. London: Routledge.

Bradley, R 2002 'The Neolithic and Bronze Age periods in the north – some matters arising', *in* Brooks, C, Daniels, R & Harding, A (eds) *Past, Present and Future: The Archaeology of Northern England*. Durham: Architectural and Archaeological Society of Durham and Northumberland Research Report 5, 37–41.

Bradley, R S & Jones P D 1992 *Climate Since AD 1500*. London: Routledge.

Bradshaw, R H W 1994 'Quaternary terrestrial sediments and spatial scale: the limits to interpretation', *in* Traverse, A (ed) *Sedimentation of Organic Particles*. Cambridge: Cambridge University Press, 239–52.

Bradshaw, R H W, Coxon, P, Greig, J R A & Hall, A R 1981 'New fossil evidence for the past cultivation and processing of hemp (*Cannabis sativa* L) in eastern England', *New Phytologist* 89, 503–10.

Bradshaw, R H W, Tolonen, K & Tolonen, M 1998 'Holocene records of fire from the boreal and temperate zones of Europe', *in* Clark, J S *et al* (eds) *Sediment Records of Biomass Burning and Global Change*. Stuttgart: Springer. NATO ASI Series 151, 347–65.

Brayshay, B A *et al* 2000 'Surface pollen-vegetation relationships on the Atlantic seaboard: South Uist, Scotland', *J Biogeography* 27, 359–78.

Brayshay, M & Williams, A 1995 'A rough and cold country: farming and landscape changes in northern Snowdonia since *c* 1600', *in* Butlin, R A & Roberts, N (eds) *Ecological Relations in Historical Times*. Oxford: Blackwell, 122–45.

Bridge, M C, Haggart, B A & Lowe, J J 1990 'The history and palaeoclimatic significance of subfossil remains of *Pinus sylvestris* in blanket peats from Scotland', *J Ecology* 78, 77–99.

Briffa, K R, Bartholin, T S, Eckstein, D, Jones, P D, Karlen, W, Schweingruber, F H & Zetterberg, P 1990 'A 1,400-year tree-ring record of summer temperatures in Fennoscandia', *Nature* 346, 434–9.

Broecker, W S 2000 'Was a change in thermohaline circulation responsible for the Little Ice Age?', *Proc National Academy of Sciences* 97, 1339–42.

Brookes, D & Thomas, K W 1967 'The distribution of pollen grains on microscope slides. I. the non-randomness of the distribution', *Pollen et Spores* 9, 621–9.

Brooks, S J, Mayle, F E & Lowe, J J 1997 'Chironomid-based lateglacial climatic reconstruction for south-east Scotland', *J Quaternary Science* 12, 161–7.

Brooks, S J & Birks, H J B 2000 'Chironomid-inferred Late-glacial air temperatures at Whitrig Bog, south-east Scotland', *J Quaternary Science* 15, 759–64.

Brown, A, Horsfield, D & Thompson, D B A 1993 'A new biogeographical classification of the Scottish uplands. I. Descriptions of vegetation blocks and their spatial variation', *J Ecology* 81, 207–29.

Brown, A, Birks, H J B & Thompson, D B A 1993 'A new biogeographical classification of the Scottish uplands. II. Vegetation – environment relationships', *J Ecology* 81, 231–51.

Brown, A G 1987a 'Long-term sediment storage in the Severn and Wye catchments', *in* Gregory, K J, Lewin, J B & Thornes, J B (eds) *Palaeohydrology in Practice*. Chichester: Wiley, 307–22.

Brown, A G 1987b 'Holocene floodplain sedimentation and channel response of the lower River Severn, United Kingdom', *Zeitschrift fur Geomorphologie* 31, 293–310.

Brown, A G 1988 'The palaeoecology of *Alnus* (alder) and the Postglacial history of floodplain vegetation. Pollen percentage and influx data from the West Midlands, United Kingdom', *New Phytologist* 110, 425–36.

Brown, A G 1997 *Alluvial Archaeology. Floodplain Archaeology and Environmental Change*. Cambridge: Cambridge University Press.

Brown, A G 1998 'Fluvial evidence for the Medieval Warm period and the Late Medieval climatic deterioration in Europe', *in* Beniot, G, Baker, V R & Gregory, K J (eds) *Palaeohydrology and Environmental Change*. Chichester: Wiley, 43–52.

Brown, A G & Barber, K E 1985 'Late Holocene palaeoecology and sedimentary history of a small lowland catchment in central England', *Quaternary Research* 24, 87–102.

Brown, A G & Keough, M 1992 'Holocene floodplain metamorphosis in the Midlands, United Kingdom', *Geomorphology* 4, 433–45.

Brown, A G & Quine, T A 1999 *Fluvial Processes and Environmental Change*. Chichester: Wiley.

Brown, A P 1971 'The *Empetrum* pollen record as a climatic indicator in the Late Weichselian and early Flandrian of the British Isles', *New Phytologist* 70, 841–9.

Bruck, J 2002 *Bronze Age Landscapes: Tradition and Transformation*. Oxford: Oxbow.

Brunsden, D 2001 'Back a'long: a millennial geomorphology', *in* Higgitt, D L & Lee, E M (eds) *Geomorphological Processes and Landscape Change: Britain in the Last 1,000 Years*. Oxford: Blackwell, 27–60.

Buckland, P C, Dugmore, A J & Edwards, K J 1997 'Bronze Age myths? Volcanic activity and human response in the Mediterranean and North Atlantic regions', *Antiquity* 71, 581–93.

Buckland, P C & Edwards, K J 1984 'The longevity of pastoral episodes of clearance activity in pollen diagrams: the role of post-occupation grazing', *J Biogeography* 11, 243–9.

Bull, I D, Simpson, I A, van Bergen, P F & Evershed, R P 1999 'Muck 'n' molecules: organic geochemical methods for detecting ancient manuring', *Antiquity* 73, 86–96.

Bunting, M J 2002 'Detecting woodland remnants in cultural landscapes: modern pollen deposition around small woodlands in north-west Scotland', *The Holocene* 12, 291–301.

Bunting, M J 2003 'Pollen-vegetation relationships in non-arboreal moorland taxa', *Review of Palaeobotany and Palynology* 125, 285–98.

Bunting, M J & Tipping, R 2000 'Sorting dross from data: possible indicators of post-depositional assemblage biasing in archaeological palynology', *in* Bailey, G, Charles, R & Winder, N (eds) *Human Ecodynamics*. Oxford: Oxbow, 63–9.

Bunting, M J & Tipping, R 2004 'Complex hydroseral vegetation succession and "dryland" pollen signals: a case study from north-west Scotland', *The Holocene* 14, 53–64.

Burgess, C 1970 'Excavations at the scooped settlement at Hetha Burn I, Hethpool, Northumberland', *Trans Architecture and Archaeol Soc of Durham & Northumberland* New Series 2, 1–26.

Burgess, C 1980 'Excavations at Houseledge, Black Law, Northumberland, 1979, and their implications for earlier Bronze Age settlement in the Cheviots', *Northern Archaeology* 1, 5–12.

Burgess, C 1984 'The prehistoric settlement of Northumberland', *in* Miket, R & Burgess, C (eds) *Between and Beyond The Walls*. Edinburgh: John Donald, 26–175.

Burgess, C 1985 'Population, climate and upland settlement', *in* Spratt, D & Burgess, C (eds) *Upland Settlement in Britain: the Second Millennium BC and After*. Oxford: BAR, 195–216.

Burgess, C 1989 'Volcanoes, catastrophe and the global crisis of the late second millennium BC', *Current Archaeology* 117, 325–9.

Burgess, C 1990 'Discontinuity and dislocation in later prehistoric settlement: some evidence from Atlantic Europe', *in* Mordant, C & Richard, A (eds) *L'Habitat et l'Occupation du Sol a l'Age du Bronze en Europe*. Paris: Actes du Colloque International de Lons-le-Saunier, 21–40.

Burgess, C 1995 'Bronze Age settlements and domestic pottery in northern Britain: some suggestions', *in* Kinnes, I & Varndell, G (eds) *'Unbaked Urns of Rudely Shape': Essays on British and Irish Pottery for Ian Longworth*. Oxford: Oxbow Monograph 55, 145–58.

Burgess, C, Ovens, M & Uribe de Kellet, A 1981 'The ground and polished stone implements of north-east England: a preliminary statement', *Northern Archaeology* 2, 6–12.

Burrin, P J 1985 'Holocene alluviation in south-east England and some implications for palaeohydrological studies', *Earth Surface Processes & Landforms* 10, 257–71.

Burrin, P J & Scaife, R G 1984 'Aspects of Holocene valley sedimentation and floodplain development in southern England', *Proc Geologists Assoc* 95, 81–96.

Burroughs, W J 1992 *Weather Cycles: Real or Imaginary?* Cambridge: Cambridge University Press.

Bush, M B 1988 'Early mesolithic disturbance: a force on the landscape', *J Archaeol Science* 15, 453–62.

Bush, M B 1989 'On the antiquity of British Chalk grasslands: a response to Thomas', *J Archaeol Science* 16, 555–60.

Butler, G 1907 'Anniversary Address', *Proc Berwickshire Naturalists Club* 19, 87–107.

Butler, S 1995 'Post-processual palynology', *Scot Archaeol Rev* 10, 15–25.

Calcote, R 1995 'Pollen source area and pollen productivity: evidence from forest hollows', *J Ecology* 83, 591–602.

Calcote, R 1998 'Identifying forest stand types using pollen from forest hollows', *The Holocene* 8, 423–32.

Campbell, C, Tipping, R & Cowley, D 2003 'Continuity and stability in past upland land uses in the western Cheviot Hills, Southern Scotland', *Landscape History* 24, 111–20.

Carcaillet, C, Bouvier, M, Frechette, B, Larouche, A C & Richard, P J H 2001 'Comparison of pollen-slide and sieving methods in lacustrine charcoal analyses for local and regional fire history', *The Holocene* 11, 467–76.

Carruthers, R G, Burnett, G A, Anderson, W & Thomas, H H 1932 *The Geology of the Cheviot Hills*. London: Memoir of the Geological Survey of Great Britain.

Carter, S P 1995 'Radiocarbon dating evidence for the age of narrow cultivation ridges in Scotland', *Tools and Tillage* 7, 83–91.

Carter, S, Tipping, R M, Davidson, D, Long, D & Tyler, A 1997 'A multi-proxy approach to the function of post-medieval ridge-and-furrow cultivation in upland northern Britain', *The Holocene* 7, 447–56.

Caseldine, C J 1999 'Archaeological and environmental change on prehistoric Dartmoor: current understanding and future directions', *Quaternary Proc* 7, 575–84.

Caseldine, C J & Hatton, J 1993 'The development of high moorland on Dartmoor: fire and the influence of Mesolithic activity on vegetation change', *in* Chambers, F M (ed) *Climate Change and Human Impact on the Landscape*. London: Chapman & Hall, 119–31.

Cayless, S M 2000 *Vegetational and Land-use History of a Late Prehistoric Landscape at Stanshiel Rig, Upper Annandale, Scotland*. Unpublished MSc thesis, University of Stirling.

Cayless, S M & Tipping, R M 2002 'Data on mid-Holocene climatic, vegetation and anthropogenic interactions in southern Scotland', *Vegetation History & Archaeobotany* 11, 201–10.

Chambers, C 1978 'A radiocarbon-dated pollen diagram from Valley Bog, on the Moor House National Nature Reserve', *New Phytologist* 80, 273–80.

Chambers, F M 1984 'Antiquity of rye in Britain', *Antiquity* 58, 219–24.

Chambers, F M 1993 *Climate Change and Human Impact on the Landscape*. London: Chapman & Hall.

Chambers, F M, Barber, K E, Maddy, D & Brew, J 1997 'A 5,500-year proxy-climate and vegetational record from blanket mire at Talla Moss, Borders, Scotland', *The Holocene* 7, 391–400.

Chambers, F M & Elliott, L 1989 'Spread and expansion of *Alnus* Mill. in the British Isles: timing, agencies and possible vectors', *J Biogeography* 16, 541–50.

Chambers, F M, Mauquoy, D & Todd, P A 1999 'Recent rise to dominance of *Molinia caerulea* in environmentally sensitive areas: new perspectives from palaeoecological data', *J Applied Ecology* 36, 719–33.

Chambers, F M & Price, S-M 1985 'Palaeoecology of *Alnus* (alder): early post-glacial rise in a valley mire, north-west Wales', *New Phytologist* 101, 333–44.

Chapman, H P & Gearey, B R 2000 'Palaeoecology and the perception of prehistoric landscapes: some comments on visual approaches to phenomenology', *Antiquity* 74, 316–19.

Charlton, D B & Day, J C 1979 'Excavation and field survey in upper Redesdale: Part II', *Archaeologia Aeliana* (5th ser) 7, 207–33.

Charman, D J 1990 *Origins and development of the Flow Country blanket mire, northern Scotland, with particular reference to patterned fens*. Unpublished PhD thesis, University of Southampton.

Charman, D J, Hendon, D & Packman, S 1999 'Multiproxy surface wetness records from replicate cores on an ombrotrophic mire: implications for Holocene palaeoclimate records', *J Quaternary Science* 14, 451–63.

Chiverrell, R C 2001 'A proxy record of late Holocene climate change from May Moss, northeast England', *J Quaternary Science* 16, 9–31.

Chiverrell, R C & Atherden, M A 1999 'Climate change and human impact – evidence from the peat stratigraphy at sites in the eastern North York Moors', *in* Bridgland, D R, Horton, B P & Innes, J B (eds) *The Quaternary of North-East England. Field Guide*. London: Quaternary Research Association, 113–30.

Chorley, R J 1969 'The drainage basin as the fundamental geomorphic unit', *in* Chorley, R J (ed) *Introduction to Fluvial Processes*. London: Methuen, 30–52.

Clack, P A G 1982 'The northern frontiers: farmers in the military zone', *in* Miles, D (ed) *The Romano-British Countryside*. Oxford: BAR, 377–402.

Clapham, A R, Tutin, T G & Moore, D M 1987 *Flora of the British Isles* (3rd edn). Cambridge: Cambridge University Press.

Clapperton, C M 1967 *The Deglaciation of the East Cheviot Area, Northumberland*. Unpublished PhD thesis, University of Edinburgh.

Clapperton, C M 1970 'The evidence for a Cheviot ice cap', *Trans Institute of British Geographers* 50, 115–28.

Clapperton, C M 1971a 'The pattern of deglaciation in part of north Northumberland', *Trans Institute of British Geographers* 53, 67–78.

Clapperton, C M 1971b 'The location and origin of glacial melt-water phenomena in the eastern Cheviot Hills', *Proc Yorkshire Geological Soc* 38, 361–80.

Clapperton, C M, Durno, S E & Squires, R H 1971 'Evidence for the Flandrian history of the Wooler Water, Northumberland, provided by pollen analysis', *Scottish Geographical Magazine* 57, 14–20.

Clark, J S 1988 'Particle motion and the theory of charcoal analysis: source area, transport, deposition and sampling', *Quaternary Research* 30, 67–80.

Clark, J S & Paterson, W A III 1997 'Background and local charcoal in sediments: scales of fire evidence in the palaeorecord', *in* Clark, J S *et al* (eds) *Sediment Records of Biomass Burning and Global Change*. Stuttgart: NATO ASI Series 151, 23–48.

Clark, J S & Royall, P D 1995 'Particle-size evidence for source areas of charcoal accumulation in late Holocene sediments of eastern North American lakes', *Quaternary Research* 43, 80–9.

Clark, R 1970 'Periglacial landforms and landscapes in Northumberland', *Proc Cumberland Geological Soc* 3, 5–20.

Clark, R L 1982 'Point count estimation of charcoal in pollen preparations and thin sections of sediments', *Pollen Spores* 24, 523–35.

Clark, R L 1984 'Effects on charcoal of pollen preparation procedures', *Pollen et Spores* 26, 559–76.

Clarke, M, Rendell, H, Tastet, J-P, Clave, B & Masse, L 2002 'Late Holocene sand invasion and North Atlantic storminess along the Aquitaine coast, south-west France', *The Holocene* 12, 231–8.

Clymo, R S 1991 'Peat growth', *in* Shane, L C K & Cushing, E J (eds) *Quaternary Landscapes*. London: Belhaven, 76–112.

Clymo, R S, Oldfield, F, Appleby, P G, Pearson, G W, Ratnesar, P & Richardson, N 1990 'The record of atmospheric deposition on a rainwater-dependent peatland', *Philosophical Trans Royal Soc London* B327, 331–8.

Coggins, D, Fairless, K J & Batey, C E 1983 'Simy Folds: an early Medieval settlement site in upper Teesdale, Co Durham', *Medieval Archaeology* 27, 1–26.

Coles, B 1992 'Further thoughts on the impact of beaver on temperate landscapes', *in* Needham, S & Macklin, M G (eds) *Alluvial Archaeology in Britain*. Oxford: Oxbow Press, 93–102.

Coles, B 1998 'Doggerland – a speculative survey', *Proc Prehist Soc* 64, 45–81.

Coles, B 2000 'Beaver territories: the resource potential for humans', *in* Bailey, G, Charles, R & Winder, N (eds) *Human Ecodynamics*. Oxford: Oxbow for the Association for Environmental Archaeology, Symposium No 19, 80–9.

Coles, B 2001 'The impact of Western European beaver on stream channels: some implications for past stream conditions and human activity', *J Wetland Archaeol* 1, 55–82.

Coles, G & Mills, C M 1998 'Clinging on for grim life: an introduction to marginality as an archaeological issue', *in* Mills, C M & Coles, G (eds) *Life on the Edge. Human Settlement and Marginality*. Oxford: Oxbow Monograph 100, vii–xii.

Coles, J M & Orme, B J 1982 'Beaver in the Somerset Levels: some new evidence', *Somerset Levels Papers* 8, 67–73.

Coles, J M & Orme, B J 1983 *Homo sapiens* or *Castor fiber*? *Antiquity* 57, 95–102.

Common, R 1953 *A Contribution to the Geomorphology of the East Cheviot Area*. Unpublished PhD thesis, University of Edinburgh.

Conroy, J W H, Kitchener, A C & Gibson, J A 1998 'The history of the beaver in Scotland and its future reintroduction', *in* Lambert, R A (ed) *Species History in Scotland*. Edinburgh: Scottish Cultural Press, 107–28.

Cosgrove, D & Daniels, S 1988 *The Iconography of Landscape*. Cambridge: Cambridge University Press.

Cotton, J A, Heritage, G L, Large, A R G & Passmore, D G 1999 'Biotic response to late Holocene floodplain evolution in the River Irthing catchment, Cumbria', *in* Marriott, S B & Alexander, J (eds) *Floodplains: Interdisciplinary Approaches*. London: Geological Society of London Special Publication 163, 163–78.

Coulthard, T J & Macklin, M G 2001 'How sensitive are river systems to climate and land-use change? A model-based evaluation', *J Quaternary Science* 16, 347–52.

Cowley, D 2000 'Site morphology and regional variation in the later prehistoric settlement of south west Scotland', *in* Harding, J & Johnston, R (eds) *Northern Pasts: Interpretations of the Later Prehistory of Northern England and Southern Scotland*. Oxford: BAR British Series 302, 167–76.

Crone, A 1998 'The development of an early historic tree-ring chronology for Scotland', *Proc Soc Antiq Scot* 128, 485–93.

Crone, A & Mills, C 2002 'Seeing the wood *and* the trees: dendrochronological studies in Scotland', *Antiquity* 76, 788–94.

Cummins, G 2000 'Fire! Accidental or strategic use of fire in the early Mesolithic of the eastern Vale of Pickering', *in* Young, R (ed) *Mesolithic Lifeways*. Leicester: Leicester Archaeological Monographs 7, 75–84.

Current Archaeology 2004 'Howick and East Barns', *Current Archaeology* 189, 394–9.

Cushing, D H 1982 *Climate and Fisheries*. London: Belhaven.

Cushing, E J 1964 'Re-deposited pollen in Late Wisconsin pollen spectra from East-Central Minnesota', *American J Science* 262, 1075–88.

Cushing, E J 1967 'Evidence for differential pollen preservation in Late Quaternary sediments in Minnesota', *Review of Palaeobotany and Palynology* 4, 87–101.

Cwynar, L C, Burden, E & McAndrews, J H 1979 'An inexpensive sieving method for concentrating pollen and spores from fine-grained sediments', *Canadian J Earth Sciences* 16, 1115–20.

Dark, K 2000 *Britain and the End of the Roman Empire*. Stroud: Tempus.

Dark, K & Dark, P 1997 *The Landscape of Roman Britain*. Stroud: Sutton.

Dark, P 2000 *The Environment of Britain in the First Millennium AD*. London: Routledge.

Darwin, T 1996 *The Scots Herbal: The Plant Lore of Scotland*. Edinburgh: Mercat Press.

Davies, A L 1999 *High Spatial Resolution Holocene Vegetation and Land-Use History in West Glen Affric and Kintail, Northern Scotland*. Unpublished PhD thesis, University of Stirling.

Davies, A L & Tipping, R M 2004 'Sensing small-scale human activity in the palaeoecological record: fine spatial resolution pollen analyses from West Glen Affric, northern Scotland', *The Holocene* 14, 233–45.

Davies, A L, Tisdall, E & Tipping, R M 2004 'Holocene climatic variability and human settlement in the Scottish Highlands: fragility and robustness', *in* Housley, R A & Coles, G M (eds) *Atlantic Connections & Adaptations*. Oxford: Oxbow, 2–11.

Davies, G & Turner, J 1979 'Pollen diagrams from Northumberland', *New Phytologist* 82, 783–804.

Davies, P 1999 'Molluscan total assemblages across a woodland-grassland boundary and their palaeoenvironmental relevance', *Environmental Archaeology* 4, 57–66.

Davies, P & Wolski, C 2001 'Later Neolithic woodland regeneration in the long barrow ditch fills of the Avebury area: the molluscan evidence', *Oxford J Archaeol* 20, 311–17.

Day, S P 1993 'Preliminary results of high-resolution palaeoecological analyses at Star Carr, Yorkshire', *Cambridge Archaeol J* 3, 129–40.

Day, S P & Mellars, P A 1994 '"Absolute" dating of Mesolithic human activity at Star Carr, Yorkshire: new palaeoecological studies and identification of the 9600 BP radiocarbon plateau', *Proc Prehist Soc* 60, 417–22.

Deacon, J 1974 'The location of refugia of *Corylus avellana* L during the Weichselian glaciation', *New Phytologist* 73, 1055–63.

Dean Jr, W E 1974 'Determination of carbonate and organic matter in calcareous sediments and sedimentary rocks by loss on ignition: comparison with other methods', *J Sedimentary Petrology* 44, 242–8.

Defoe, D 1974 *A Tour through the Whole Island of Great Britain*. London: Dent & Sons.

Delcourt, H R & Delcourt, P A 1981 *Quaternary Ecology: A Paleoecological Perspective*. London: Chapman & Hall.

Delcourt, P A & Delcourt, H R 1980 'Pollen preservation and Quaternary environmental history in the southeastern United States', *Palynology* 4, 215–31.

Dent, J & McDonald, R 1997 *Early Settlers in the Borders*. Melrose: Scottish Borders Council.

Devine, T M 1994 *The Transformation of Rural Scotland: Social Change and the Agrarian Economy, 1660–1815*. Edinburgh: Edinburgh University Press.

Dickinson, W 1975 'Recurrence surfaces in Rusland Moss, Cumbria (formerly North Lancashire)', *J Ecology* 63, 913–35.

Dickson, C 1988 'Distinguishing cereal from wild grass pollen: some limitations', *Circaea* 5, 67–72.

Dickson, C & Dickson, J 2000 *Plants and People in Ancient Scotland*. Stroud: Tempus Publishing.

Dickson, J H 1973 *Bryophytes of the Pleistocene*. Cambridge: Cambridge University Press.

Dickson, J H 1978 'Bronze Age mead', *Antiquity* 52, 108–13.

Dickson, J H 1988 'Post-glacial pine stumps in central Scotland', *Scottish Forestry* 42, 192–9.

Dickson, J H 1992 'Scottish woodlands: their ancient past and precarious present', *Botanical J Scotland* 46, 155–65.

Dickson, J H 1994 'The yew tree (*Taxus baccata* L) in Scotland – native or early introduction or both?', *Scottish Forestry* 48, 253–61.

Digerfeldt, G 1989 'Reconstruction and regional correlation of Holocene lake-level fluctuations in Lake Bysjon, South Sweden', *Boreas* 17, 165–82.

Dimbleby, G W 1960 'Iron Age land use on Bonchester Hill', *Proc Soc Antiq Scot* 93, 237–8.

Dimbleby, G W & Evans, J G 1974 'Pollen and land-snail analysis of calcareous soils', *J Archaeol Science* 1, 117–33.

Dixon, P 1979 'Towerhouses, pelehouses and Border society', *Archaeological J* 136, 240–52.

Dixon, P J 1985 *The Deserted Medieval Villages of North Northumberland*. Unpublished PhD thesis, University of Wales.

Dixon, P J 1994 'Field systems, rig and other cultivation remains in Scotland: the field evidence', *in* Foster, S & Smout, T C (eds) *The History of Soils and Field Systems*. Aberdeen: Scottish Cultural Press, 26–52.

Dixon, P J 1998 'A rural settlement in Roxburghshire: excavations at Springwood Park, Kelso, 1985–6', *Proc Soc Antiq Scot* 128, 671–751.

Dixon, P J 2003 'Champagne country: a review of medieval rural settlement in lowland Scotland', *in* Govan, S (ed) *Medieval or Later Rural Settlement in Scotland: 10 Years On*. Edinburgh: Historic Scotland, 53–64.

Dobson, R B 1973 *Durham Priory 1400–1450*. Cambridge: Cambridge University Press.

Dodds, J F 1997. *Bastions and Belligerents. Medieval Strongholds in Northumberland*. Jesmond: Keepdate.

Dodgshon, R A 1972 'The removal of runrig in Roxburghshire and Berwickshire 1680–1766', *Scottish Studies* 16, 121–37.

Dodgshon, R A 1975 'Farming in Roxburghshire and Berwickshire on the eve of Improvement', *Scot Hist Rev* 54, 140–54.

Dodgshon, R A 1976 'The economics of sheep farming in the Southern Uplands during the Age of Improvement, 1750–1833', *Economic History Review* 29, 551–69.

Dodgshon, R A 1983 'Medieval rural Scotland', *in* Whittington, G & Whyte, I D (eds) *An Historical Geography of Scotland*. London: Academic Press, 47–71.

Dodgshon, R A, Gilbertson, D D & Grattan, J P 2000 'Endemic stress, farming communities and the influence of Icelandic volcanic eruptions in the Scottish Highlands', *in* McGuire, W G, Hancock, D R & Stewart, I S (eds) *The Archaeology of Geological Catastrophes*. London: Geological Society of London Special Publication 171, 267–80.

Donaldson, A M & Turner, J 1977 'A pollen diagram from Hallowell Moss, near Durham City, UK', *J Biogeography* 4, 25–33.

Donkin, R A 1978 *The Cistercians: Studies in the Geography of Medieval England and Wales*. Toronto: Pontifical Institute of Medieval Studies.

Douglas, D D 1798 *General View of the Agriculture in the Counties of Roxburgh and Selkirk*. Edinburgh.

Douglas, T D & Harrison, S 1984 *Solifluction sheets: a review and case study from the Cheviot Hills*. Newcastle: Newcastle upon Tyne Polytechnic, School of Geography and Environmental Sciences.

Douglas, T D & Harrison, S 1985 'Periglacial landforms and sediments in the Cheviots', *in* Boardman, J (ed) *Field Guide to the Periglacial Landforms of Northern England*. Cambridge: Quaternary Research Association, 68–75.

Douglas, T D & Harrison, S 1987 'Late Devensian periglacial slope deposits in the Cheviot Hills', *in* Boardman, J (ed) *Periglacial Processes in Britain and Ireland*. Cambridge: Cambridge University Press, 237–44.

Dugmore, A J 1989 'Icelandic volcanic ash in Scotland', *Scottish Geographical Magazine* 105, 168–72.

Dumayne, L 1992 *Late Holocene Palaeoecology and Human Impact on the Environment of North Britain*. Unpublished PhD thesis, University of Southampton.

Dumayne, L 1993a 'Invader or native? – vegetation clearance in northern Britain during Romano-British time', *Vegetation History and Archaeobotany* 2, 29–36.

Dumayne, L 1993b 'Iron Age and Roman vegetation clearance in northern Britain: further evidence', *Botanical J Scotland* 46, 385–92.

Dumayne, L 1994 'The effect of the Roman occupation on the environment of Hadrian's Wall: a pollen diagram from Fozy Moss, Northumbria', *Britannia* 32, 217–24.

Dumayne, L 1995 'Human impact on vegetation in northern Cumbria since the Bronze Age: relating palynological and archaeological evidence', *Trans Cumberland & Westmorland Antiq and Archaeol Soc* 95, 23–33.

Dumayne-Peaty, L 1998a 'Forest clearance in northern Britain during Romano-British times: re-addressing the palynological evidence', *Britannia* 26, 315–22.

Dumayne-Peaty, L 1998b 'Human impact on the environment during the Iron Age and Romano-British times: palynological evidence from three sites near the Antonine Wall', *J Archaeol Science* 25, 203–14.

Dumayne-Peaty, L 1999a 'Continuity or discontinuity? Vegetation change in the Hadrianic-Antonine frontier zone of northern Britain at the end of the Roman occupation', *J Biogeography* 26, 643–65.

Dumayne-Peaty, L 1999b 'Late Holocene human impact on the vegetation of south-eastern Scotland: a pollen diagram from Dogden Moss, Berwickshire', *Review of Palaeobotany & Palynology* 105, 121–41.

Dumayne, L, Stoneman, R E, Barber, K E & Harkness, D D 1995 'Problems associated with correlating calibrated radiocarbon-dated pollen diagrams with historical events', *The Holocene* 5, 118–24.

Dumayne-Peaty, L & Barber, K E 1998 'Late Holocene vegetation history, human impact and pollen representivity variations in northern Cumbria, England', *J Quaternary Science* 13, 147–64.

Dunsford, H M *The Response of Alluvial Fans and Debris Cones to Changes in Sediment Supply in Upland Britain*. Unpublished PhD thesis, University of Durham.

Dunwell, A 1999 'Edin's Hall fort, broch and settlement, Berwickshire (Scottish Borders): recent fieldwork and new perceptions', *Proc Soc Antiq Scot* 129, 303–58.

Dunwell, A & Coles, G 1998 'Archaeological and palynological investigations on the Antonine Wall near Glasgow Bridge, Kirkintilloch', *Proc Soc Antiq Scot* 128, 461–80.

Dupont, L M 1986 'Temperature and rainfall variations in the Holocene based on comparative palaeoecology and isotope geology of a hummock and a hollow (Boutangerveen, The Netherlands)', *Review of Palaeobotany and Palynology* 48, 71–159.

Dupont, L M & Brenninkmeier, C A M 1984 'Palaeobotanic and isotopic analysis of Late Subboreal and early Subatlantic peat from Engbertsdijksveen VII, The Netherlands', *Review of Palaeobotany and Palynology* 41, 241–71.

Durno, S E 1956 'Pollen analysis of peat deposits in Scotland', *Scottish Geographical Magazine* 72, 177–87.

Durno, S E & McVean, D N 1959 'Forest history of the Beinn Eighe Nature Reserve', *New Phytologist* 58, 228–36.

Durno, S E & Romans, J C C 1969 'Evidence for variations in the altitudinal zonation of climate in Scotland and northern England since the Boreal period', *Scottish Geographical Magazine* 85, 31–3.

Edmonds, M 1999 *Ancestral Geographies of the Neolithic: Landscapes, Monuments and Memory*. London: Routledge.

Edwards, K J 1981 'The separation of *Corylus* and *Myrica* pollen in modern and fossil samples', *Pollen et Spores* 23, 205–18.

Edwards, K J 1982 'Man, space and the woodland edge – speculations on the detection and interpretation of human impact in pollen profiles', *in* Bell, M & Limbrey, S (eds) *Archaeological Aspects of Woodland Ecology*. Oxford: BAR International Series 46, 5–22.

Edwards, K J 1988 'The hunter-gatherer/agricultural transition and the pollen record in the British Isles', *in* Birks, H H *et al* (eds) *The Cultural Landscape: Past, Present and Future*. Cambridge: Cambridge University Press, 255–66.

Edwards, K J 1989a 'Meso-Neolithic vegetation impacts in Scotland and beyond: palynological considerations', *in* Bonsall, C (ed) *The Mesolithic in Europe*. Edinburgh: John Donald, 143–63.

Edwards, K J 1989b 'The cereal pollen record and early agriculture', *in* Milles, A, Williams, D & Gardner, N (eds) *The Beginnings of Agriculture*. Oxford: BAR International Series 496 and Symposia for the Association for Environmental Archaeology 8, 113–36.

Edwards, K J 1990 'Fire and the Scottish mesolithic: evidence from microscopic charcoal', *in* Vermeesch, P M & van Peer, P (eds) *Contributions to the Mesolithic in Europe*. Leeuven: Leeuven University Press, 71–9.

Edwards, K J 1991 'Using space in cultural palynology: the value of the off-site pollen record', *in* Harris, D R & Thomas, K D (eds) *Modelling Ecological Change*. London: Institute of Archaeology, University College, 61–74.

Edwards, K J 1993 'Models of mid-Holocene forest farming for north-west Europe', *in* Chambers, F M (ed) *Climate Change and Human Impact on the Landscape*. London: Chapman & Hall, 133–46.

Edwards, K J 1999 'Palynology and people – observations on the British record', *Quaternary Proceedings* 7, 531–44.

Edwards, K J & Hirons, K R 1982 'Date of blanket peat initiation and rates of spread – a problem in research design', *Quaternary Newsletter* 36, 32–7.

Edwards, K J & Hirons, K R 1984 'Cereal pollen grains in pre-elm decline deposits: implications for the earliest agriculture in Britain and Ireland', *J Archaeol Science* 11, 71–80.

Edwards, K J & Ralston, I B M 1984 'Postglacial hunter-gatherers and vegetational history in Scotland', *Proc Soc Antiq Scot* 114, 15–34.

Edwards, K J & Whittington, G 1990 'Palynological evidence for the growing of *Cannabis sativa* L (hemp) in medieval and historical Scotland', *Trans Inst British Geog* New Series 15, 60–9.

Ellis, C & Brown, A G 1999 'Alluvial microfabrics, anisotropy of magnetic susceptibility and overbank processes', *in* Brown, A G & Quine, T A (eds) *Fluvial Processes and Environmental Change*. Chichester: Wiley, 181–206.

Erdrich, M, Giannotta, K M & Hanson, W S 2000 'Traprain Law: native and Roman on the northern frontier', *Proc Soc Antiq Scot* 130, 441–56.

Evans, A T & Moore, P D 1985 'Surface pollen studies of *Calluna vulgaris* (L) Hull and their relevance to the interpretation of bog and moorland pollen diagrams', *Circaea* 3, 173–8.

Evans, J G 1975 *The Environment of Early Man in the British Isles*. London: Elek Books.

Evans, J G 1999 *Land & Archaeology. Histories of Human Environment in the British Isles*. Stroud: Tempus.

Evans, J G, Limbrey, S & Cleere, H 1975 *The effect of man on the landscape: the Highland Zone*. London: Council for British Archaeology.

Evans, R 1977 'Overgrazing and soil erosion on hill pastures with particular reference to the Peak District', *J British Grassland Soc* 32, 65–76.

Evans, R 1990 'Erosion studies in the Dark Peak', *North of England Soils Discussion Group Proceedings* 24, 39–61.

Everson, P & Williamson, T 1998 *The Archaeology of Landscape*. Manchester: Manchester University Press.

Faegri, K & Iversen, J 1975 *Textbook of Pollen Analysis* (3rd edn). Oxford: Blackwell Scientific.

Faegri, K & Iversen, J 1989 *Textbook of Pollen Analysis* (4th edn) (revised by Faegri, K, Kaland, P E & Krzywinski, K). Chichester: Wiley.

Fagan, B 2000 *The Little Ice Age: How Climate Made History 1300–1850*. New York: Basic Books.

Feachem, R W 1966 'The hill-forts of northern Britain', *in* Rivet, A L F (ed) *The Iron Age in Northern Britain*. Edinburgh: Edinburgh University Press, 59–87.

Fenton, E W 1935 'The influence of sheep on the vegetation of hill grazings in Scotland', *J Ecology* 25, 424–30.

Fenton-Thomas, C 1992 'Pollen analysis as an aid to the reconstruction of patterns of land-use and settlement in the Tyne-Tees region during the first millennia BC and AD', *Durham Archaeol J* 8, 51–62.

Fernandez-Armesto, F 2000 *Civilizations*. London: Macmillan.

Ferrell, G 1995 'Space and society: new perspectives on the Iron Age of north-east England', *in* Hill, J D & Cumberpatch, C G (eds) *Different Iron Ages: Studies on the Iron Age in Temperate Europe*. Oxford: BAR International Series 602, 129–47.

Ferrell, G 1997 'Space and society in the Iron Age of north-east England', *in* Gwilt, A & Haselgrove, C (eds) *Reconstructing Iron Age Societies: New Approaches to the British Iron Age*. Oxford: Oxbow Monograph 71, 228–38.

Ficken, K J, Barber, K E & Eglinton, G 1998 'Lipid biomarker, δ^{13}C and plant macrofossil stratigraphy of a Scottish montane peat bog over the last two millennia', *Organic Geochemistry* 28, 217–37.

Fleming, A 1978 *The Dartmoor Reaves*. London: Batsford.

Fleming, A 1998 *Swaledale. Valley of the Wild River*. Edinburgh: Edinburgh University Press.

Flinn, M 1977 *Scottish Population History from the 17th Century to the 1930s*. Cambridge: Cambridge University Press.

Ford, B, Deakin, P & Walker, M 2000 'The tri-radial cairns of Northumberland', *Current Archaeology* 182, 82–5.

Fowler, P 1998 'Moving through the landscape', *in* Everson, P & Williamson, T (eds) *The Archaeology of Landscape*. Manchester: Manchester University Press, 25–41.

Fowler, P 2002 *Farming in the First Millennium AD. British Agriculture between Julius Caesar and William the Conqueror*. Cambridge: Cambridge University Press.

Frazer, J 1983 *Traditional Scottish Dyes*. Edinburgh: Canongate.

French, C N & Moore, P D 1986 'Deforestation, *Cannabis* cultivation and schwingmoor formation at Cors Llyn (Llyn Mire), Central Wales', *New Phytologist* 102, 469–82.

Frenzel, B 1995 *European River Activity and Climatic Change during the Lateglacial and early Holocene*. Stuttgart: Gustav Fischer Verlag.

Frodsham, P & Rushton, S 1994 'Yet more rock art in Northumberland. Morpeth: Northumberland County Council', *Archaeology in Northumberland 1993–1994*, 5.

Fulford, M 1990 'The landscape of Roman Britain: a review', *Landscape History* 12, 25–31.

Gaillard, M-J 1985 'Postglacial palaeoclimatic changes in Scandinavia and central Europe. A tentative correlation based on studies of lake-level fluctuations', *Ecologia Meditteranea* 11, 159–75.

Gaillard, M-J & Berglund, B E 1988 'Land-use history during the last 2,700 years in the area of Bjaresjo, southern Sweden', *in* Birks, H H *et al* (eds) *The Cultural Landscape: Past, Present and Future*. Cambridge: Cambridge University Press, 409–28.

Gardiner, V 1975 *Drainage Basin Morphometry*. Wolverhampton: British Geomorphological Research Group Technical Bulletin No. 14.

Gates, T 1981 'Farming on the frontier: Romano-British fields in Northumberland', *in* Clack, P & Haselgrove, S (eds) *Rural Settlement in the Roman North*. Durham: Council for British Archaeology, 21–42.

Gates, T 1983 'Unenclosed settlements in Northumberland', *in* Chapman, J C & Mytum, H C (eds) *Settlement in North Britain 1000 BC–AD 1000*. Oxford: BAR, 103–48.

Gates, T & O'Brien, C 1988 'Cropmarks at Milfield and New Bewick and the recognition of *grubenhauser* in Northumberland', *Archaeologia Aeliana* (5th ser) 16, 1–9.

Gear, A J & Huntley, B 1991 'Rapid changes in the range limits of Scots Pine 4,000 years ago', *Science* 251, 544–7.

Gearey, B & Gilbertson, D D 1997 'Pollen taphonomy of trees in a windy climate: Northbay Plantation, Barra, Outer Hebrides', *Scottish Geographical Magazine* 113, 113–20.

Geiger, R 1965 *The Climate near the Ground*. London: Harvard University Press.

Geikie, A 1887 *The Scenery of Scotland*. London: Macmillan.

Geikie, J 1876 'The Cheviot Hills', *Good Words* 17, 550–6.

Gibson, A 2002 'A matter of pegs and labels: a review of some of the prehistoric pottery from the Milfield Basin', *Archaeologia Aeliana* 30, 175–80.

Gilbert, J 1983 'The monastic record of a Border landscape 1136 to 1236', *Scottish Geographical Magazine* 99, 4–15.

Gilbert, J M 1979 *Hunting and Hunting Reserves in Scotland*. Edinburgh: John Donald.

Giller, K E & Wheeler, B D 1986 'Past peat cutting and present vegetation patterns in an undrained fen in the Norfolk Broadland', *J Ecology* 74, 219–47.

Godwin, H E 1956 *History of the British Flora*. Cambridge: Cambridge University Press.

Godwin, H E 1975 *History of the British Flora* (2nd edn). Cambridge: Cambridge University Press.

Goodman, A 1987 'The Anglo-Scottish Marches in the fifteenth century', *in* Mason, R A (ed) *Scotland and England 1286–1815*. Edinburgh: John Donald.

Goransson, H 1986 'Man and the forests of nemoral broad-leaved trees during the Stone Age', *Striae* 24, 143–52.

Gordon, A D & Birks, H J B 1972 'Numerical methods in Quaternary palaeoecology. I. Zonation of pollen diagrams', *New Phytologist* 71, 961–79.

Gordon, J E & Sutherland, D G 1993 *Quaternary of Scotland*. London: Chapman & Hall.

Hodgson, J 1828. *A History of Northumberland*. Newcastle.

Hodgson, J C 1923 'The Manors of Brandon and Branton', *Archaeologia Aeliana* (3rd ser) 20, 28–54.

Honeyman, A 1985 *Studies in the Holocene Vegetation History of Wensleydale*. Unpublished PhD thesis, University of Leeds.

Hope-Taylor, B 1977 *Yeavering*. London: HMSO.

Horden, P & Purcell, N 2000 *The Corrupting Sea: A Study of Mediterranean History*. Oxford: Blackwell.

House, S & Dingwall, C 2003 '"A Nation of Planters": introducing the new trees, 1650–1950', *in* Smout, T C (ed) *People and Woods in Scotland: A History*. Edinburgh: Edinburgh University Press, 128–57.

Howard, A J, Keen, D H, Mighall, T M, Field, M H, Coope, G R, Griffiths, H I & Macklin, M G 2000 'Early Holocene environments of the River Ure, near Ripon, North Yorkshire, UK', *Proc Yorkshire Geological Soc* 53, 31–42.

Howard, A J & Macklin, M G 1999 'A generic geomorphological approach to archaeological interpretation and prospection in British river valleys: a guide for archaeologists investigating Holocene landscapes', *Antiquity* 73, 527–41.

Hudson-Edwards, K A, Macklin, M G, Finlayson, R & Passmore, D G 1997 'Mediaeval lead polution in the River Ouse at York, England', *J Archaeol Science* 26, 809–19.

Hughes, J & Huntley, B 1988 'Upland hay meadows in Britain – their vegetation, management and future', *in* Birks, H H *et al* (eds) *The Cultural Landscape: Past, Present and Future*. Cambridge: Cambridge University Press, 91–110.

Hughes, M K & Diaz, H F 1994 'Was there a "Medieval Warm Period", and if so, where and when? *Climatic Change* 26, 109–42.

Hughes, P D M & Barber, K E 2004 'Contrasting pathways to ombrotrophy in three raised bogs from Ireland and Cumbria, England', *The Holocene* 14, 65–79.

Hughes, P D M, Mauquoy, D M, Barber, K E & Langdon, P G 2000 'Mire-development pathways and palaeoclimatic records from a full Holocene peat archive at Walton Moss, Cumbria', *The Holocene* 10, 465–80.

Hunter, F 1997 'Iron Age hoarding in Scotland and northern England', *in* Gwilt, A & Haselgrove, C (eds) *Reconstructing Iron Age Societies. New Approaches to the British Iron Age*. Oxford: Oxbow Monograph 71, 108–33.

Hunter, R F 1962 'Hill sheep and their pasture: a study of sheep-grazing in south-east Scotland', *J Ecology* 30, 651–80.

Huntley, B 1993 'Rapid early Holocene migration and high abundance of hazel (*Corylus avellana* L): alternative hypotheses', *in* Chambers, F M (ed) *Climate Change and Human Impact on the Landscape*. London: Chapman & Hall, 205–15.

Huntley, B 1999 'Climatic change and reconstruction', *in* Edwards, K J & Sadler, J P (eds) *Holocene Environments of Prehistoric Britain*. Chichester: Wiley. Quaternary Proceedings No 7, 513–21.

Huntley, B & Birks, H J B 1983 *An Atlas of Past and Present Pollen maps for Europe 0–13,000 Years Ago*. Cambridge: Cambridge University Press.

Huntley, B & Webb, T III 1988 *Vegetation History: Handbook of Vegetation Science*, Vol 7. Dordrecht: Kluwer.

Huntley, J P 2000 'Late Roman transition in the north: the palynological evidence', *in* Wilmott, T & Wilson, P (eds) *The Late Roman Transition in the North*. Oxford: BAR British Series 299, 67–71.

Ingram, H A P 1978 'Soil layers in mires: function and terminology', *J Soil Science* 29, 224–7.

Ingrouille, M 1995 *Historical Ecology of the British Flora*. London: Chapman & Hall.

Innes, C 1854 *Origines Parochiales Scotiae*. Edinburgh: Bannatyne Club.

Innes, J B, Blackford, J J & Davey, P J 2003 'Dating the introduction of cereal cultivation to the British Isles: early palaeoecological evidence from the Isle of Man', *J Quaternary Science* 18, 603–14.

Innes, J B & Shennan, I 1991 'Palynology of archaeological and mire sediments from Dod, Borders Region, Scotland', *Archaeol J* 148, 1–45.

Innes, J L 1983 'Landuse changes in the Scottish Highlands during the 19th century: the role of pasture degeneration', *Scottish Geographical Magazine* 99, 141–9.

International Study Group 1982 'An inter-laboratory comparison of radiocarbon measurements in tree rings', *Nature* 298, 619–23.

Jacobson Jr, G J & Bradshaw, R H W 1981 'The selection of sites for paleovegetational studies', *Quaternary Research* 16, 80–96.

Janssen, C R 1973 'Local and regional pollen deposition', *in* Birks, H J B & West, R G (eds) *Quaternary Plant Ecology*. Oxford: Blackwell Scientific, 31–42.

Jarman, M R, Bailey, G N & Jarman, H N 1982 *Early European Agriculture. Its Foundation and Development*. Cambridge: Cambridge University Press.

Jeffrey, A 1855 *The History and Antiquities of Roxburghshire*. Jedburgh: Walter Easton.

Jennings, I 1981 *Studies of accelerated soil erosion in parts of south-east Scotland*. Unpublished PhD thesis, University of Edinburgh.

Jobey, G 1961 'Three polished stone axes from Northumberland', *Archaeologia Aeliana* (4th ser) 39, 370–80.

Jobey, G 1964 'Enclosed stone-built settlements in north Northumberland', *Archaeologia Aeliana* (4th ser) 42, 41–64.

Jobey, G 1966 'Homesteads and settlements of the Frontier area', *in* Thomas, C (ed) *Rural Settlement in Roman Britain*. London: Council for British Archaeology, 1–14.

Jobey, G 1978 'Burnswark Hill', *Trans Dumfries & Galloway Natural History & Antiq Soc* 53, 57–104.

Jobey, G 1980 'Unenclosed platforms and settlements of the later second millennium BC in northern Britain', *Scot Archaeol Forum* 10, 12–26.

Jobey, G 1981 'Between Tyne and Forth: some problems', *in* Clack, P A G & Haselgrove, S (eds) *Rural Settlement in the*

Roman North. Durham: Council for British Archaeology, 7–20.

Jobey, G 1983 'Excavation of an unenclosed settlement on Standrop Rigg, Northumberland, and some problems related to similar settlements between Tyne and Forth', *Archaeologia Aeliana* (5th ser) 11, 1–22.

Jobey, G 1985 'The unenclosed settlements of Tyne–Forth: a summary', *in* Spratt, D & Burgess, C (eds) *Upland Settlement in Britain: the Second Millennium* BC *and After*. Oxford: BAR, 177–94.

Johnston, R 2000 'Dying, becoming and being the field: prehistoric cairnfields in Northumberland', *in* Harding, J & Johnston, R (eds) *Northern Pasts: Interpretations of the Later Prehistory of Northern England and Southern Scotland*. Oxford: BAR British Series 302, 57–70.

Johnston, R 2002 '"Breaking new ground": land tenure and fieldstone clearance during the Bronze Age', *in* Bruck, J (ed) *Bronze Age Landscapes. Tradition and Transformation*. Oxford: Oxbow, 99–108.

Jones, A 2002 *Archaeological Theory and Scientific Practice*. Cambridge: Cambridge University Press.

Jones, G D B & Walker, J 1983 'Towards a minimalist view of Romano-British agricultural settlement in the north west', *in* Chapman, J C & Mytum, H C (eds) *Settlement in North Britain 1000* BC–AD *1000*. Oxford: BAR British Series 118, 185–204.

Jones, M 1981 'The development of crop husbandry', *in* Jones, M & Dimbleby, G W (eds) *The Environment of Man: the Iron Age to the Anglo-Saxon Period*. Oxford: BAR, 95–127.

Jones, M 1983 *Integrating the Subsistence Economy*. Oxford: BAR International Series 181.

Jones, M E 1996 *The End of Roman Britain*. London: Cornell University Press.

Jones, P D & Bradley, R S 1992 'Climatic variations over the last 500 years', *in* Bradley, R S & Jones, P D (eds) *Climate Since* AD *1500*. London: Routledge, 649–55.

Jones, R A, Keen, D H & Robinson, J E 2000 'Devensian Lateglacial and early Holocene floral and faunal records from north-east Northumberland', *Proc Yorkshire Geological Soc* 53, 97–110.

Jones, V J, Stevenson, A C & Battarbee, R W 1989 'Acidification of lakes in Galloway, south-west Scotland: a diatom and pollen study of the post-glacial history of the Round Loch of Glenhead', *J Ecology* 77, 1–23.

Kelly, P M, Leuschner, H H, Briffa, K R & Harris, I C 2002 'The climatic interpretation of pan-European signature years in oak ring-width series', *The Holocene* 12, 689–94.

Keppie, L J F, Fitzpatrick, A, Walker, J J, Webster, P V, Young, A & Tipping, R M 1997 'Excavations on the Roman fort at Westerwood on the Antonine Wall, 1985–8', *Glasgow Archaeol J* 19, 83–99.

Kerr, R J 1978 *The Nature and Derivation of Glacial Till in part of the Tweed Basin*. Unpublished PhD thesis, University of Edinburgh.

Kerr, W B 1977 'Soils and "later prehistoric" settlement in south-east Scotland', *Trans Dumfries & Galloway Natural History and Antiq Soc* 52, 66–76.

Kershaw, I 1973 *Bolton Priory. The Economy of a Northern Monastery 1286–1325*. Oxford: Oxford University Press.

Kilian, M R, van der Plicht, J & van Geel, B 1995 'Dating raised bogs: new aspects of AMS ^{14}C wiggle matching, a reservoir effect and climatic change', *Quaternary Science Reviews* 14, 959–66.

King, J 1955 *The Ecology of Certain Hill Communities in the Cheviots with particular reference to* Nardus stricta. Unpublished PhD thesis, University of Edinburgh.

King, J 1960 'Observations on the seedling establishment and growth of *Nardus stricta* in burned Callunetum', *J Ecology* 48, 667–77.

King, J 1962 'The *Festuca-Agrostis* grassland complex in south-east Scotland', *J Ecology* 50, 321–55.

King, J & Nicholson, J A 1964 'Grasslands of the forest and sub-alpine zones', *in* Burnett, J H (ed) *The Vegetation of Scotland*. Edinburgh: Oliver & Boyd, 168–231.

Kirkby, M J 1967 'Measurement and theory of soil creep', *J Geology* 75, 359–78.

Kitchener, A C & Bonsall, C 1997 'AMS radiocarbon dates for some extinct Scottish mammals', *Quaternary Newsletter* 83, 1–11.

Kitchener, A C & Bonsall, C 1999 'Further AMS radiocarbon dates for extinct Scottish mammals', *Quaternary Newsletter* 88, 1–11.

Kitchener, A C & Conroy, J W H 1997 'The history of the Eurasian beaver *Castor fiber* in Scotland', *Mammal Review* 27, 95–108.

Klanderud, K & Birks, H J B 2003 'Recent increases in species richness and shifts in altitudinal distributions of Norwegian mountain plants', *The Holocene* 13, 1–6.

Klitgaard-Kristensen, D, Sejrup, H P, Haflidason, H, Johnsen, S & Spurk, M 1998 'A regional 8200 cal. year BP cooling event in north-west Europe, induced by final stages of the Laurentide ice-sheet deglaciation?', *J Quaternary Science* 13, 165–70.

Konigsson, L-K 1969 'Pollen dispersion and the destruction degree', *Bulletin of the Geological Institution of Uppsala* New Series 6, 161–5.

Kooistra, L I 1996 *Borderland Farming. Possibilities and Limitations of Farming in the Roman Period and Early Middle Ages between the Rhine and Meuse*. Assen: van Gorcum & Co.

Kreutz, K J *et al* 1997 'Bipolar changes in atmospheric circulation during the Little Ice Age', *Science* 277, 1294–6.

Kristiansen, K 1993 'Neolithic farming practice – an archaeological response to the Goransson hypothesis', *Fornvannen* 88, 247–51.

Lamb, H H 1977 *Climate: Present, Past and Future*. London: Methuen.

Lamb, H H 1981 'Climate from 1000 BC to 1000 AD', *in* Jones, M & Dimbleby, G W (eds) *The Environment of Man: the Iron Age to the Anglo-Saxon Period*. Oxford: BAR, 53–65.

Lamb, H H 1985 *Climate, History and the Modern World*. London: Routledge.

Lamb, H H & Frydendahl, K 1991 *Historical Storms of the North Sea, British Isles and north-west Europe*. Cambridge: Cambridge University Press.

Langdon, P G & Barber, K E 2004 'Snapshots in time: precise correlations of peat-based proxy climate records in Scotland using mid-Holocene tephras', *The Holocene* 14, 21–34.

Langdon, P G, Barber, K E & Hughes, P D M 2003 'A 7,500-year peat-based palaeoclimatic reconstruction and evidence for an 1,100-year cyclicity in bog surface wetness from Temple Hill Moss, Pentland Hills, south-east Scotland', *Quaternary Science Reviews* 22, 259–74.

Law, C 1998 'The uses and fire ecology of reedswamp vegetation', *in* Mellars, P & Dark, P (eds) *Star Carr in Context: new archaeological and palaeoecological investigations at the Early Mesolithic site of Star Carr, North Yorkshire*. Cambridge: McDonald Institute Monographs, 197–206.

Lee, J A, Tallis, J H & Woodin, S J 1988 'Acidic deposition and British upland vegetation', *in* Usher, M B & Thompson, D B A (eds) *Ecological Change in the Uplands*. Oxford: Blackwell, 151–62.

Lelong, O & Pollard, T 1998 'The excavation and survey of prehistoric enclosures at Blackshouse Burn, Lanarkshire', *Proc Soc Antiq Scot* 128, 13–53.

Leuschner, H H, Sass-Klaassen, U, Jansma, E, Baillie, M G L & Spurk, M 2002 'Subfossil European bog oaks: population dynamics and long-term growth depressions as indicators of changes in the Holocene hydro-regime and climate', *The Holocene* 12, 695–706.

Lewin, J 1981 *British Rivers*. London: George Allen & Unwin.

Lewin, J & Macklin, M G 2003 'Preservation potential for Late Quaternary river alluvium', *J Quaternary Science* 18, 107–20.

Limbrey, S & Evans, J G 1978 *The Effect of Man on the Landscape: the Lowland Zone*. London: Council for British Archaeology

Linnman, G 1981 'Some aspects of the colonization of *Corylus avellana* in north west Europe during early Flandrian times', *Striae* 14, 72–5.

Linton, D L 1955 'The problem of tors', *Geographical J* 121, 470–87.

Long, D J, Tipping, R, Carter, S, Davidson, D A, Boag, B & Tyler, A 2000 'The replication of pollen stratigraphies in soil pollen profiles: a test', *in* Harley, M M, Morton, C M & Blackmore, S (eds) *Pollen and Spores: Morphology and Biology*. Kew: Royal Botanic Gardens, 481–97.

Lowe, J J 1982 'Three Flandrian pollen profiles from the Teith Valley, Scotland. II. Analyses of deteriorated pollen', *New Phytologist* 90, 371–85.

Lowe, J J 1993 'Isolating the climatic factors in early- and mid-Holocene palaeobotanical records from Scotland', *in* Chambers, F M (ed) *Climate Change and Human Impact on the Landscape*. London: Chapman & Hall, 67–82.

Lowe, J J & Walker, M J C 1984 *Reconstructing Quaternary Environments*. Oxford: Pergamon.

Lowe, J J & Walker, M J C 1997 *Reconstructing Quaternary Environments* (2nd edn). London: Longman.

Macinnes, L 1982 'Pattern and purpose: the settlement evidence', *in* Harding, D W (ed) *Late Prehistoric Settlement in South-east Scotland*. Edinburgh: Department of Archaeology, Edinburgh University, 57–74.

Mack, J L 1924 *The Border Line*. Edinburgh: Oliver & Boyd.

Mackay, A & Tallis, J H 1992 'Possible causes of erosion of the blanket mires of the Bowland Fells, north-west England', *Proc 9th International Peat Congress* 1, 244–55.

Mackay, A W & Tallis, J H 1994 'The recent vegetational history of the Forest of Bowland, Lancashire, UK', *New Phytologist* 128, 571–84.

Mackay, A W & Tallis, J H 1996 'Summit-type blanket mire erosion in the Forest of Bowland, Lancashire, UK: predisposing factors and implications for conservation', *Biological Conservation* 76, 31–44.

Mackenzie, N A & Callander, R F 1997 'Birchwoods in a Deeside parish', *in* Smout, T C (ed) *Scottish Woodland History*. Edinburgh: Scottish Cultural Press, 135–46.

Macklin, M G 1999 'Holocene river environments in prehistoric Britain: human interaction and impact', *Quaternary Proc* 7, 521–30.

Macklin, M G & Aspinall, R J 1986 'Historic floodplain sedimentation in the River West Allen, Northumberland: a case study of channel change in an upland, gravel-bed river in the Northern Pennines', *in* Macklin, M G & Rose, J (eds) *Quaternary River Landforms and Sediments in the Northern Pennines, England. Field Guide*. London: British Geomorphological Research Group/Quaternary Research Association, 7–17.

Macklin, M G & Lewin, J 1986 'Terraced fills of Pleistocene and Holocene age in the Rheidol Valley, Wales', *J Quaternary Science* 1, 21–34.

Macklin, M G & Lewin, J 1993 'Holocene river alluviation in Britain', *Zeitschrift fur Geomorphologie (Supplement)* 88, 109–22.

Macklin, M G & Lewin, J 2003 'River sediments, great floods and centennial-scale Holocene climate change', *J Quaternary Science* 18, 101–06.

Macklin, M G & Needham, S 1992 'Studies in British alluvial archaeology: potential and prospect', *in* Needham, S & Macklin, M G (eds) *Alluvial Archaeology in Britain*. Oxford: Oxbow Press, 123–40.

Macklin, M G, Passmore, D G, Cowley, D C, Stevenson, A C & O'Brien, C F 1992a 'Geoarchaeological enhancement of river valley archaeology in north-east England', *in* Spoerry, P (ed) *Geoprospection in the Archaeological Landscape*. Oxford: Oxbow, 43–58.

Macklin, M G, Passmore, D G & Rumsby, B T 1992b 'Climatic and cultural signals in Holocene alluvial sequences: the Tyne basin', *in* Needham, S & Macklin, M G (ed) *Alluvial Archaeology in Britain*. Oxford: Oxbow, 123–40.

Macklin, M G, Passmore, D G, Stevenson, A C, Cowley, D C, Edwards, D N & O'Brien, C F 1991 'Holocene alluviation and land-use change on Callaly Moor, Northumberland, England', *J Quaternary Science* 6, 225–32.

Macklin, M G, Rumsby, B T & Heap, T 1992 'Flood alluviation and entrenchment: Holocene valley-floor development and transformation in the British uplands', *Geological Soc of America Bulletin* 104, 631–43.

Macklin, M G, Taylor, M P, Hudson-Edwards, K A & Howard, A J 2000 'Holocene environmental changes in the Yorkshire Ouse basin and its influence on river dynamics and sediment fluxes to the coastal zone', *in* Shennan, I & Andrews, J (eds) *Holocene Land-Ocean Interaction and Environmental Change around the North Sea*. London: Geological Society of London Special Publication 166, 87–96.

MacPherson, J B 1980 'Environmental change during the Loch Lomond Stadial: evidence from a site in the Upper Spey Valley, Scotland', *in* Lowe, J J, Gray, J M & Robinson, J E (eds) *Studies in the Lateglacial of North-West Europe*. Oxford: Pergamon, 89–102.

Magny, M 1992 'Holocene lake-level fluctuations in Jura and the northern subalpine ranges, France: regional pattern and climatic implications', *Boreas* 21, 319–34.

Magny, M 1995 'Successive oceanic and solar forcing indicated by Younger Dryas and early Holocene climatic oscillations in the Jura', *Quaternary Research* 43, 279–85.

Magny, M, Begeot, C, Guiot, J & Peyron, O 2003 'Contrasting patterns of hydrological changes in Europe in response to Holocene climatic cooling phases', *Quaternary Science Reviews* 22, 1589–96.

Mallik, A U, Gimingham, C H & Rahman, A A 1984 'Ecological effects of heather burning. I. Water infiltration, moisture retention and porosity of surface soil', *J Ecology* 72, 767–76.

Maltby, E, Legg, C J & Proctor, M F C 1990 'The ecology of a severe moorland fire on the North York Moors: effects of the 1976 fires, and subsequent surface and vegetation development', *J Ecology* 78, 490–518.

Manning, A, Tipping, R M & Birley, R 1997 'Roman impact on the environment at Hadrian's Wall: precisely dated pollen analyses from Vindolanda, northern England', *The Holocene* 7, 175–86.

Manning, W H 1975 'Economic influences on land use in the military areas of the highland zone during the Roman period', *in* Evans, J G, Limbrey, S & Cleere, H (eds) *The Effect of Man on the Landscape: the Highland Zone*. London: Council for British Archaeology Research Report 11, 112–16.

Mannion, A M 1975 *Late Quaternary Palaeogeographic Environments. A Study from Roxburghshire*. Unpublished PhD thesis, University of Bristol.

Mannion, A M 1978 'Late Quaternary deposits from Linton Loch, south-east Scotland. 1. Absolute and relative pollen analyses of limnic sediments', *J Biogeography* 5, 193–206.

Mannion, A M 1982 'Palynological evidence for lake-level changes during the Flandrian in Scotland', *Trans Bot Soc Edinburgh* 44, 13–18.

Mares, F H 1972 *The Memoirs of Robert Carey*. Oxford: Clarendon Press.

Markgraf, V 1980 'Pollen dispersion in a mountain area', *Grana* 19, 127–46.

Marsden, J 1990 *The Illustrated Border Ballads*. London: Macmillan.

Mather, A 1993 'The environmental impact of sheep farming in the Scottish Highlands', *in* Smout, T C (ed) *Scotland Since Prehistory: Natural Change and Human Impact*. Aberdeen: Scottish Cultural Press, 79–88.

Matthews, J A 1993 'Radiocarbon dating of arctic-alpine palaeosols and the reconstruction of Holocene palaeoenvironmental change', *in* Chambers, F M (ed) *Climate Change and Human Impact on the Landscape*. London: Chapman & Hall, 83–96.

Matthews, J R 1955 *The Origin and Distribution of the British Flora*. London: Hutchinson.

Mauquoy, D & Barber, K E 1999 'A replicated 3,000-year proxy-climate record from Coom Rigg and Felicia Moss, the Border Mires, northern England', *J Quaternary Science* 14, 263–75.

Mauquoy, D, van Geel, B, Blaauw, M & van der Plicht, J 2002 'Evidence from north-west European bogs show "Little Ice Age" climatic changes driven by variations in solar activity', *The Holocene* 12, 1–6.

Mauquoy, D, van Geel, B, Blaauw, M, Speranza, A & van der Plicht, J 2004 'Changes in solar activity and Holocene climatic shifts derived from ^{14}C wiggle-match dated peat deposits', *The Holocene* 14, 45–52.

May, J & Thrift, N 2001 *Timespace: Geographies and Temporality*. London: Routledge.

Mayle, F E, Lowe, J J & Sheldrick, C 1997 'The Late Devensian Lateglacial palaeoenvironmental record from Whitrig Bog, south-east Scotland. I. Lithostratigraphy, geochemistry and palaeobotany', *Boreas* 26, 279–95.

McCabe, M, Knight, J & McCarron, S 1998 'Evidence for Heinrich event 1 in the British Isles', *J Quaternary Science* 13, 549–68.

McCarthy, M 1995 'Archaeological evidence for the Roman impact on vegetation near Carlisle', *The Holocene* 5, 491–5.

McCarthy, M 2000 'Prehistoric settlement in northern Cumbria', *in* Harding, J & Johnston, R (eds) *Northern Pasts: Interpretations of the Later Prehistory of Northern England and Southern Scotland*. Oxford: BAR British Series 302, 131–40.

McCord, N & Thompson, R 1998 *The Northern Counties from AD 1000*. London: Longman.

McCullagh, R & Tipping, R 1998 *The Lairg Project 1988–1996: The Evolution of an Archaeological Landscape in Northern Scotland*. Edinburgh: STAR.

McDonnell, J 1988 'The role of transhumance in northern England', *Northern History* 24, 1–17.

McDonnell, J 1990 'Upland pennine hamlets', *Northern History* 26, 20–39.

McEwen, L 1985 *River Channel Planform Changes in Upland Scotland, with specific reference to Climatic Fluctuations and Landuse Changes over the Last 250 Years*. Unpublished PhD thesis, University of St Andrews.

McEwen, L J 1989 'Extreme rainfall and its implications for flood frequency: a case study of the middle River Tweed basin, Scotland', *Trans Inst of Brit Geog* NS14, 287–98.

McNeill, J 2000 *Something New Under the Sun: An Environmental History of the Twentieth Century*. London: The Penguin Press.

McVean, D N 1953 'Biological flora of the British Isles: *Alnus glutinosa*', *J Ecology* 41, 447–66.

McVean, D N 1955 'Ecology of *Alnus glutinosa* (L) Gaertn. 2. Seed distribution and germination', *J Ecology* 43, 67–71.

McVean, D N 1958 'Snow cover and vegetation in the Scottish Highlands', *Weather* 13, 197–200.

McVean, D N 1964 'Woodland and scrub', *in* Burnett, J H (ed) *The vegetation of Scotland*. Edinburgh: Oliver & Boyd, 144–67.

McVean, D N & Lockie, J D 1969 *Ecology and Land Use in Upland Scotland*. Edinburgh: Edinburgh University Press.

McVean, D N & Ratcliffe, D A 1962 *Plant Communities of the Scottish Highlands*. London: HMSO.

Meeker, L D & Mayewski, P A 2002 'A 1,400-year high-resolution record of atmospheric circulation over the North Atlantic and Asia', *The Holocene* 12, 257–66.

Mellars, P A 1976 'Fire ecology, animal populations and man: a study of some ecological relationships in prehistory', *Proc Prehist Soc* 42, 15–45.

Mercer, R J 1987 *Bowmont Valley*. Unpublished Field Guide for the Hillfort Studies Group.

Mercer, R J 1991 'The highland zone: reaction and reality 5000 BC–2000 AD', *Proc British Academy* 76, 129–50.

Mercer, R J & Tipping, R M 1994 'The prehistory of soil erosion in the northern and eastern Cheviot Hills, Anglo-Scottish Borders', *in* Foster, S & Smout, T C (eds) *The History of Soils and Field Systems*. Aberdeen: Scottish Cultural Press, 1–26.

Merrett, S P & Macklin, M G 1999 'Historic river response to extreme flooding in the Yorkshire Dales, northern England', *in* Brown, A G & Quine, T A (eds) *Fluvial Processes and Environmental Change*. Chichester: Wiley, 345–60.

Middeldorp, A A 1986 'Functional palaeoecology of the Hahnenmoor raised bog ecosystem – a study of vegetation history, production and decomposition by means of pollen density dating', *Review of Palaeobotany and Palynology* 49, 1–73.

Miket, R 1976 'The evidence for neolithic activity in the Milfield Basin, Northumberland', *in* Burgess, C & Miket, R (ed) *Settlement and Economy in the Third and Second Millennium BC*. Oxford: BAR, 113–42.

Miket, R 1981 'Pit alignments in the Milfield Basin and the excavation of Ewart I', *Proc Prehist Soc* 47, 137–46.

Milburn, P 1996 *Palaeoenvironmental Investigations into Aspects of the Vegetation History of North Fife and South Perthshire, Scotland*. Unpublished PhD thesis, University of Edinburgh.

Miles, J 1985 'The pedogenic effects of different species and vegetation types and the implications of succession', *J Soil Science* 36, 571–84.

Miles, J 1988 'Vegetation and soil change in the uplands', *in* Usher, M B & Thompson, D B A (eds) *Ecological Change in the Uplands*. Oxford: Blackwell, 57–70.

Miles, J, Welch, D & Chapman, S B 1978 'Vegetation and management in the uplands', *in* Heal, O W (ed) *Upland Land Use in England and Wales*. Cheltenham: Countryside Commission, 77–95.

Milne, J A 1982 *River channel change in the Harthope Valley, Northumberland, since 1897*. Newcastle: University of Newcastle upon Tyne Department of Geography Research Series No 13.

Mitchell, G F 1948 'Late-glacial deposits in Berwickshire', *New Phytologist* 47, 262–4.

Mithen, S, Finlay, N, Carruthers, W, Carter, S & Ashmore, P 2001 'Plant use in the Mesolithic: evidence from Staosnaig, Isle of Colonsay, Scotland', *J Archaeol Science* 28, 223–34.

Moffat, A 1985 *Kelsae: A History of Moffat from Earliest Times*. Edinburgh: Mainstream Publishing.

Moffat, B 1989 *Third Report on Researches into the Medieval Hospital at Soutra, Lothian/Borders Region, Scotland*. Edinburgh: SHARP.

Molen, P C van der & Hoekstra, S P 1988 'A palaeo-ecological study of a hummock-hollow complex from Engbertsdijksveen, in The Netherlands', *Review of Palaeobotany and Palynology* 56, 213–74.

Moore, J 1996 'Damp squib: how to fire a major deciduous forest in an inclement climate', *in* Pollard, T & Morrison, A (eds) *The Early Prehistory of Scotland*. Edinburgh: Edinburgh University Press, 62–73.

Moore, P D 1993 'The origin of blanket mire, revisited', *in* Chambers, F M (ed) *Climate Change and Human Impact on the Landscape*. London: Chapman & Hall, 217–24.

Moore, P D & Webb, J A 1978 *An Illustrated Guide to Pollen Analysis*. London: Hodder & Stoughton.

Moore, P D, Webb, J A & Collinson, M E 1991 *Pollen Analysis*. Oxford: Blackwell Scientific.

Moores, A J, Passmore, D G & Stevenson, A C 1999 'High resolution palaeochannel records of Holocene valley floor environments in the North Tyne basin, northern England', *in* Brown, A G & Quine, T A (eds) *Fluvial Processes and Environmental Change*. Chichester: Wiley, 283–311.

Morris, C D 1977 'Northumbria and the Viking settlement: the evidence for land-holding', *Archaeologia Aeliana* (5th ser) 5, 81–103.

Morris, C D 1995 'The early historic period', *in* Omand, D (ed) *The Borders Book*. Edinburgh: Birlinn, 53–64.

Morrison, K D 1994 'Monitoring regional fire history through size-specific analysis of microscopic charcoal: the last 600 years in south India', *J of Archaeol Science* 21, 675–85.

Moyle, D W 1980 *Pollen Analysis of Peat Deposits near Edlingham, Northumberland.* Unpublished MSc thesis, University of Durham.

Muir, J W 1956 *The Soils of the Country round Jedburgh & Morebattle.* Memoirs of the Soil Survey of Great Britain. Edinburgh: HMSO.

Mulholland, H 1970 'The microlithic industries of the Tweed Valley', *Trans Dumfries & Galloway Natural History & Antiq Soc* 47, 81–110.

National Research Council 2002 *Abrupt Climate Change: Inevitable Surprises.* Washington: National Academy of Sciences.

Needham, S & Macklin, M G 1992 *Alluvial Archaeology in Britain.* Oxford: Oxbow.

Newey, W W 1967 'Pollen analyses from south-east Scotland', *Trans Bot Soc Scot* 40, 424–34.

Newman, R 2001 *The Historical Archaeology of Britain, c 1540–1900.* Stroud: Sutton.

Newson, M D 1981 'Mountain streams', *in* Lewin, J (ed) *British Rivers.* London: George Allen & Unwin, 59–89.

Nichols, H 1967 'Vegetational change, shoreline displacement and the human factor in the late Quaternary history of south-west Scotland', *Trans Royal Soc Edinburgh* 67, 145–87.

Nicolaisen, W F H 1964 'Celts and Anglo-Saxons in the Scottish Border counties', *Scottish Studies* 8, 141–70.

O'Brien, S R, Mayewski, P A, Meeker, L D, Meese, D A, Twickler, M S & Whitlow, S I 1995 'Complexity of Holocene climate as reconstructed from a Greenland ice core', *Science* 270, 1962–4.

O'Connell, M 1987 'Early cereal-type pollen records from Connemara, western Ireland and their possible significance', *Pollen et Spores* 29, 207–24.

O'Connor, T P 1991 'Science, evidential archaeology and the new scholasticism', *Scot Archaeol Rev* 8, 1–7.

O'Sullivan, P E 1975 'Early and middle Flandrian pollen zonation in the eastern Highlands of Scotland', *Boreas* 4, 197–207.

Oldfield, F A 1959 'The pollen morphology of some of the West European Ericales', *Pollen et Spores* 1, 19–48.

Oldfield, F A 1969 'Pollen analysis and the history of land use', *Advancement in Science* 125, 298–311.

Oldfield, F, Crooks, P R J, Gedye, S, Jones, R, Plaer, A J, Richardspon, N, Nijampurkar, V N, Renberg, I, Rose, N J & Thompson, R 1994 'The geochronology of the last millennium', *in* Funnell, B M & Kay, R L F (eds) *Palaeoclimate of the Last Glacial/Interglacial Cycle.* Swindon: NERC Earth Sciences Directorate Special Publication 94/2, 77–80.

Oldfield, F, Richardson, N & Appleby, P G 1995 'Radiometric dating (^{210}Pb, ^{137}Cs) of recent ombrotrophic peat accumulation and evidence for changes in mass balance', *The Holocene* 5, 141–8.

Oldfield, F, Wake, R, Boyle, J, Jones, R, Nolan, S, Gibbs, Z, Appleby, P, Fisher, E & Wolff, G 2003 'The late-Holocene history of Gormire Lake (north-east England) and its catchment: a multiproxy reconstruction of past human impact', *The Holocene* 13, 677–90.

Orford, J D, Wilson, P, Wintle, A G, Knight, J & Braley, S 2000 'Holocene coastal dune initiation in Northumberland and Norfolk, eastern UK: climate and sea-level changes as possible forcing agents for dune initiation', *in* Shennan, I & Andrews, J (eds) *Holocene Land-Ocean Interaction and Environmental Change around the North Sea.* London: Geological Society of London Special Publication 166, 197–218.

Overton, M 1996 *Agricultural Revolution in England. The Transformation of the Agrarian Economy 1500–1850.* Cambridge: Cambridge University Press.

Owen, O A 1992 'Eildon Hill North, Roxburgh, Borders', *in* Rideout, J, Owen, O A & Halpin, E (eds) *Hillforts of Southern Scotland.* Edinburgh: STAR Monograph 1, 21–72.

Parker, A G, Goudie, A S, Anderson, D E, Robinson, M A & Bonsall, C 2001 'A review of the mid-Holocene elm decline in the British Isles', *Progress in Physical Geography* 26, 1–45.

Parker Pearson, M 1993 *Bronze Age Britain.* London: Batsford.

Parker Pearson, M 2000 'Ancestors, bones and stones in Neolithic and Early Bronze Age Britain and Ireland', *in* Ritchie, A (ed) *Neolithic Orkney in its European Context.* Cambridge: McDonald Institute Monographs, 203–14.

Parry, M L 1973 *Changes in the Upper Limit to Cultivation in South-east Scotland, 1600–1900.* Unpublished PhD thesis, University of Edinburgh.

Parry, M L 1975 'Secular climatic change and marginal land', *Trans Inst Brit Geog* 64, 1–13.

Parry, M L 1978 *Climate Change, Agriculture and Settlement.* Folkestone: Dawson & Sons.

Parry, M L 1981 'Climatic change and the agricultural frontier: a research strategy', *in* Wigley, T M L, Ingram, M J & Farmer, G (eds) *Climate and History.* Cambridge: Cambridge University Press, 319–36.

Parry, M L & Carter, T R 1985 'The effect of climatic variations on agricultural risk', *Climatic Change* 7, 95–110.

Passmore, D G & Macklin, M G 1997 'Geoarchaeology of the Tyne Basin: Holocene river valley environments and the archaeological record', *in* Tolan-Smith, C (ed) *Landscape Archaeology in Tynedale.* Newcastle: Department of Archaeology, 11–27.

Passmore, D G & Macklin, M G 2000 'Late Holocene channel and floodplain development in a wandering gravel-bed river: the River South Tyne at Lambley, northern England', *Earth Surface Processes & Landforms* 25, 1237–56.

Passmore, D G & Macklin, M G 2002 'Holocene sediment budgets in an upland gravel bed river: the River South Tyne, northern England', *in* Maddy, D, Macklin, M G & Woodward, J C (eds) *River Basin Sediment Systems: Archives of Environmental Change.* Lisse: Balkema, 423–44.

Passmore, D G, Macklin, M G, Brewer, P A, Lewin, J, Rumsby, B T & Newson, M D 1993 'Variability of late Holocene braiding in Britain', *in* Best, J L & Bristow, C S (eds) *Braided Rivers*. London: Geological Society, 205–29.

Passmore, D G, Macklin, M G, Heap, T & Anderson, J 1991 'Geoarchaeological investigations of late Holocene alluvial fills and valley side sediments at *Habitancum* Roman fort, West Woodburn, Northumberland: a re-evaluation of *The Piercebridge Formula*', Durham: Universities of Durham and Newcastle upon Tyne Archaeological Reports 14, 29–32.

Passmore, D G, Macklin, M G, Stevenson, A C, O'Brien, C F & Davis, B A S 1992 'A Holocene alluvial sequence in the lower Tyne Valley, northern Britain: a record of river response to environmental change', *The Holocene* 2, 138–47.

Patterson III, W A, Edwards, K J & Maguire, D J 1987 'Microscopic charcoal as a fossil indicator of fire', *Quaternary Science Reviews* 6, 3–23.

Payton, R W 1980 'Soils of the Milfield Plain, Northumberland', *North of England Soils Discussion Group Proceedings* 16, 1–52.

Payton, R W 1987 'Podzolic soils of the Fell Sandstones, Northumberland: their characteristics and genesis', *North of England Soils Discussion Group Proceedings* 22, 1–43.

Payton, R W 1992 'Fragipan formation in argillic brown earths (Fragiudalfs) of the Milfield Plain, north-east England. I. Evidence for a periglacial stage of development', *J Soil Science* 43, 621–44.

Peacock, J D 1997 'Was there a readvance of the British ice sheet into the North Sea between 15 ka and 14 ka BP?' *Quaternary Newsletter* 81, 1–8.

Peck, R M 1973 'Pollen budget studies in a small Yorkshire catchment', *in* Birks, H J B & West, R G (eds) *Quaternary Plant Ecology*. Oxford: Blackwell Scientific, 43–60.

Peglar, S 1993 'The mid-Holocene *Ulmus* decline at Diss Mere, Norfolk, UK: a year-by-year pollen stratigraphy from annual laminations', *The Holocene* 3, 1–13.

Peglar, S, Fritz, S C, Alapieti, T, Saarnisto, M & Birks, H J B 1984 'Composition and formation of laminated sediments in Diss Mere, Norfolk, England', *Boreas* 13, 13–28.

Pennington, W 1964 'Pollen analyses from the deposits of six upland tarns in the Lake District', *Phil Trans Royal Soc London* B248, 205–44.

Pennington, W 1969 *The History of British Vegetation*. London: Hodder & Stoughton.

Pennington, W 1970 'Vegetation history in the north-west of England: a regional synthesis', *in* Walker, D & West, R G (eds) *Studies in the Vegetational History of the British Isles*. Cambridge: Cambridge University Press, 41–80.

Pennington, W 1979 'The origin of pollen in lake sediments: an enclosed lake compared with one receiving inflow streams', *New Phytologist* 83, 189–213.

Pennington, W, Haworth, E Y, Bonny, A P & Lishman, J P 1972 'Lake sediments in northern Scotland', *Philo Trans Royal Soc London* B264, 191–294.

Phythian-Adams, C 2000 'Frontier valleys', *in* Thirsk, J (ed) *The English Rural Landscape*. Oxford: Oxford University Press, 236–64.

Piggott, C M 1948 'The excavations at Hownam Rings, Roxburghshire', *Proc Soc Antiq Scot* 82, 193–225.

Piggott, C M 1949 'The Iron Age settlement at Hayhope Knowe, Roxburghshire. Excavations 1949', *Proc Soc Antiq Scot* 83, 45–67.

Piggott, S 1972 'A note on climatic deterioration in the first millennium BC in Britain', *Scottish Archaeological Forum* 4, 109–13.

Pigott, C D 1975 'Natural regeneration of *Tilia cordata* in relation to forest-structure in the forest of Bialowieza, Poland', *Phil Trans Royal Soc London* B270, 151–79.

Pigott, C D & Huntley, J P 1978 'Factors controlling the distribution of *Tilia cordata* at the northern limits of its geographical range. I. Distribution in north-west England', *New Phytologist* 81, 429–41.

Pigott, C D & Huntley, J P 1980 'Factors controlling the distribution of *Tilia cordata* at the northern limits of its geographical range. II. History in north-west England', *New Phytologist* 84, 145–64.

Pigott, C D & Huntley, J P 1981 'Factors controlling the distribution of *Tilia cordata* at the northern limits of its geographical range. III. Nature and causes of seed sterility', *New Phytologist* 87, 817–39.

Pilcher, J 1991 'Radiocarbon dating for the Quaternary scientist', *in* Lowe, J J (ed) *Radiocarbon dating: Recent Applications and Future Potential*. Cambridge: Quaternary Research Association, Quaternary Proceedings 1, 27–34.

Plaut, G, Ghil, M & Vautard, R 1995 'Interannual and interdecadal variability in 335 years of Central England temperatures', *Science* 268, 710–13.

Potter, T W 1976 'Valleys and settlement: some new evidence', *World Archaeology* 8, 207–19.

Potter, T W 1979 *Romans in North West England: Excavations at the Roman Forts of Ravenglass, Watercrook and Bowness on Solway*. Cumberland & Westmorland Antiquarian and Archaeological Society Research Series 1.

Prentice, I C 1985 'Pollen representation, source area and basin size: toward a unified theory of pollen analysis', *Quaternary Research* 23, 76–86.

Price, M D R & Moore, P D 1984 'Pollen dispersion in the hills of Wales: a pollen shed hypothesis', *Pollen et Spores* 26, 127–36.

Pryor, F 1995 'Abandonment and the role of ritual sites in the landscape', *Scot Archaeol Rev* 9–10, 96–109.

Probert-Jones, J R 1984 'On the homogeneity of the annual temperature of central England since 1659', *J Climatology* 4, 241–53.

Proctor, M F C & Lambert, C A 1961 'Pollen spectra from Recent *Helianthemum* communities', *New Phytologist* 60, 21–6.

Puffer, J H, Russell, E W B & Rampino, M R 1980 'Distribution and origin of magnetite spherules in air, waters and sediments of the Greater New York City area and the North Atlantic Ocean', *J Sedimentary Petrology* 50, 247–56.

Punt, W & den Breejen, P 1981 'The North-west European Pollen Flora 27: Linaceae', *Review of Palaeobotany and Palynology* 33, 75–115.

Punt, W & Reumer, J W 1981 'The North-west European Pollen Flora 22: Alismataceae', *Review of Palaeobotany and Palynology* 33, 27–44.

Rackham, O 1980 *Ancient Woodland: Its History, Vegetation and Uses in England.* London: Edward Arnold.

Rackham, O 2000 'Prospects for landscape history and historical ecology', *Landcapes* 2, 3–15.

Rackham, O 2003 *Ancient Woodland: Its History, Vegetation and Uses in England* (2nd edn). Dalbeattie: Castlepoint Press.

Rae, T I 1966 *The Administration of the Scottish Frontier, 1513–1603.* Edinburgh: Edinburgh University Press.

Ragg, J M 1960 *The Soils of the Country round Kelso & Lauder.* Memoirs of the Soil Survey of Great Britain. Edinburgh: HMSO.

Ragg, J M & Bibby, J S 1966 'Frost weathering and solifluction deposits in southern Scotland', *Geografiska Annaler* 48A, 12–23.

Ramm, H G, McDowall, R W & Mercer, E 1970 *Shielings and Bastles.* London: HMSO.

Ramsay, S & Dickson, J H 1997 'Vegetation history of central Scotland', *Botanical J Scotland* 49, 141–50.

Randall, R E, Andrew, R & West, R G 1986 'Pollen catchment in relation to local vegetation: Creann ear, Monach Isles National Nature Reserve, Outer Hebrides', *New Phytologist* 104, 271–310.

Ratcliffe, D A 1977 *A Nature Conservation Review.* Cambridge: Cambridge University Press.

Ray, K & Thomas, J 2003 'In the kinship of cows: the social centrality of cattle in the earlier Neolithic of southern Britain', *in* Parker Pearson, M (ed) *Food, Culture and Identity in the Neolithic and Early Bronze Age.* Oxford: BAR International Series 1117, 37–44.

RCAHMS 1956 *Roxburghshire: An Inventory of the Ancient and Historical Monuments.* Edinburgh: HMSO.

RCAHMS 1994 *Southdean, Borders: An Archaeological Survey.* Edinburgh: RCAHMS.

RCAHMS 1997 *Eastern Dumfriesshire: An Archaeological Landscape.* Edinburgh: HMSO.

Reece 1980 'Town and country: the end of Roman Britain', *World Archaeology* 12, 77–93.

Renfrew, C 1985 *The Prehistory of Orkney 4000 BC–AD 1000.* Edinburgh: Edinburgh University Press.

Reynolds, D M 1982 'Aspects of later prehistoric timber construction in south-east Scotland', *in* Harding, D W (ed) *Late Prehistoric Settlement in South-east Scotland.* Edinburgh: Department of Archaeology, University of Edinburgh, 44–56.

Rhind, D W 1969 *The Terraces of the Tweed Valley.* Unpublished PhD thesis, University of Edinburgh.

Rhodes, N & Stevenson, A C 1997 'Palaeoenvironmental evidence for the importance of fire as a cause of erosion in British and Irish blanket peats', *in* Tallis, J H, Meade, R & Hulme, P D (eds) *Blanket Mire Degradation. Causes, Consequences and Challenges.* Aberdeen: Macaulay Land Use Research Institute, 64–79.

Richards, C 1996 'Henges and water: towards an elemental understanding of monumentality and landscape in late Neolithic Britain', *J Material Culture* 1, 313–36.

Richards, K S, Peters, N S, Robertson-Rintoul, M S E & Switsur, V R 1986 'Recent valley sediments in the North York Moors: evidence and interpretation', *in* Gardiner, V (ed) *International Geomorphology Part I.* Chichester: Wiley, 869–83.

Richards, M P 2003 'Explaining the dietary isotope evidence for the rapid adoption of the Neolithic in Britain', *in* Parker Pearson, M (ed) *Food, Culture and Identity in the Neolithic and Early Bronze Age.* Oxford: BAR International Series 1117, 31–6.

Richards, M P & Hedges, R E M 1999a 'A Neolithic revolution? New evidence of diet in the British Neolithic', *Antiquity* 73, 891–7.

Richards, M P & Hedges, R E M 1999b 'Stable isotope evidence for similarities in the types of marine foods used by late Mesolithic humans at sites along the Atlantic coast of Europe', *J Archaeol Science* 26, 717–22.

Richmond, A 1999 *Preferred Economies.* Oxford: BAR British Series 290.

Richmond, I A & Keeney, G S 1937 'The Roman works at Chew Green, Coquetdalehead', *Archaeologia Aeliana* (4th ser) 14, 129–40.

Rideout, J, Owen, O A & Halpin, E (eds) *Hillforts of Southern Scotland.* Edinburgh: STAR Monograph 1.

Ridpath, R 1848 *Border History.* Berwick.

Roberts, B K, Turner, J & Ward, P F 1973 'Recent forest history and land use in Weardale, northern England', *in* Birks, H J B & West, R G (eds) *Quaternary Plant Ecology.* Oxford: Blackwell Scientific, 207–21.

Robertson-Rintoul, M S E 1986 'A quantitative soil-stratigraphic approach to the correlation and dating of post-glacial river terraces in Glen Feshie, western Cairngorms', *Earth Surface Processes and Landforms* 11, 605–17.

Robinson, M A & Lambrick, G H 1984 'Holocene alluviation and hydrology in the Upper Thames basin', *Nature* 308, 809–14.

Robson, M J H 1987 *Ride with the Moonlight: The Mosstroopers of the Border.* Newcastleton.

Robson, R 1989 *The English Highland Clans.* Edinburgh: John Donald.

Romans, J C C & Robertson, L 1975 'Some genetic characteristics of the freely drained soils of the Ettrick Association in east Scotland', *Geoderma* 14, 297–317.

Rose, J & Boardman, J 1983 'River activity in relation to short-term climatic deterioration', *Quaternary Studies in Poland* 4, 189–98.

Rose, J, Turner, C, Coope, G R & Bryan, M D 1980 'Channel changes in a lowland river over the last 13,000 years', *in* Cullingford, R A, Davidson, D A & Lewin, J (eds) *Timescales in Geomorphology*. Chichester: Wiley, 159–75.

Rose, N L 1990 'A method for the extraction of carbonaceous particles from lake sediment', *J Palaeolimnology* 3, 45–53.

Rose, N L 1994 Characterization of carbonaceous particles from lake sediments', *Hydrobiologia* 274, 127–32.

Rose, N L, Harlock, S, Appleby, P G & Battarbee, R W 1995 'Dating of recent lake sediments in the United Kingdom and Ireland using spheroidal carbonaceous particle (SCP) concentration profiles', *The Holocene* 5, 328–35.

Rothlisberger, F 1986 *10,000 Jahre Gletschergergeschichte der Erde*. Aarau: Sauerlander.

Rowell, T K & Turner, J 1985 'Litho-, humic- and pollen-stratigraphy at Quick Moss, Northumberland', *J Ecology* 73, 11–25.

Rumsby, B T & Macklin, M G 1994 'Channel and floodplain response to recent abrupt climate change: the Tyne Basin, northern England', *Earth Surface Processes & Landforms* 19, 499–515.

Rumsby, B T & Macklin, M G 1996 'River response to the last neoglacial (the "Little Ice Age") in northern, western and central Europe', *in* Branson, J, Brown, A G, & Gregory, K J (eds) *Global Continental Changes: The Context of Palaeohydrology*. London: Geological Society of London Special Publication 115, 217–34.

Ryder, M L 1983 *Sheep & Man*. London: Duckworth.

Rymer, L 1976 'The history and ethnobotany of bracken', *Botanical J Linnean Soc* 73, 151–76.

Sagar, G R & Harper, J L 1964 'Biological Flora of the British Isles: *Plantago major* L', *J Ecology* 52, 189–205.

Sanderson, R P 1891 *Survey of the Debateable and Border Lands adjoining the Realm of Scotland, and belonging to the Crown of England, Taken 1604*. Alnwick.

Sarmaja-Korjonen, K 2001 'Correlation of fluctuations in cladoceran planktonic-littoral ratio between three cores from a small lake in southern Finland: Holocene water-level changes', *The Holocene* 11, 53–64.

Schmidt, P K& Burgess, C B 1981 *The Axes of Scotland and Northern England*. Munich: Praehistorische Bronzefunden.

Schulting, R K 1998 'Slighting the sea: stable isotope evidence for the transition to farming in north-western Europe', *Documenta Prehistorica* 25, 203–18.

Schulting, R J & Richards, M P 2002 'The wet, the wild and the domesticated: the Mesolithic-Neolithic transition on the west coast of Scotland', *European J of Archaeology* 5, 147–89.

Schumm, S A 1977 *The Fluvial System*. New York: Wiley.

Schweizer, A 1997 *Mid-Late Holocene Landscape Development in the Cheviot Hills, Scotland*. Department of Geography, Johann Wolfgang Goethe University, Frankfurt. Unpublished Diploma Dissertation.

Scott, A C, Moore, J & Brayshay, B 2000 *Fire and the Palaeo-environment. Palaeogeography, Palaeoclimatology, Palaeoecology* Special Issue 164.

Segerstrom, U & Emanuelsson, M 2002 'Extensive forest grazing and hay-making on mires – vegetation changes in south-central Sweden due to land use since Medieval times', *Vegetation History & Archaeobotany* 11, 181–90.

Shennan, I & Innes, J B 1986 'Late Devensian and Flandrian environmental changes at The Dod, Borders Region', *Scot Archaeol Rev* 4, 17–26.

Shore, J S, Bartley, D D & Harkness, D D 1995 'Problems encountered with the ^{14}C dating of peat', *Quaternary Science Reviews* 14, 373–83.

Shotton, F W 1978 'Archaeological inferences from the study of alluvium in the lower Severn-Avon valleys', *in* Limbrey, S & Evans, J G (eds) *Man's Effect on the Landscape: the Lowland Zone*. London: Council for British Archaeology, 27–32.

Shreve, R L 1967 'Infinite topologically random channel networks', *J Geology* 75, 175–86.

Simmons, I G 1975 'Towards an ecology of Mesolithic man in the uplands of Great Britain', *J Archaeol Science* 2, 1–15.

Simmons, I G 1993 'Vegetation change during the Mesolithic in the British Isles: some amplifications', *in* Chambers, F M (ed) *Climate Change and Human Impact on the Landscape*. London: Chapman & Hall, 109–18.

Simmons, I G 1996 *The Environmental Impact of Later Mesolithic Cultures. The Creation of Moorland Landscape in England & Wales*. Edinburgh: Edinburgh University Press.

Simmons, I G 2001 *An Environmental History of the Great Britain from 10,000 Years Ago to the Present*. Edinburgh: Edinburgh University Press.

Simmons, I G 2003 *The Moorlands of England and Wales. An Environmental History 8000 BC–AD 2000*. Edinburgh: Edinburgh University Press.

Simmons, I G & Innes, J B 1981 'Tree remains in a North York Moors peat profile', *Nature* 294, 76–8.

Simmons, I G & Innes, J B 1987 'Mid-Holocene adaptations and Later Mesolithic forest disturbance in northern England', *J Archaeol Science* 14, 385–403.

Simmons, I G & Innes, J B 1988a 'The later Mesolithic period (6000–5000 BP) on Glaisdale Moor, North Yorkshire', *Archaeol J* 145, 1–12.

Simmons, I G & Innes, J B 1988b 'Late Quaternary vegetational history of the North York Moors. X. Investigations on East Bilsdale Moor', *J Biogeography* 15, 299–324.

Simmons, I G & Innes, J B 1996 'Disturbance phases in the mid-Holocene vegetation at North Gill, North York Moors: form and process', *J Archaeol Science* 23, 183–91.

Simmons, I G & Tooley, M J 1981 *The Environment in British Prehistory*. London: Duckworth.

Simmons, I G, Turner, J & Innes, J B 1989 'An application of fine-resolution pollen analysis to later Mesolithic peats of an English upland', *in* Bonsall, C (ed) *The Mesolithic in Europe*. Edinburgh: John Donald, 206–17.

Sinclair, Sir J 1979 *The Statistical Account of Scotland 1791–1799. III. The Eastern Borders*. Wakefield: EP Publishing.

Sissons, J B 1967 *The Evolution of Scotland's Scenery*. Edinburgh: Oliver & Boyd.

Skelton, R A 1967 'The military survey of Scotland 1747–55', *Scottish Geographical Magazine* 83, 5–16.

Skinner, C J & Brown, A G 1999 'Mid-Holocene vegetation diversity in eastern Cumbria', *J Biogeography* 26, 45–54.

Smith, A G 1970 'The influence of Mesolithic and Neolithic man on British vegetation: a discussion', *in* Walker, D & West, R G (eds) *Studies in the Vegetational History of the British Isles*. Cambridge: Cambridge University Press, 81–96.

Smith, A G 1981 'The Neolithic', *in* Simmons, I G & Tooley, M J (eds) *The Environment in British Prehistory* London: Routledge, 125–209.

Smith, A G 1984 'Newferry and the Boreal-Atlantic transition', *New Phytologist* 98, 35–55.

Smith, A G & Pilcher, J R 1973 'Radiocarbon dates and vegetational history of the British Isles', *New Phytologist* 72, 903–14.

Smith, B W, Rhodes, E J, Stokes, S, Spooner, N A & Aitken, M J 1990 'Optical dating of sediments: initial quartz results from Oxford', *Archaeometry* 32, 19–31.

Smith, C 1988–9 'Excavations at Dod Law West hillfort, Northumberland', *Northern Archaeology* 9, 1–55.

Smith, R F & Boardman, J 1989 'The use of soil information in the assessment of the incidence and magnitude of historical flood events in upland Britain', *in* Beven, K & Carling, P (eds) *Floods: Hydrological, Sedimentological and Geomorphological Implications*. Chichester: Wiley, 185–97.

Smith, R S & Charman, D J 1988 'The vegetation of upland mires within conifer plantations in Northumberland', *J Applied Ecology* 25, 579–94.

Smout, T C 1997 *Scottish Woodland History*. Edinburgh: Scottish Cultural Press.

Smout, T C 2002 *People and Woods in Scotland: A History*. Edinburgh: Edinburgh University Press.

Snape, M E 1989 'Roman and native: *vici* on the north British frontier', *in* Maxfield, V A & Dobson, M J (eds) *Roman Frontier Studies 1989*. Exeter: Exeter University Press, 468–71.

Spedding, C R W & Diekmahns, E C 1972 *Grasses and Legumes in British Agriculture*. Farnham: Commonwealth Agricultural Bureaux.

Spikins, P 1999 *Mesolithic Northern England. Environment, Population and Settlement*. Oxford: BAR British Series 283.

Spurk, M, Leuschner, H H, Baillie, M G L, Briffa, K R & Friedrich, M 2002 'Depositional frequency of German sub-fossil oaks: climatically and non-climatically induced fluctuations in the Holocene', *The Holocene* 12, 707–16.

Stace, C 1991 *New Flora of the British Isles*. Cambridge: Cambridge University Press.

Stager, J C & Mayewski, P A 1997 'Abrupt early to mid-Holocene climatic transition registered at the equator and the poles', *Science* 276, 1834–6.

Stallibrass, S 1998 'On the outside looking in: a view of animal bones in Roman Britain from the north-west frontier', *in* Mills, C M & Coles, G (eds) *Life on the Edge: Human Settlement and Marginality*. Oxford: Oxbow Monograph 100, 53–60.

Stallibrass, S & Huntley, J P 1996 'Slim evidence: a review of the faunal and botanical data from the Neolithic of northern England', *in* Frodsham, P (ed) *The Neolithic of Northern England*. Newcastle: Northern Archaeology Group, 35–42.

Starkel, L 1991 'Environmental changes at the Younger Dryas-Preboreal transition and during the early Holocene: some distinctive aspects in central Europe', *The Holocene* 1, 234–42.

Starkel, L, Gregory, K J & Thornes, J B 1991 *Temperate Palaeohydrology: Fluvial Processes in the Temperate Zone during the last 15,000 Years*. Chichester: Wiley.

Steer, K A & Keeney, G S 1947 'Excavations in two homesteads at Crock Cleugh, Roxburghshire', *Proc Soc Antiq Scot* 81, 138–57.

Steven, H M & Carlisle, A 1959 *The Native Pinewoods of Scotland*. Edinburgh: Oliver & Boyd.

Stevenson, A C & Harrison, R J 1992 'Ancient forests in Spain: a model for land-use and dry forest management in south-west Spain from 4000 BC to AD 1900', *Proc Prehist Soc* 58, 227–47.

Stevenson, A C, Jones, V J & Battarbee, R W 1990 'The cause of peat erosion: a palaeolimnological approach', *New Phytologist* 114, 727–35.

Stevenson, A C & Thompson, D B A 1993 'Long-term changes in heather moorland in upland Britain and Ireland: palaeoecological evidence for the importance of grazing', *The Holocene* 3, 70–6.

Stewart, M 2003 'Using the woods, 1600–1850. (2) Managing for profit', *in* Smout, T C (ed) *People and Woods in Scotland: A History*. Edinburgh: Edinburgh University Press, 105–27.

Stockmarr, J 1971 'Tablets with spores used in absolute pollen analysis', *Pollen et Spores* 13, 614–621.

Strahler, A N 1952 'Hypsometric (area-altitude) analysis of erosional topography', *Bulletin of the Geological Society of America* 63, 1117–42.

Stuiver, M & Kra, R S 1986 'Twelfth International Radiocarbon Conference, 24–28 June 1985, Trondheim, Norway', *Radiocarbon* 28 (2B).

Sturlodottir, S A & Turner, J 1985 'The elm decline at Pawlaw Mire: an anthropogenic interpretation', *New Phytologist* 99, 323–9.

Sugden, D E 1968 'The selectivity of glacial erosion in the Cairngorm Mountains, Scotland', *Trans Inst Brit Geog* 45, 79–92.

Sugita, S 1993 'A model of pollen source area for an entire lake surface', *Quaternary Research* 39, 239–44.

Sugita, S, Gaillard, M-J & Bröstrom, A 1999 'Landscape openness and pollen records: a simulation approach', *The Holocene* 9, 409–21.

Swain, A M 1973 'A history of fire and vegetation in northeastern Minnesota as recorded in lake sediments', *Quaternary Research* 3, 383–96.

Tallantire, P A 1992 'The alder [*Alnus glutinosa* (L) Gaertn.] problem in the British Isles: a third approach to its palaeohistory', *New Phytologist* 122, 717–31.

Tallantire, P A 2002 'The early Holocene spread of hazel (*Corylus avellana* L) in Europe north and west of the Alps: an ecological hypothesis', *The Holocene* 12, 81–96.

Tallis, J H 1985 'Erosion of blanket peat in the southern Pennines: new light on an old problem', *in* Johnston, R H (ed) *The Geomorphology of North-West England*. Manchester: Manchester University Press, 313–36.

Tallis, J H 1987 'Fire and flood at Holme Moss: erosion processes in an upland blanket mire', *J Ecology* 75, 1099–129.

Tallis, J H 1991 'Forest and moorland in the south Pennine uplands in the mid-Flandrian period. III. The spread of moorland – local, regional and national', *J Ecology* 79, 401–15.

Tallis, J H 1994 'Pool-and-hummock patterning in a southern Pennine blanket mire. II. The formation and erosion of the pool system', *J Ecology* 82, 793–803.

Tallis, J H 1995 'Climate and erosion signals in British blanket peats: the significance of *Racomitrium lanuginosum* remains', *J Ecology* 83, 1021–030.

Tallis, J H 1997 'The pollen record of *Empetrum nigrum* in southern Pennine peats: implications for erosion and climate change', *J Ecology* 85, 455–65.

Tallis, J H 1998 'Growth and degradation of British and Irish blanket mires', *Environmental Reviews* 6, 81–122.

Tallis, J H & Switsur, V R 1990 'Forest and moorland in the south Pennine uplands in the mid-Flandrian period. II. The hill-slope forests', *J Ecology* 78, 857–83.

Tansley, A G 1939 *The British Islands and Their Vegetation*. Cambridge: Cambridge University Press.

Tauber, H 1965 'Differential pollen dispersion and the interpretation of pollen diagrams', *Danmarks Geologiske Undersögelse* II. Raekke 89, 7–69.

Taylor, C 2001 'The plus fours in the wardobe: a personal view of landscape history', *in* Hooke, D (ed) *Landscape. The Richest Historical Record*. Birmingham: Society for Landscape Studies Supplementary Series 1, 157–62.

Teasdale, D & Hughes, D 1999 'The glacial history of north-east England', *in* Bridgland, D R, Horton, B P & Innes, J B (eds) *The Quaternary of North-East England. Field Guide*. London: Quaternary Research Association, 10–17.

Terry, J 1993 'Bodsberry Hill unenclosed platform settlement, near Elvanfoot, Strathclyde', *Glasgow Archaeol J* 18, 49–63.

Terry, J 1995 'Excavations at Lintshie Gutter unenclosed platform settlement, Crawford, Lanarkshire, 1991', *Proc Soc Antiq Scot* 125, 369–427.

Thirsk, J 2000 *The English Rural Landscape*. Oxford: Oxford University Press.

Thomas, J 1990 'Silent running: the ills of environmental archaeology', *Scot Archaeol Rev* 7, 2–7.

Thomas, J 1999 *Rethinking the Neolithic*. Cambridge: Cambridge University Press.

Thomas, K D 1989 'Vegetation of the British chalklands in the Flandrian period: a response to Bush', *J Archaeol Science* 16, 549–53.

Tight, J A 1987 *The Late Quaternary History of WesterBranxholme and Kingside Lochs, South-east Scotland*. Unpublished PhD thesis, University of Reading.

Tilley, C 1994 *A Phenomenology of Landscape*. Oxford: Berg.

Tinner, W & Feng Sheng Hu 2003 'Size parameters, size-class distribution and area-number relationship of microscopic charcoal: relevance for fire reconstruction', *The Holocene* 13, 499–505.

Tipping, R M 1985 'A problem with pollen concentration procedures', *Pollen et Spores* 27, 121–30.

Tipping, R M 1987a 'A note concerning possible increased pollen deterioration in sediments containing *Lycopodium* tablets', *Pollen et Spores* 29, 323–8.

Tipping, R M 1987b 'The origins of corroded pollen grains at five early postglacial pollen sites in western Scotland', *Review of Palaeobotany and Palynology* 53, 151–61.

Tipping, R M 1987c 'The prospects for establishing synchroneity in the early postglacial pollen peak of *Juniperus* in the British Isles', *Boreas* 16, 155–63.

Tipping, R M 1991 'Climatic change in Scotland during the Devensian Lateglacial: the palynological record', *in* Barton, N, Roberts, A J & Roe, D A (eds) *The Lateglacial in North West Europe: Human Adaptation and Environmental Change at the end of the Pleistocene*. London: Council for British Archaeology, 7–21.

Tipping, R M 1992 'The determination of cause in the generation of major prehistoric valley fills in the Cheviot Hills, Anglo-Scottish Border', *in* Needham, S & Macklin, M G (eds) *Alluvial Archaeology in Britain*. Oxford: Oxbow, 111–21.

Tipping, R M 1993 'Fluvial chronology and valley floor evolution of the upper Bowmont Valley, Borders Region, Scotland', *Earth Surface Processes and Landforms* 19, 641–57.

Tipping, R M 1994 'The form and fate of Scotland's woodlands', *Proc Soc Antiq Scot* 124, 1–54.

Tipping, R M 1995a 'Holocene evolution of a lowland Scottish landscape: Kirkpatrick Fleming. I. Peat- and pollen-stratigraphic evidence for raised moss development and climatic change', *The Holocene* 5, 69–81.

Tipping, R M 1995b 'Holocene evolution of a lowland Scottish landscape: Kirkpatrick Fleming. II. Regional vegetation and land-use change', *The Holocene* 5, 83–96.

Tipping, R M 1995c 'Holocene evolution of a lowland Scottish landscape: Kirkpatrick Fleming. III. Fluvial history', *The Holocene* 5, 184–95.

Tipping, R M 1995d 'Holocene landscape change at Carn Dubh, near Pitlochry, Perthshire', *J Quaternary Science* 10, 59–75.

Tipping, R M 1996a 'The neolithic landscapes of the Cheviot Hills and hinterland – palaeoenvironmental evidence', *in* Frodsham, P (ed) *The Neolithic of Northern England*. Newcastle: Northern Archaeology Group, 17–35.

Tipping, R M 1996b 'Microscopic charcoal records, inferred human activity and climate change in the mesolithic of northernmost Scotland', *in* Pollard, A & Morrison, A (eds) *The Early Prehistory of Scotland*. Edinburgh: Edinburgh University Press, 39–61.

Tipping, R M 1997a 'Pollen analysis, late Iron Age and Roman agriculture around Hadrian's Wall', *in* Gwilt, A & Haselgrove, C (eds) *Reconstructing Iron Age Societies*. Oxford: Oxbow, 239–47.

Tipping, R M 1997b 'Environment and environmental change in Eastern Dumfriesshire', *in* RCAHMS *Eastern Dumfriesshire: An Archaeological Landscape*. Edinburgh: HMSO.

Tipping, R M 1997c 'Medieval woodland history from the Scottish Southern Uplands: fine spatial-scale pollen data from a small woodland hollow', *in* Smout, T C (ed) *Scottish Woodland History*. Edinburgh: Scottish Cultural Press, 49–72.

Tipping, R M 1997d 'Vegetation history of southern Scotland', *Botanical J of Scotland* 49, 151–62.

Tipping, R M 1998a 'The chronology of Late Quaternary fluvial activity in part of the Milfield Basin, north-east England', *Earth Surface Processes & Landforms* 23, 845–56.

Tipping, R M 1998b 'Cereal cultivation on the Anglo-Scottish Border during the "Little Ice Age"', *in* Mills, C & Coles, G (eds) *Life on the Edge: Human Settlement and Marginality*. Oxford: Oxbow Monograph 100, 1–11.

Tipping, R M 1998c 'The application of palaeoecology to native woodland restoration: Carrifrans as a case-study', *in* Newton, A C & Ashmole, P (eds) *Native Woodland Restoration in Southern Scotland: Principles and Practice*. Borders Forest Trust Occasional Paper 2. Jedburgh: Borders Forest Trust, 9–21.

Tipping, R M 1999a 'Towards an environmental history of the Bowmont Valley and the Northern Cheviot Hills', *Landscape History* 20, 41–50.

Tipping, R M 1999b 'Moffat Basin: Holocene fluvial stratigraphy and chronology', *in* Tipping, R M (ed) *The Quaternary of Dumfries & Galloway. Field Guide*. London: Quaternary Research Association, 153–9.

Tipping, R M 1999c 'Rotten Bottom – Holocene upland environments', *in* Tipping, R M (ed) *The Quaternary of Dumfries & Galloway: Field Guide*. London: Quaternary Research Association, 171–81.

Tipping, R M 2000a 'Accelerated geomorphic activity and human causation: problems in proving the links in proxy records', *in* Nicholson, R A & O'Connor, T P (eds) *People as an Agent of Environmental Change*. Oxford: Oxbow, 1–5.

Tipping, R M 2000b 'Palaeoecological approaches to historic problems: a comparison of sheep-grazing intensities in the Cheviot Hills in the Medieval and later periods', *in* Atkinson, J, Banks, I & MacGregor, G (eds) *Townships to Farmsteads: Rural Settlement Studies in Scotland, England and Wales*. Oxford: BAR 293, 30–43.

Tipping, R M 2000c 'Pollen preservation analysis as a necessity in Holocene pollen analysis', *in* Stallybrass, S & Huntley, J P (eds) *Taphonomy and Interpretation*. Oxford: Oxbow, 23–34.

Tipping, R M 2002a 'Living in the past: woods and people in prehistory to 1000 BC', *in* Smout, T C (ed) *People and Woods in Scotland: A History*. Edinburgh: Edinburgh University Press, 14–39.

Tipping, R M 2002b 'Climatic variability and "marginal" settlement in upland British landscapes: a re-evaluation', *Landscapes* 3, 10–28.

Tipping, R M 2004 'Interpretative issues concerning the driving forces of vegetation change in the early Holocene of the British Isles', *in* Saville, A (ed) *Mesolithic Scotland: The Early Holocene Prehistory of Scotland and its European Context*. Edinburgh: Society of Antiquaries of Scotland, 45–54.

Tipping, R M 2005 'Palaeoecology and political history: evaluating driving forces in historic landscape change in southern Scotland', *in* Whyte, I & Winchester, A J L (eds) *Society, Landcape, Environment in Upland Britain*. Exeter: Exeter University Press, 11–21.

Tipping, R M, Carter, S C & Johnston, D A 1994 'Soil pollen and soil micromorphological analyses of old ground surfaces on Biggar Common, Borders Region, Scotland', *J Archaeol Science* 21, 387–401.

Tipping, R M, Carter, S P, Davidson, D A, Long, D J & Tyler, A N 1997 'Soil pollen analysis: a new approach to understanding the stratigraphic integrity of data', *in* Sinclair, A *et al* (eds) *Archaeological Sciences*. Oxford: Oxbow, 221–32.

Tipping, R M, Edmonds, M & Sheridan, A 1993 'Palaeoenvironmental investigations directly associated with a neolithic axe "quarry" on Beinn Lawers, near Killin, Perthshire, Scotland', *New Phytologist* 123, 585–97.

Tipping, R M, Haggart, B A, Milburn, P A & Thomas, J 2004 'Landscape perception in early Bronze Age henge construction at The Pict's Knowe, southern Scotland: a palaeoenvironmental perspective', *in* Carver, E & Lelong, O (eds) *Modern Views: Ancient Lands. New Work and Thought on Cultural Landscapes*. Oxford: Archaeopress, 33–40.

Tipping, R M & Halliday, S 1994 'The age of alluvial fan deposition at Hopecarton in the upper Tweed valley, Scotland', *Earth Surface Processes and Landforms* 19, 333–48.

Tipping, R M & McCulloch, R (in press) 'Identifying the prehistory of woodland management: problems and potential from a case-study in northern Scotland', *in* Rotherham, I D (ed) *Ecology, Archaeology and Management of Ancient Woods*. Sheffield.

Tipping, R M & Milburn, P 2000 'The mid-Holocene charcoal fall in southern Scotland: spatial and temporal variability', *Palaeogeography, Palaeoclimatology, Palaeoecology* 164, 193–209.

Tipping, R M, Milburn, P & Halliday, S 1999 'Fluvial processes, land use and climate change 2000 years ago in upper Annandale, southern Scotland', *in* Brown, A G & Quine, T (eds) *Fluvial Processes and Environmental Change*. Chichester: Wiley, 311–28.

Tipping, R M & Tisdall, E 2004 'Continuity, crisis and climate change in the Neolithic and early Bronze Periods of North West Europe', *in* Shepherd, I A G & Barclay, G (eds) *Scotland in Ancient Europe. The Neolithic and Early Bronze Age of Scotland in their European Context*. Edinburgh: Society of Antiquaries of Scotland, 71–82.

Tipping, R M & Watson, F 1999 'Environmental history in Scotland – the past as the key to the future', *Scottish Association of Geography Teachers J* 28, 23–30.

Tisdall, E W 2000 *Holocene Climate Change in Glen Affric, northern Scotland: A Multiproxy Approach*. Unpublished PhD thesis, University of Stirling.

Tivy, J 1957 'Influence des facteurs biologiques sur l'érosion dans les Southern Uplands écossais', *Revue Géomorphique Dynamique* 8, 9–19.

Tivy, J 1962 'An investigation of certain slope deposits in the Lowther Hills, Southern Uplands of Scotland', *Trans Inst Brit Geog* 30, 59–73.

Tolonen, K 1986 'Charred particle analysis', *in* Berglund, B E (ed) *Handbook of Holocene Palaeoecology and Palaeohydrology*. Chichester: Wiley, 484–95.

Topping, P 1981 'The prehistoric field systems of College Valley, north Northumberland', *Northern Archaeology* 2, 14–33.

Topping, P 1983 'Observations on the stratigraphy of early agricultural remains in the Kirknewton area of the Northumberland Cheviots', *Northern Archaeology* 4, 21–31.

Topping, P 1987 'The Linhope Burn excavations, Northumberland, 1989: interim report', *Northern Archaeology* 8, 29–33.

Topping, P 1989a 'Early cultivation in Northumberland and the Borders', *Proc Prehist Soc* 55, 161–79.

Topping, P 1989b 'The context of cord rig cultivation in later prehistoric Northumberland', *in* Bowden, M, Mackay, D & Topping, P (eds) *From Cornwall to Caithness. Some Aspects of British Field Archaeology*. Oxford: BAR British Series 209, 145–59.

Topping, P 1993 'The excavation of an unenclosed settlement, field system and cord rig at Linhope Burn, Northumberland, 1989', *Northern Archaeology* 11, 1–42.

Topping, P 1997 'Different realities: the Neolithic in the Northumberland Cheviots', *in* Topping, P (ed) *Neolithic Landscapes*. Oxford: Oxbow Monograph 86 and Neolithic Studies Group Seminar Papers 2, 113–24.

Topping, P 1998 'The excavation of burnt mounds at Titlington Mount, north Northumberland, 1992–3', *Northern Archaeology* 15/16, 3–24.

Topping, P 1999a 'Late prehistoric landscapes in the Northumberland Cheviots', *in* Pattison, P, Field, D & Ainsworth, S (eds) *Patterns in the Past: Essays in Landscape Archaeology for Christopher Taylor*. Oxford: Oxbow Books, 11–22.

Topping, P 1999b 'Wether Hill, Northumberland: excavations 1993–8', *NAGNews* May 1999, 1–6.

Tough, D L W 1928 *The Last Years of a Frontier*. Oxford: Oxford University Press.

Triscott, J 1982 'Excavations at Dryburn Bridge, East Lothian', *in* Harding, D W (ed) *Late Prehistoric Settlement in South-east Scotland*. Edinburgh: Department of Archaeology, University of Edinburgh, 117–24.

Trow-Smith, R 1957 *A History of British Livestock to 1700*. London: Routledge & Kegan Paul.

Tuck, J A 1985 'War and society in the Medieval north', *Northern History* 21, 33–52.

Turner, C H 1968 *Studies on a Small Post-glacial Peat Deposit in Northumberland*. Unpublished MSc thesis, University of Durham.

Turner, J 1970 'Post-Neolithic disturbance of British vegetation', *in* Walker, D & West, R G (eds) *Studies in the Vegetational History of the British Isles*. Cambridge: Cambridge University Press, 97–116.

Turner, J 1979 'The environment of northeast England during Roman times as shown by pollen analysis', *J Archaeol Science* 6, 285–90.

Turner, J 1981a 'The Iron Age', *in* Simmons, I G & Tooley, M J (eds) *The Environment in British Prehistory*. London: Duckworth, 250–81.

Turner, J 1981b 'The vegetation', *in* Jones, M & Dimbleby, G W (eds) *The Environment of Man: the Iron Age to the Anglo-Saxon Period*. Oxford: BAR, 67–73.

Turner, J 1983 'Some pollen evidence for the environment of northern Britain 1000 BC – AD 1000', *in* Chapman, J C & Mytum, H C (eds) *Settlement in North Britain 1000 BC – AD 1000*. Oxford: BAR, 3–27.

Turner, J 1984 'Pollen diagrams from Cross Fell and their implications for former tree-lines', *in* Haworth, E Y & Lund, J W G (eds) *Lake Sediments and Environmental History*. Leicester: Leicester University Press, 317–57.

Turner, J 1987 'Principal components analyses of pollen data with special reference to anthropogenic indicators', *in* Behre, K-E (ed) *Anthropogenic Indicators in Pollen Diagrams*. Rotterdam: Balkema, 221–32.

Turner, J, Hewetson, V P, Hibbert, F A, Lowry, K H & Chambers, C 1973 'The history of the vegetation and flora of Widdybank Fell and the Cow Green Reservoir Basin, Upper Teesdale', *Phil Trans Royal Soc London* B265, 328–407.

Turner, J & Hodgson, J 1979 'Studies in the vegetational history of the northern Pennines. I. Variations in the composition of the early Flandrian forests', *J Ecology* 67, 629–46.

Turner, J & Hodgson, J 1981 'Studies in the vegetational history of the northern Pennines. II. An atypical pollen diagram from Pow Hill, Co. Durham', *J Ecology* 69, 71–188.

Turner, J & Hodgson, J 1983 'Studies in the vegetational history of the northern Pennines. III. Variations in the composition of the mid-Flandrian forests', *J Ecology* 71, 95–118.

Turner, J, Innes, J & Simmons, I G 1993 'Spatial diversity in the mid-Flandrian vegetation history of North Gill, North Yorkshire', *New Phytologist* 123, 599–647.

Turner, J & Peglar, S M 1988 'Temporally precise studies of vegetation history', *in* Huntley, B & Webb, T III (eds) *Vegetation History*. Kluwer, Dordrecht, 753–77.

Turner, J Simmons, I G & Innes, J B 1989 'Two pollen diagrams from the same site', *New Phytologist* 113, 409–16.

Turney, C S M, Harkness, D D & Lowe, J J 1997 'The use of microtephra horizons to correlate Late-glacial lake sediment successions in Scotland', *J Quaternary Science* 12, 525–33.

Tyldesley, J B 1973 'Long-range transmission of tree pollen to Shetland. I. sampling and trajectories', *New Phytologist* 72, 175–81.

Tyler, A N, Carter, S, Davidson, D A, Long, D J & Tipping, R M 2001 'The extent and significance of bioturbation on ^{137}Cs distributions in five upland soil profiles', *Catena* 43, 81–99.

Urban, N, Eisenreich, S J, Grigal, D F & Schurr, K T 1990 'Mobility and diagenesis of Pb and Pb–210 in peat', *Geochimica et Cosmochimica Acta* 54, 3329–46.

van Geel, B 1978 'A palaeoecological study of Holocene peat bog sections in Germany and The Netherlands, based on the analysis of pollen, spores, and macro- and micro-scopic remains of fungi, algae, cormophytes and animals', *Review of Palaeobotany and Palynology* 25, 1–120.

van Geel, B, Buurmman, J & Waterbolk, H T 1996 'Archaeological and palaeoclimatic indications of an abrupt change in The Netherlands, and evidence for climatological teleconnections around 2650 BP', *J Quaternary Science* 11, 451–60.

van Geel, B van der Plicht, J, Kilian, M R, Klaver, E R, Kouwenberg, J H M, Renssen, H, Reynaud-Ferrara, I & Waterbolk, H T 1998 'The sharp rise of Δ^{14}C *ca.* 800 cal BC: possible causes, related climatic teleconnections and the impact on human environments', *Radiocarbon* 40, 535–50.

van Geel, B, Raspopov, O M, van der Plicht, J & Renssen, H 1998 'Solar forcing of abrupt climate change around 850 calendar years BC', *in* Peiser, B J, Palmer, T & Bailey, M E (eds) *Natural Catastrophes during Bronze Age Civilizations*. Oxford: BAR International Series 728, 162–8.

Vasari, Y & Väänänen, K 1986 'Stratigraphical indications of the former use of wetlands', *in* Behre, K-E (ed) *Anthropogenic Indicators in Pollen Diagrams*. Rotterdam: Balkema, 65–71.

Veen, M van der 1985 'Evidence for crop plants from north-east England: an interim overview with discussion of new results', *in* Fieller, N R J, Gilbertson, D D & Ralph, N G A (eds) *Palaeobiological Investigations: Research Design, Methods and Data Analysis*. Oxford: BAR, 197–219.

Veen, M van der 1989 'Native communities in the frontier zone – uniformity or diversity?', *in* Maxfield, V A & Dobson, M J (eds) *Roman Frontier Studies 1989*. Exeter: Exeter University Press, 446–50.

Veen, M van der 1992 *Crop Husbandry Regimes: An Archaeological Study of Farming in Northern England 1000 BC–AD 500*. Sheffield: Department of Archaeology and Prehistory, University of Sheffield.

Vera, F W M 2000 *Grazing Ecology and Forest History*. Wallingford: CABI Publishing.

von Graffenstein, U *et al* 1998 'The cold event 8,200 years ago documented in oxygen isotope records of precipitation in Europe and Greenland', *Climate Dynamics* 14, 73–81.

Vuorela, I 1973 'The indication of farming in pollen diagrams from southern Finland', *Acta Botanica Fennici* 87, 3–41.

Vyner, B E 1994 'The territory of ritual: cross-ridge boundaries and the prehistoric landscape of the Cleveland Hills, northeast England', *Antiquity* 68, 27–38.

Waddington, C 1996 'Putting rock art to use: a model of early Nelithic transhumance in north Northumberland', *in* Frodsham, P (ed) *The Neolithic of Northern England*. Newcastle: Northern Archaeology Group, 147–78.

Waddington, C 1999 *A Landscape Archaeological Study of the Mesolithic-Neolithic in the Milfield Basin, Northumberland*. Oxford: BAR British Series 291.

Wainwright, A 1968 *Pennine Way Companion*. Kendal: Westmorland Gazette.

Walker, D 1966 'The late Quaternary history of the Cumberland Lowland', *Philo Trans Royal Soc London* B251, 1–210.

Walker, D 1970 'Direction and rate in some British post-glacial hydroseres', *in* Walker, D & West, R G (eds) *Studies in the Vegetational History of the British Isles*. Cambridge: Cambridge University Press, 117–40.

Walker, D & West, R G 1970 *Studies in the Vegetational History of the British Isles*. Cambridge: Cambridge University Press.

Walker, M J C, Bohncke, S J P, Coope, G R, O'Connell, M, Usinger, H & Verbruggen, C 1994 'The Devensian/Weichselian Late-glacial in north-west Europe (Ireland, Britain, north Belgium, The Netherlands, north-west Germany)', *J Quaternary Science* 9, 109–18.

Walker, M J C, Bjorck, S, Lowe, J J, Cwynar, L C, Johnsen, S, Knudsen, K-L, Wolhlfarth, B *et al* 1999 'Isotopic "events" in the GRIP ice core: a stratotype for the Late Pleistocene', *Quaternary Science Reviews* 18, 1143–150.

Walsh, K 1995 'The changing environment of Lindisfarne', *in* O'Sullivan, D & Young, R (eds) *Lindisfarne Holy Island*. London: Batsford, 18–27.

Warren, G 2001 *Towards a Social Archaeology of the Mesolithic in Scotland: Landscapes, Contexts and Experiences*. Unpublished PhD thesis, University of Edinburgh.

Watts, S J 1975 *From Border to Middle Shire: Northumberland 1586–1625.* Leicester: Leicester University Press.

Webb, J A & Moore, P D 1982 'The Late Devensian vegetational history of the Whitlaw Mosses, southeast Scotland', *New Phytologist* 91, 341–98.

Welfare, A unpublished *An assessment of the potential archaeological and cultural heritage constraints respecting the extension of the existing sand and gravel workings south of the River Breamish, at Powburn, Northumberland.* Heritage Site and Landscape Surveys Ltd. 1992.

Welfare, H 2002 'The uplands of the northern counties in the first millennium BC', *in* Brooks, C, Daniels, R & Harding, A (eds) *Past, Present and Future. The Archaeology of Northern England.* Durham: Architectural and Archaeological Society of Durham & Northumberland Research Report 5, 71–7.

Wells, C E, Hodgkinson, D & Huckerby, E 2000 'Evidence for the role of beaver (*Castor fiber* L) in the prehistoric ontogenesis of a mire in north-west England, UK', *The Holocene* 10, 503–08.

West, R G 1977 *Pleistocene Geology and Biology.* London: Longman.

West, R G 1980 'Pleistocene forest history of East Anglia', *New Phytologist* 85, 571–622.

White, J T 1973 *The Scottish Border and Northumberland.* London: Eyre Methuen.

Whitfield, W A D & Furley, P A 1971 'The relationship between soil patterns and slope form in the Ettrick Association, south-east Scotland', *in* Brunsden, D (ed) *Slopes: Form and Process.* London: Institute of British Geographers, 165–75.

Whittington, G & Edwards, K J 1989 'Problems in the interpretation of Cannabaceae pollen in the stratigraphic record', *Pollen et Spores* 31, 79–96.

Whittington, G & Edwards, K J 1990 'The cultivation and utilization of hemp in Scotland', *Scottish Geographical Magazine* 106, 167–73.

Whittington, G & Edwards, K J 1993 '*Ubi solitudinem faciunt pacem appellant*: the Romans in Scotland, a palaeoenvironmental contribution', *Britannia* 24, 13–25.

Whittington, G & Edwards, K J 1994 'Palynology as a predictive tool in archaeology', *Proc Soc Antiq Scot* 124, 55–65.

Whittington, G & Edwards, K J 1997 'Vegetation change', *in* Edwards, K J & Ralston, I B M (eds) *Scotland: Environment and Archaeology 8000 BC – AD 1000.* Chichester: Wiley, 63–82.

Whittington, G, Edwards, K J & Caseldine, C J 1991 'Late- and post-glacial pollen-analytical and environmental data from a near-coastal site in north-east Fife, Scotland', *Review of Palaeobotany & Palynology* 68, 65–85.

Whittington, G, Edwards, K J & Cundill, P R 1990 *Palaeoenvironmental Investigations at Black Loch in the Ochil Hills of Fife, Scotland.* Aberdeen: Department of Geography, Aberdeen University. O'Dell Memorial Monograph 22.

Whittington, G, Edwards, K J & Cundill, P R 1991a 'Palaeoecological investigations of multiple elm declines at a site in north Fife, Scotland', *J Biogeography* 18, 71–87.

Whittington, G, Edwards, K J & Cundill, P R 1991b 'Late-glacial and Holocene vegetation change at Black Loch, Fife, eastern Scotland – a multiple core approach', *New Phytologist* 118, 147–66.

Whittington, G & Gordon, A D 1987 'The differentiation of the pollen of *Cannabis sativa* L from that of *Humulus lupulus* L', *Pollen et Spores* 29, 111–20.

Whittington, G & Jarvis, J 1986 'Kilconquhar Loch, Fife: an historical and palynological investigation', *Proc Soc Antiq Scot* 116, 413–28.

Whittle, A 1978 'Resources and population in the British Neolithic', *Antiquity* 52, 34–42.

Whittle, A 1996 *Europe in the Neolithic: the Creation of New Worlds.* Cambridge: Cambridge University Press.

Whittle, A 1999 'The Neolithic period, *c* 4000–2500/2000 BC: changing the world', *in* Hunter, J & Ralston, I (eds) *The Archaeology of Britain.* London: Routledge, 58–76.

Whittle, A, Keith-Lucas, M, Milles, A, Noddle, B, Rees, S & Romans, S 1978. *Scord of Brouster: An Early Agricultural Settlement on Shetland.* Oxford: Oxford University Committee for Archaeology Monograph 9.

Whyte, I 1981 'Human response to short- and long-term climatic fluctuations: the example of early Scotland', in Delano Smith, C & Parry, M L (eds) *Consequences of Climatic Change.* Nottingham: Nottingham University Press, 17–29.

Whyte, I D 1997 *Scotland's Society and Economy in Transition, c 1500–c 1760.* London: Macmillan.

Wigley, T M L & Kelly, P M 1990 'Holocene climatic change, ^{14}C wiggles and variations in solar irradiance', *Phil Trans Royal Soc London* A330, 547–60.

Wik, M & Natkanski, J 1990 'British and Scandinavian lake sediment records of carbonaceous particles from fossil-fuel combustion', *Phil Trans Royal Soc London* B327, 319–323.

Wik, M, Renberg, I & Darley, J 1986 'Sedimentary records of carbonaceous particles from fossil fuel combustion', *Hydrobiologia* 143, 387–94.

Wild, C Wells, C, Anderson, D, Boardman, J & Parker, A 2001 'Evidence for Medieval clearance in the Seathwaite Valley, Cumbria', *Trans Cumberland & Westmorland Antiq and Archaeol Soc* 1, 53–68.

Williams, C T 1985 *Mesolithic Exploitation Patterns in the Central Pennines. A Palynological Study of Soyland Moor.* Oxford: BAR British Series 139.

Williams, E 1989 'Dating the introduction of food production into Britain and Ireland', *Antiquity* 63, 510–21.

Williamson, T 2002 *The Transformation of Rural England. Farming and the Landscape 1700–1870.* Exeter: Exeter University Press.

Williamson, T 2003 *Shaping Medieval Landscapes. Settlement, Society & Environment.* Macclesfield: Windgather Press.

Wilmott, T 2001 *Birdoswald Roman Fort. 1,800 Years on Hadrian's Wall.* Stroud: Tempus.

Wilson, B 1995 'On the curious distortions behind the charge of scientism against environmental archaeology', *Scot Archaeol Rev* 10, 67–70.

Wilson, C 1855 'Notes on the prior existence of the *Castor fiber* in Scotland', *Proc Berwickshire Naturalists Club* 4, 76–86.

Wilson, C 1858 'Notes on the prior existence of the *Castor fiber* in Scotland, with its ancient and present distribution in Europe, and on the use of castoreum', *Edinburgh New Philosophical J* New Series 8, 1–40.

Wilson, D H 1981 *Pollen Analysis and Settlement Archaeology of the First Millennium* BC *from North-east England*. Unpublished MSc thesis, University of Oxford.

Wilson, P, Orford, J D, Knight, J, Braley, S M & Wintle, A G 2001 'Late Holocene (post-4,000 years BP) coastal dune development in Northumberland, northeast England', *The Holocene* 11, 215–30.

Wiltshire, P E J 1997 'The pre-Roman environment', *in* Wilmott, T (ed) *Birdoswald. Excavations of a Roman fort on Hadrians's Wall and its successor settlements: 1987–1992*. London: English Heritage Archaeological Report 14, 25–40.

Wiltshire, P A, Edwards, K J & Bond, S 1994 'Microbially derived metallic sulphide spherules, pollen and the waterlogging of archaeological sites', *American Association of Stratigraphic Palynologists Contribution Series* 29, 207–21.

Wimble, G T 1986 *The Palaeoecology of the Lowland Coastal Raised Mires of South Cumbria*. Unpublished PhD thesis, University of Wales.

Winchester, A J L 2000 *The Harvest of the Hills: Rural Life in Northern England and the Scottish Borders, 1400–1700*. Edinburgh: Edinburgh University Press.

Wise, A 2000 'Late prehistoric settlement and society: recent research in the central Tweed Valley', *in* Harding, J & Johnston, R (eds) *Northern Pasts: Interpretations of the Later Prehistory of Northern England and Southern Scotland*. Oxford: BAR British Series 302, 93–100.

Wishart, D & Warburton, J 2001 'An assessment of blanket mire degradation and peatland gully development in the Cheviot Hills, Northumberland', *Scottish Geographical J* 117, 185–206.

Worster, D 1993 'Paths across the levee', *in* Worster, D *The Wealth of Nature: Environmental History and the Ecological Imagination*. Oxford: Oxford University Press, 16–29.

Wright Jr, H E & Patten, H L 1963 'The pollen sum', *Pollen et Spores* 5, 445–50.

Yang, H, Rose, N L & Battarbee, R W 2001 'Dating of recent catchment peats using spheroidal carbonaceous spherules (SCP) concentration profiles with particular reference to Lochnagar, Scotland', *The Holocene* 11, 593–97.

Young, A 1972 *Slopes*. Edinburgh: Oliver & Boyd.

Young, R 1987 'Barrows clearance and land use: some suggestions from the north-east of England', *Landscape History* 9, 27–34.

Young, R 2000 'Continuity and change: marginality and later prehistoric settlement in the northern uplands', *in* Harding, J & Johnston, R (eds) *Northern Pasts: Interpretations of the Later Prehistory of Northern England and Southern Scotland*. Oxford: BAR British Series 302, 71–80.

Young, R & Simmonds, T 1995 'Marginality and the nature of later prehistoric upland settlement in the north of England', *Landscape History* 17, 5–16.

Zvelebil, M 1994 'Plant use in the Mesolithic and its role in the transition to farming', *Proc Prehist Soc* 60, 35–74.

INDEX